Marriage
His Convenience

A passionate paper marriage!

By Request™

Marriage at His Convenience

AFTER THE AFFAIR
by
Miranda Lee

A HUSBAND'S PRICE
by
Diana Hamilton

AN ARRANGED MARRIAGE
by
Susan Fox

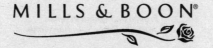

MILLS & BOON®

*MILLS & BOON and MILLS & BOON with the Rose Device
are registered trademarks of the publisher.*
*Harlequin Mills & Boon Limited,
Eton House, 18-24 Paradise Road, Richmond, Surrey, TW9 1SR*

MARRIAGE AT HIS CONVENIENCE
© by Harlequin Enterprises II B.V., 2003

After the Affair, A Husband's Price and *An Arranged Marriage*
were first published in Great Britain by Harlequin Mills & Boon
Limited in separate, single volumes.

After the Affair © Miranda Lee 1990
A Husband's Price © Diana Hamilton 1998
An Arranged Marriage © Susan Fox 1998

ISBN 0 263 83596 0

05-1103

*Printed and bound in Spain
by Litografia Rosés S.A., Barcelona*

Miranda Lee is Australian, living near Sydney. Born and raised in the bush, she was boarding-school educated and briefly pursued a career in classical music, before moving to Sydney and embracing the world of computers. Happily married, with three daughters, she began writing when family commitments kept her at home. She likes to create stories that are believable, modern, fast-paced and sexy. Her interests include meaty sagas, doing word puzzles, gambling and going to the movies.

AFTER THE AFFAIR
by
Miranda Lee

CHAPTER ONE

'SOLD! To the lady here in the front row.'

Cassie glanced at the successful buyer sitting next to her, then watched dispiritedly as Lot Forty-Seven was carried away. She sighed. The lovely blue vase would have been a perfect wedding present for her mother and Roger, but seventeen hundred dollars was ridiculously expensive.

'Lot Forty-Eight, ladies and gentlemen. . .a tea-service. . .a fine example of nineteenth-century silver. . .'

Cassie wrinkled her nose and sat back. She didn't like silver. No doubt it was a rare antique, but it was not to her taste.

The bidding started, again without her taking part. Really, the whole auction was proving to be a disappointment. When she'd heard that the river island of Strath-haven had been sold and selected items from the homestead were to be auctioned on site, Cassie had pictured a small affair, with every opportunity of picking up a bargain gift.

Instead, collectors had descended on the property in droves, coming from as far afield as Sydney and Brisbane. Cassie had even noticed a helicopter landing in the grounds when she was arriving.

The prices had been exorbitant, with Cassie growing more and more pessimistic. Her only consolation at the wasted afternoon was that she'd actually been able to visit this place without turning a hair. In nine long years she had avoided even looking at Strath-haven, which wasn't easy, since the island sat in the river directly opposite the Palmer farm.

Admittedly, when she'd driven down to the river and crossed the footbridge that connected the mainland to the island, she had refrained from looking down to the far point and the small building nestling there. But that was only to be expected. She was not a masochist!

The bidding continued, the auctioneer going through another twenty lots with amazing speed. Those Cassie could afford, she didn't like. Those she liked, she couldn't afford.

A glance at her watch told her it was nearly four-thirty. Jason's Saturday afternoon cricket match would be over soon, and if Cassie wasn't home by five her son would badger his grandmother into walking over to the auction. Cassie knew that her mother would be tired after an afternoon keeping the score at cricket, and Cassie already felt guilty over how often her mother looked after Jason, despite the older woman's insistence that she enjoyed it.

'Don't be silly, darling,' her mother had said more than once when Cassie had expressed her concern. 'You are my only child, Jason my only grandchild. I love being with him!'

Nevertheless, Cassie made up her mind to leave the auction after the next few lots.

'And finally, the paintings,' the auctioneer announced. He turned and indicated a selection leaning against the wall behind him. His assistant presented a rather small square-framed canvas, holding it up high before resting it on the table in front of Cassie.

'The first one is Lot Seventy. An untitled, unsigned work by an unknown artist. Yet clearly a work of some merit. And an attractive local landscape, too. Now, ladies and gentlemen, what am I bid. . .?'

Cassie stared.

And stared.

She could hardly believe it.

Her heart began to thud.

She recognised the distinctive use of the pale colours, the broad sweeps of the palette knife, the impressionistic style.

Shocked eyes swept over the scene.

Cassie's stomach churned as she realised that there was only one place where the artist could have set up his easel to paint this picture – where the river was on the left, the suspension bridge in the distance, and the impressive two-storeyed house in which she was now sitting on the right. She had seen that particular view herself many

many times. From the far point of the island, on the riverbank, right next to the small studio.

The studio. . .where Dan had come to stay and paint that fateful summer; where she had posed so innocently for a portrait; where their affair had begun. . .and ended.

A wave of irony washed over Cassie. She thought of all the hours – the *days* – she had spent, wheeling Jason's pram through art galleries in Sydney, searching for one of Dan's paintings. It was a perverse desire. . .wanting to own one, wanting some tangible evidence of his existence. Her mind had kept telling her quite categorically that she should despise the man and never want to see him, or anything belonging to him, again.

Still, she had gone on searching during the entire time it had taken her to complete her veterinary science degree – a foolish, obsessive quest. She had returned home to Riversbend empty-handed, yet this particular painting had been here all along, barely a mile from her home.

'Two thousand. . . Last bid was yours, sir. Any advance on two thousand?'

Cassie came back to the reality of the auction with a jolt. The painting was being sold! Her mouth opened of its own accord. 'Twenty-one hundred.'

Eyes snapped her way. She had not bid before.

Cassie's pulse started racing. She knew that she was doing a mad thing. She was supposed to be buying a present, not giving in to some ghastly sentimental indulgence. It wasn't as though she felt anything for the man any more. Her love for him was well and truly dead. She felt absolutely and positively nothing.

Her heart pounded even faster. Somehow the knowledge that she was acting crazily made no difference. She could not seem to help herself. She wanted that painting!

'Twenty-five!' snapped the man whom she had overbid.

Cassie gritted her teeth. 'Twenty-six.'

There was an electric silence. Cassie held her breath.

'Twenty-seven,' the other bidder gruffed.

Cassie breathed in deeply, trying to calm her growing tension. Should she bid twenty-eight, or leap to three thousand? Which would be the better tactic? Her chest felt as if a vice were squeezing it.

'Three thousand,' she blurted out. And held her breath.

'Thirty-five hundred.'

Disappointment knifed through Cassie, and her chest sagged. She could not go on. She really couldn't. Three thousand had to be her limit.

'It's against you, madam,' the auctioneer said.

She could feel expectant eyes upon her. But she slowly shook her head, her eyes dropping to the floor. She could no longer bear to look at the painting.

'Five thousand dollars!'

A murmur swept through the crowd at the astonishing new bid. Cassie's head snapped round. She knew that voice! Her eyes clawed through the sea of faces. It couldn't be him. It *couldn't*. . .

There was no reason why he should be here. No reason at all. . .

And then she saw him, standing near one of the back windows, looking as devastating as ever.

Dan McKay.

His black eyes locked fiercely on to hers, and a stab of pure pain sliced through Cassie. She jerked her head round to face the front, shaken to the core of her being.

'Going once, twice. . . Sold!'

Cassie jumped when the gavel banged down. Then she sat. At first frozen, then suddenly trembling. If someone had asked her before this moment what was left of her feelings for Dan McKay she would have said nothing. *Nothing*! She would have sworn that he could not move a single emotion in her.

But she had been wrong. Something dark and destructive, something unexpected and shocking, had stirred inside her. It spun her head back to seek him out again.

He was moving towards the front of the room,

his gaze never leaving hers. But his eyes were guarded, making it impossible to tell what he was thinking. Cassie's mouth grew dry as she watched him approach. He was so handsome still, each line of his strong, angular face and tall, lean body achingly familiar.

Yet there were differences, Cassie conceded ruefully. The unruly black waves of nine years ago had been cut short and, while the well-groomed style complemented his dark suit and white shirt, he was a far cry from the informal, bejeaned Dan whom Cassie had once known. This man was smooth and suave and sophisticated, the epitome of city elegance.

Dan was watching her as well, waiting perhaps for a visible reaction to his shock return. When she gave none, sitting silent and staring, he smiled, his straight black eyebrows lifting enquiringly.

Again it sliced through her, sharper now and more definite, tightening her stomach, setting her teeth hard in her jaw. Hatred! Pure and utter hatred!

The feeling was so shockingly intense that she must have projected it in her eyes, for the smile was instantly wiped from his face, his expression changing to one of puzzlement.

A wave of fierce resentment swept through Cassie at his lack of sensitivity. Who did he think he was, coming back here, smiling at her as if everything had been forgiven and forgotten? Nothing was forgiven! Nothing was forgotten!

No doubt his return had something to do with buying back his painting. Nothing else would have brought him back, she decided cynically. And no doubt he would be gone again at the end of the auction.

Meanwhile. . .

Cassie gritted her teeth and looked up. He was talking to the auctioneer's assistant, yet glancing impatiently her way. A jolt of sudden panic set her heart racing. Jason! Oh, God, she had forgotten about Jason!

Her mind whirled. It was imperative that Dan didn't accidentally find out about the boy during his visit. Imperative! Instinct told Cassie that Dan was not a man who would ignore a son, even if the mother meant nothing to him any longer.

Cassie knew that she had to get out of this room, away from him. To meet him and talk to him – however briefly – was a risk she wasn't prepared to take.

She should have left without looking back. She should have just stood up and walked away. But something – female curiosity, perhaps – drew her to one final glance.

It was a mistake. He was staring at her over the man's shoulder, and when their eyes met he held hers easily. They had always been her undoing. His eyes. They were like molten ebony, their deep-set, penetrating scrutiny searing its way into her soul, evoking long-buried memories from deep inside.

She tried to look away, but could not.

She was transfixed, hypnotised. Her heart began to pound and, as his gaze went deeper and deeper, Cassie's mind plunged her back...back...till she was lying on the rug on the studio floor, gazing passionately up at him. He was standing over her, proud and virile, his eyes devouring her, arousing her, teasing her, till she could bear it no longer. She held her arms out to him, and as he knelt down she reached out, gathering his naked body to hers with a sighing, tormented groan.

Cassie jerked back to the present, a cold sweat breaking out on her forehead. She wrenched her eyes away from his and jumped up, clusmy in her haste, but intent only on one purpose. To flee.

CHAPTER TWO

DAN caught her on the veranda.

'Cassie?' His hand closed over a wrist, spinning her to a halt.

Terrified eyes lifted to him.

'You're not leaving, are you?' He peered down at her with that inscrutable black gaze of his.

Cassie tried desperately to pull herself together. You are twenty-nine years old, she reassured herself. You are a competent veterinary surgeon. You are an independent, clear-thinking woman. You are *not* a vulnerable, naïve girl barely out of her teens.

She dragged in a steadying breath and schooled her face into a bland smile. 'Hello, Dan,' she said. 'I thought it was you in there. It's been a long time. You're looking well. Sorry, but I can't stay and chat. I'm running late.'

His hand remained closed around her wrist, effectively staying her. 'Then you didn't leave the auction because of me?' His eyes were searching hers, trying no doubt to gauge her reaction to him.

The intensity of his expression unnerved and annoyed Cassie. Who did he think he was, giving her the third degree after running into her out of sheer coincidence? He couldn't possibly have known that she would attend this auction.

Her laugh carried the right amount of dry disdain. 'Good heavens, no. Why should I do that?'

He frowned. Clearly her attitude puzzled him. The reason why eluded Cassie. 'Then could you spare me a few minutes?' he asked, still frowning. 'I won't keep you long.'

She glanced at her watch, then up. 'Perhaps a minute, then.' Her voice held an impatient note.

'So kind,' he muttered, and dropped her wrist.

Cassie tried not to let her relief show. It was unbearable having him touch her. Unbearable!

'You'll have to make it snappy, Dan. I really must be going.'

His head tilted slightly to one side, eyes narrowing. His gaze flicked down over her body, clad casually in faded blue jeans and a pink cotton shirt. When he looked back up at her face, his expression thoughtful, Cassie found herself wishing she'd had time to change before coming to the auction. But she'd been running late after an emergency at the surgery, and had had only a minute to dash on some pink lipstick and flick a quick brush through her fine blonde hair.

At that moment she wanted more than anything to be able to present an image as cool and sophisticated as Dan's. The feeling that she was at a physical disadvantage was as annoying as his close scrutiny.

'You know, you've hardly changed,' he said slowly. 'You're still incredibly beautiful. . .still without artifice.'

Her cheeks burnt with hot resentment. Her jaw clenched in anger. Trust him to resort to flattery. What a hide he had! And what a fool she was to let him still affect her, even if it was just irritation now. But two could play that game.

'You're hardly the worse for wear, either,' she countered in an offhand tone.

His mouth lifted in a dry smile. 'You flatter me. I'll be forty next year, and I feel every day of it.'

Cassie was taken aback. She hadn't realised he was that old. Nine years ago he had looked as if he were in his middle twenties, no more. But it didn't change anything. In fact, it made his guilt even worse. He should have known better than to toy with a young girl's life.

She waited for him to say something further, but he didn't. He had always been a man of few words.

'What is it you want, then?' she snapped irritably.

He drew back a step and flourished his hand in the direction of the front doors. 'If you will accompany me inside, I'll show you.'

'What do you mean. . .inside? I'm not going back into the auction. I told you. I have to go.'

'I know what you told me. . .' His determined glance indicated that he'd totally ignored all she had said. 'We'll go into the library. It's the first door on the right.'

'We can't do that!'

'Why not?'

'The owner might not like it.'

'He won't mind.'

Her eyes grew wary. 'How do you know that? Do you know him?'

'Very well.'

Cassie tried to control her growing alarm. She'd heard that the new owner of Strath-haven was a wealthy businessman from Sydney, intent on using the island as a rural retreat, in much the same way as the van Aarks had done. If Dan was a friend of his, as he had been of the van Aarks, perhaps he would be staying here as a guest sometimes. Oh, God. . .

'Stop frowning, Cassie,' he advised. 'It spoils your lovely forehead.'

She threw him a scornful look. 'I'll come inside, but please. . .stop the flattery. Keep that for your current victims. It won't work on me any more.'

He stiffened at her barb, but she gained no satisfaction from it. Strange, she puzzled, that she didn't enjoy hurting him. Surely he deserved it? Surely he deserved anything she could dish out?

'Come along,' he ground out, taking her elbow in a firm grip.

When she instinctively pulled back, he sighed and lessened the force of his hold. But he still urged her towards the front doors. Cassie went, not knowing what else to do. He wasn't going to take no for an answer, that was obvious. And she knew that she should find out what the situation was – if he was going to be around on a regular basis.

A churning thought had come to her. Perhaps he worked for the new owner of Strath-haven. After all, artists rarely made enough to live on.

Going with him proved to be a mistake. She had underestimated the physical effect he still had on her. His fingers felt like silken threads on the soft flesh of her inner arm, sending warm shivers through her veins, and when he stopped to open the library door the still reality of his closeness became particularly disturbing. All she had to do was turn and she would be in his arms. All she had to do was signal her willingness and he would sweep her into the room, shut the door and kiss her.

She knew that this was so, for Dan McKay was that sort of man. The type who would take a woman quite ruthlessly – if she showed weakness – all the while pretending she was someone special, then discard her if and when it was expedient.

'This won't take long, will it?' she asked sharply, and took a step backwards. She was worried that he might grow aware of her quickened heartbeat, her flush of sexual awareness.

He pushed the door open, then glared down at her. Light from the room slanted brilliantly across his face and Cassie was shocked to see that he *had* aged, though he still didn't look anywhere near forty. A smattering of grey was hiding within the thick black waves and there were lines around his dark eyes.

But neither detracted from his appeal. If anything, they added a dimension of rugged sophistication to his looks that he had perhaps lacked all those years ago. Or perhaps it appealed to her now because she herself was older.

'If you'd stop backing away from me,' he said curtly, 'we'd be a damned sight quicker!'

Cassie tipped up her chin and strode past him, dropping her holdall in a distant chair before whirling round to face him.

He was watching her closely. 'Far enough away for you?' he mocked. 'Shall I keep the door open as well?'

She said nothing. But her stomach muscles tightened as he swung the door shut. An impatient sigh betrayed his frustration.

'I won't hold you up now,' he said brusquely, moving to pick up the painting, which she hadn't noticed lying on top of a large desk, 'but I wanted you to have this.'

Cassie's mouth dropped open. Confusion and

anger warred with an irrational pleasure. 'But why?' she blurted out before recovering. 'I. . . No, thank you. I don't want it. I won't take it!'

His face was annoyingly passive. 'Why not? You were bidding for it.'

She gulped down a gathering lump of panic. 'That doesn't mean I'll take it from you.'

'Why not?'

His persistence brought an agitated mutter. 'This is ridiculous!'

'Is there someone who would object to your taking a gift from me? A lover, perhaps?'

She glared at him. 'I don't have to answer your questions, Dan McKay!'

'No, you don't,' he said with maddening composure.

There was a short, sharp silence.

'I could well have a husband by now, for all you know,' she threw at him.

'But you don't, do you?'

She gasped. 'How do you know that? Have you been spying on me?'

She saw the surprise on his face and knew that she was over-reacting badly.

He walked over and picked up her hand. Her stomach somersaulted as his long, elegant fingers stroked her palm, her fingers. 'You're not wearing a ring,' he explained.

She snatched her hand away, but not before her

breathing had gone absolutely haywire. 'I might have taken it off,' she argued breathlessly.

'And have you?' His black eyes were watchful.

She lifted her chin. 'No.'

'So there's no husband. What about lovers? Any of those around at the moment?'

Her blue eyes flashed angrily at his hounding of her private life. 'My having or not having a lover is none of your business.'

'I'm making it my business.'

She was shocked by the implication of his statement. 'My God!' she exclaimed. 'Do you honestly think you can come back here after all these years and take up where you left off?'

His eyes were giving her no peace. They were devouring her, yet telling her nothing.

'I didn't think anything, Cassie,' he said matter-of-factly. 'But when I saw you in there, bidding for my painting, I thought ——'

'Thought what?' she cut in savagely. 'That I was buying it as a sentimental reminder of you?' She laughed – a harsh, cynical sound. 'You do have a colossal ego, don't you? I'll tell you why I wanted that painting of yours. Yes, it was as a reminder. A reminder of the mistake I made in loving and believing in a man like you! But now I don't need it, do I? I've seen you again, experienced at first hand another sample of your amazing sense of opportunity.' She glared at him in disgust. 'I can just imagine what you felt in there when you saw me bidding for your painting. An initial surprise, perhaps, but quickly followed by a smug satisfaction. An old flame, you would have thought, who hasn't forgotten the good times we once shared. She even wants my painting as a memento. What good luck! I wonder what would happen if I bought the painting and made a grand gesture of giving it to her. She would be bound to be grateful, maybe even *very* grateful. . .'

Cassie stopped, and let a mask of stone drop over her heated features. 'Isn't that how it was, Dan? Did I get anything wrong?'

He was staring at her with such a look of horror that for a moment Cassie wondered if she could indeed be wrong.

He shook his head. 'You couldn't be more wrong. I never intended to hurt you, Cassie. Not then. . .or now.'

His rich voice reverberated with such apparent sincerity that Cassie almost weakened. But she didn't. For this was Dan McKay speaking, she reminded herself coldly. Accomplished artist, lover, liar and adulterer!

'Hurt me?' she tossed off airily. 'Don't lose any sleep on my account. I'm well and truly over you now, believe me.'

He frowned at her, but said nothing. Cassie hated his silence. She remembered how when she'd posed for him hours had gone by without his saying a word. She had chattered away, telling him everything about herself, but he'd never reciprocated. It wasn't until he'd left her that she'd known why.

'What are you doing here, anyway?' she demanded. 'Riversbend is a long way from the bright lights of Sydney.'

When her tart words brought an assessing look from Dan, Cassie regretted asking. She hoped he wouldn't think she was interested in him, despite her outburst.

'A change is as good as a rest,' he said cryptically.

A prickle of apprehension darted up Cassie's spine. 'Oh?'

'I needed some fresh air.' He walked over to stare through the large window at the river below. 'I've always loved this place. When I found out it was on the market. . .'

Cassie's heart stopped. Surely he couldn't mean. . .?

He turned slowly, saw her widening eyes. 'I decided to buy it. Yes, Cassie, I'm the new owner of Strath-haven.'

CHAPTER THREE

CASSIE went weak at the knees.

'I'll be your next-door neighbour,' Dan added, his hands slipping into his trouser pockets. 'That is. . .if you still live on the farm across the river.'

She didn't know what to say. The feeling of impending doom was overwhelming. It was all she could do to keep standing.

'I gather that idea doesn't find favour,' Dan said drily.

Cassie stared at him. 'You really o-own Strath-haven?' she stammered.

'You sound doubtful.'

'But how?' she blurted out. 'I mean. . .'

He gave her a sharp look. 'I've done well enough over the years.'

'But. . .but you're an artist. I was told that the new owner was a businessman!'

'Can't I be both?' His face softened for a moment. 'Look, Cassie, I'm not an artist by profession. Painting's a hobby of mine. . .a pastime.'

His admission swept all thought of Jason aside for the moment. All Cassie could think of was how little she'd known about Dan at the time of their affair, how little he had told her! It hurt terribly to be reminded of her foolish naïveté.

'Do forgive my stupidity,' she said tartly. 'A pastime. . . How quaint! Just as your models were pastimes?'

His sigh carried frustration. 'You know that's not true. And I never said I made my living as an artist.'

'You never said much at all, Dan,' she accused.

Silence descended. They looked at each other for several seconds, Cassie with bitter resentment, Dan with an undermining concern.

'Why are you so hostile, Cassie? After all this time.'

'Hostile, Dan? I'm not hostile. I'm merely saying a few of the things I never had the opportunity to say nine years ago. You did leave rather quickly.' Her glare held shivers of ice. 'But that's all water under the bridge, isn't it? The present is far more to the point. I gather you won't be living here permanently? This will be a weekender, or some such?'

Already she was devising a plan to protect herself and her son. Her mother and Roger were getting married soon. They could have the house across the river. She could move, to Roger's place in town maybe, or to another town altogether!

'I shall be travelling back and forth to Sydney,' he admitted slowly, 'but I *had* intended spending as much time here as I could.'

Her mind jumped on the way he'd said '*had* intended'. She clutched at the straw. 'And you've changed your mind?'

'That depends.'

'On what?'

He shrugged. 'On a lot of things.' He gave her the oddest look. It was vaguely challenging. 'Meanwhile. . .don't you think we could at least be friends? After all, we will be neighbours. How about coming back when this auction is over? Have dinner with me this evening. You could advise me on what to buy for the house. I did keep the essentials in furniture, but the rest will need a woman's touch.'

Cassie stared at him in utter astonishment. 'You don't give up easily, do you?'

'No.'

'I can't,' she said sharply. 'Sorry.'

'Can't or won't?'

'Both!'

'Why not?'

Cassie's head was whirling. Why not? God, if only he knew. . .

But he would know, she thought frantically, if he meant to really live here. Even if she moved, some day, someone would say something about Jason. And Dan would come looking for him.

Fear made her aggressive. 'I think your wife is a good reason for me not to come, don't you?'

There was no doubting his shock, but he

recovered quickly. 'I see... So that's it. You found out.'

'The van Aarks were only too pleased to enlighten me.'

'And what exactly did they tell you?' he said angrily, and paced towards her. 'For pity's sake, Cassie, they didn't even know the whole truth.' His hands closed over her shoulders. 'They weren't close friends, just social acquaintances. God! Do you think I confided my private affairs to people like them?'

Cassie was crazily aware of the bruising fingers digging into her shoulders. Her breathing grew fast and shallow. Her face flushed. 'Let me go!' she gasped in a panic.

'No!' he snarled. 'Not till you've listened to the truth. I was separated from my wife when I came here to stay at the island. We were getting a divorce. I didn't mean to fall in love with you, dammit! But you were so lovely...so goddamned lovely. I convinced myself that I'd be content with painting you, being with you, listening to you give voice to your bright, sweet dreams for the future. What a fool I was to think that I wouldn't end up making love to you! But I did *love* you, Cassie, and I meant to marry you at the time. You have to believe that!'

Believe him? He expected her to believe him? *Believing* in Dan had been her greatest mistake.

She wrenched out of his hold with a violent

twist. 'Save your breath, Dan,' she said savagely. 'You're wasting it on me.'

He visibly fought anger at her rejection of his plea.

'Something wrong, Dan?' she mocked. 'Your plans going awry?'

New resolve firmed his face. 'Cassie, I understand how bad it must have looked. I really do. And I can see how hurt you've been, but you must listen. My wife had an accident – a terrible accident. She——'

'I know about the accident,' she interrupted bluntly. 'The van Aarks told me that, too. But *you* didn't, Dan, when you sent me my "Dear John" letter. No mention of any accident. No mention of any wife. Shall I tell you what you said? Shall I remind you?'

His mouth clamped shut in thinly disguised frustration.

'"Dear Cassie,"' she went on in sharp, bitter tones. '"I hate having to write to you like this. I would much rather be able to see you personally. To explain. But it is best that I stay right away. You are young. You will forget me in time. And, I hope, forgive me. I want you to get on with your life, my darling girl. Be a wonderful veterinary surgeon, make some man a wonderful wife, some child a wonderful mother. My love always. Dan."'

She glared at him when she had finished, head

held high, eyes smarting with the salt of unshed tears.

He looked appalled. 'You know it...off by heart?'

She turned away from his sight, unwilling to have him witness her distress. She heard him approach, felt his warm breath on the back of her neck. Her heart stopped when his hands closed gently over her shoulders.

'Oh, Cassie, Cassie,' he murmured in her hair. 'I didn't tell you about my wife in the letter because I thought it would only add to your hurt. She needed me in a way I didn't think I could adequately explain. It was far too complex.'

'But *I* needed you, Dan,' Cassie choked out, forgetting everything but the way he was enfolding her back against his chest, forgetting every...single...thing.

'I know...I know...' He was holding her tightly, his lips against her ear. 'But you were young and strong, my darling. You could cope... I had no option then. But I'm back now. Can't you see? I'm back...'

He turned her slowly, tilted up her chin. She caught her breath as his mouth descended.

His kiss was soft and tender...sweet. His thumb was tracing her jawline, a finger stroking the sensitive flesh of her throat.

Subtly, slowly, his mouth grew more insistent, his tongue probing at her hypnotised lips. They parted slightly, allowing him entry, then further and further. Fire ignited along her veins, and before she knew it she was kissing him back with all the fervour of passions that had been buried for nine lonely years. This was the man she had once loved. This was the man who——

'My God!'

She wrenched herself out of his arms, shocked and shaking.

'My God!' she repeated, chest heaving, eyes awash.

'Cassie, I. . .' He reached for her.

'Don't!' she sobbed. 'Don't touch me! Don't say a word.'

He didn't do either. But he was clearly upset.

And why wouldn't he be? Cassie thought with bitter fury as she struggled to get control of herself. For a moment there he must have thought he'd struck the jackpot! Only back at Riversbend for an hour and, with a few half-truths smoothly delivered, he already had a willing bedmate in his clutches.

The glaring facts catapulted into her brain. He'd run into her by sheer coincidence at the auction. He certainly hadn't come back for *her*. He hadn't even known till he'd seen her hand whether she was married or not. In nine years she could very well have moved away somewhere. Or died! And as for that pathetic excuse about his wife not being able to cope. . .

Oh, God! His wife! And what about children? Had the marriage produced children? She hated the very thought, but she had to find out.

Her eyes slashed at him. 'What about your wife? Your children?' she demanded, heart racing.

'I have no children,' came the brusque reply.

Cassie swallowed. 'And your wife? Where's she? Will she be living here with you?'

'No.'

'Another convenient separation?'

'No.'

'What, then?'

His face was grim. 'My wife. . .is dead.'

Cassie was rocked, as much by the announcement as by an unwanted sympathy for Dan. He sounded so. . .desolate.

'When?' she rasped.

'Just over a year ago.'

Any sympathy vanished. 'A year ago,' she repeated flatly. Twelve whole months. Fifty-two weeks. Three hundred and sixty-five days. More than enough time to contact her. . . If he truly cared. It was the final nail in his coffin. 'I see,' she said in a flat, lifeless voice.

'You don't see at all!' Dan growled. 'You've taken everything the wrong way. You don't believe I still care about you!'

'No,' she stated with cruel honesty. 'I don't.'

'Hell!' He raked his hands through his hair,

disturbing the veneer of polished elegance. The dishevelled waves reminded her of the Dan she had first met – the slightly messy, struggling artist. Or so she had believed at the time.

But it had all been an act, a game, a fantasy.

Cassie turned away. She didn't want to be reminded of the past. She had been such a little fool then. She had no intention of being one again.

Suddenly, she remembered and looked at her watch. After five. . . If she wasn't home soon her mother would be sure to come looking for her.

'I have to go,' she said brusquely, and moved towards the door.

Dan was there before her. He opened it, but barred her exit. 'No. Let's get it all straight between us, Cassie. There's too much that's been left unexplained.'

Her eyes were hard. 'You're too late, Dan. Get out of my way.'

He glared at her for a moment, then stepped aside. 'I won't let it finish like this, Cassie,' he said as she walked past him. 'You must know that.'

She stopped and eyed him fiercely over her shoulder. 'And you must know, Dan, that I'm a grown woman now. I have a mind of my own. No one, least of all you, forces me to do anything!'

She set her jaw, suddenly determined to act out her strong words. She would not run away. She would not move. If and when Dan found out about Jason, she would deal with it. He might not discover the boy's existence for ages. He might even quit Strath-haven before doing so.

Dan was watching her with a reproachful expression. 'You've grown hard, Cassie.'

'No, Dan, just wise. . .wise to men like you.'

'I'm not what you think.'

Her smile was cold. 'Goodbye, Dan. Live here if you must, but don't cross that bridge. Don't try to see me.'

'And if I do?'

She swept on, away from his veiled threat, away from her treacherous responses. She should never have let him kiss her. Never! But, oh. . .the pleasure his lips evoked, the desire his touch uncurled.

She stuffed a fist in her mouth to stifle her moan of dismay and hurried on, down the hall, past the noisy auction-room, out into the bright, bright sunshine, there to grind to a horrified halt.

Her mother was coming across the suspension bridge. And running ahead, up the hill, through the hedge, his legs going like pistons, his hair flying, was Jason.

A noise behind her had Cassie whirling.

It was Dan, holding her denim bag. 'You forgot this,' he said.

Stricken, she didn't know where to turn, where to look.

'Mum! Mum!' Jason called as he raced up the stairs to meet her.

CHAPTER FOUR

CASSIE heard Dan's sharp intake of breath. When he stepped forward to be level with her, a swift glance verified his utter shock.

Her eyes flew back to her son, travelling anxiously over his slight figure as he bounced up on to the veranda. Jason was not overly big for his age, so there was some hope that Dan would not put two and two together.

But it was a slim hope. She only had to look frankly at the boy to know that Dan wouldn't be fooled for long. He might not be an artist by profession, but he had an artist's keen observation, and while Jason's hair was mid-brown and quite straight, not at all like Dan's thick black waves, the eyes were a dead giveaway. They were jet black, deep-set and piercing. The exact image of his father's.

Jason reached the veranda, coming to an untidy halt in front of her. 'We won, Mum. We won! Isn't that terrific? And guess what – next week I'm going to have a go as wicket-keeper.'

She dared not look Dan's way, but she could feel the electric tension emanating from his rock-like body. 'That's wonderful, love,' she said, and gave Jason a hug. Be damned with you, Dan McKay! she thought defiantly.

'Hey, Mum, did you see that helicopter over there? Isn't it terrific? Wouldn't I just love to have a ride in that!'

Cassie grimaced at her son's prattle. All she wanted to do was get away. The situation was excruciating for her. She was afraid that the penny would drop and Dan would make a scene. 'Jason, I don't think——'

'That could be arranged,' Dan interrupted curtly, 'since it's my helicopter to do with as I wish.'

Cassie whirled to face him. '*Yours*?' She was still unable to take in Dan's unexpected wealth.

'Mine!' He gave her a hard, penetrating look before returning his attention to Jason, a grim concentration drawing his dark eyebrows together.

'Oh, boy! Did you hear that, Mum?'

She gave a weak nod.

Jason glanced from his mother to Dan. 'Are you a friend of Mum's, mister?'

The corner of Dan's mouth twisted. 'I was. . .a long time ago.'

'And you really own that helicopter?'

Dan flicked a caustic glance Cassie's way. 'I seem to be having trouble making people believe anything I say. Yes, Jason, it is indisputably my helicopter.'

'Wow! Can I have a ride in it today? Now?'

'If you like.'

'Jason, I don't——'

'A ride in a helicopter!' Jason exclaimed, not even hearing his mother's objection. His beaming face was turned towards the helicopter. 'Oh, boy! Wait till Gran hears about this!'

Cassie groaned.

The sound drew a puzzled glance from her son. 'Are you all right, Mum? You look kinda sick, or something.'

'I. . .I have a headache. I'm afraid you'll have to leave Mr McKay's offer of a ride for today.'

'Aw, gee. . .'

Dan knelt down to Jason's eye level. 'Not to worry,' he said kindly. 'There'll be plenty of other days. By the way, how old are you, Jason?'

Cassie's heart stopped.

'Eight,' her son announced proudly, then added, 'I'll be nine in November.'

'Nine, eh?' Dan lifted his dark eyes to glare daggers at Cassie. 'In November, no less. . .'

It took all her inner strength to glare proudly back at him.

So now he knew for certain! It had been inevitable that he would. But what was he going to do about it? Cassie was so upset by the possibilities that her head was indeed pounding.

Dan straightened up, just as Cassie's mother

puffed up the steep steps. 'My goodness, but that's a walk! Jason, you shouldn't tear ahead like that.'

Mrs Palmer's arrival did nothing to alleviate Cassie's distress. Her mother wouldn't recognise Dan, as they had never actually met, but she would know his name. Cassie hoped and prayed that she would be able to escape without effecting an introduction, but, knowing her mother, that was unlikely.

Joan Palmer was still a good-looking woman at fifty-five, with stylishly cut grey-blonde hair and a shapely figure. People said that Cassie was the spitting image of her mother as a young girl, but where Cassie was a modern, independent woman, her mother was one of the old school, who believed that the female sex was put on earth solely for the purpose of marriage. She would not miss a chance of meeting a handsome man, especially one whom she might be able to push in her daughter's direction.

Cassie's anti-social behaviour had been a source of several heated discussions over the years. The 'once bitten, twice shy' principle did not go down well at all, though Cassie could have pointed out that it had taken her mother almost nine years herself to get over her own husband's death. Roger Nolan, Cassie's employer, had been wanting to marry the attractive widow Palmer for years, but Joan had only recently given him the nod. The wedding was due to take place in two weeks' time.

Perhaps finally aware that she was staring at Dan, Joan swung her attention to her daughter. 'Well, love? Did you have any luck at the auction?'

'I'm afraid not, Mum. Everything was much too dear.'

'Guess what, Gran,' Jason piped in. 'This man here's an old friend of Mum's and he owns that helicopter over there and he's going to give me a ride in it some time, aren't you, mister?'

'I guarantee it.'

'See? He——'

'Hush, Jason.' Joan smiled apologetically at Dan. 'That's very kind of you, Mr...er... Cassie, aren't you going to introduce us?'

Cassie steeled herself. It wasn't going to be easy introducing a mother to the man who'd made her unmarried daughter pregnant. And Joan was bound to recognise the name at once.

Cassie's sigh carried a weary resignation. 'Mum, this is the new owner of Strath-haven, Mr McKay...Mr *Dan McKay*.'

'Pleased to meet you, Mr Mc... Oh...' Her ready smile faded, her outstretched hand dropped. 'Oh, dear...'

It was a dreadful moment, saved by a child's innocence.

'Pleased to meet you, Mr McKay.' Jason's hand shot out like a fast ball at cricket.

'You can call me Dan, Jason.'

Cassie stiffened. It had sounded like 'Dad'. 'I think Jason should——'

'Dan will be fine,' he overrode her firmly. 'I prefer it.'

'Are you really going to be living here, Dan?' Jason asked, black eyes shining with uninhibited joy.

'I certainly am.'

'Oh, boy! Can I come over and visit sometimes? I won't be a bother. Really I won't.'

'Any time. . .son.'

The word sent a stab of fear into Cassie. She looked at Dan appealingly. Please, don't tell him, her eyes said. Please. . .

His returning look was so cold, it sent shivers up her spine.

'Did you hear that, Mum?'

'Yes, Jason, I heard,' Cassie choked out. 'Now we really must be going. Nice to have seen you again, Dan,' she added stiffly and took her bag from him. 'Are you coming, Mum?'

Joan looked as if she'd been struck by lightning. 'Oh. . . Yes. . . Of course. . . Goodbye, Mr. . . er. . . Goodbye. . .'

Cassie took her mother's arm and helped her down the steps, not once looking back over her shoulder. Jason, as was his habit, skipped on ahead, shouting, 'Oh, boy! Oh, boy!' in a happy, excited voice.

Cassie kept a firm grip on herself as she walked away. But it wasn't easy. She was tempted to turn round, to run back, to beg Dan not to spoil what she had built up for herself and her son over the last nine years. He had no right, no right at all to come back into her life now and turn it upside-down again. She didn't need him. *Jason* didn't need him. Her son had never suffered from not having a father. And he would gain little from acquiring one now. Particularly one not married to his mother. Riversbend would be agog!

'Cassie. . .'

'What?' she snapped, her angry thoughts having fuelled a short fuse. 'Sorry, Mum,' she added quickly. 'I'm still a bit. . .upset.'

'I don't blame you, love. It must have come as a big shock, seeing Dan McKay again, finding out he'd bought Strath-haven. Then having Jason burst in on you like he did.'

Cassie sighed. They were about to step on to the suspension bridge. Jason was up ahead in the centre, jumping up and down, enjoying the effect he was having. Not so his mother.

'Jason! For Pete's sake, stand still or move along. Do you want your Gran and myself to end up in the river?'

He looked up, not at all chastened. 'Sorry, Mum,' he shouted back, and ran on, which wasn't much of an improvement on using the bridge as a trampoline. It swooped and swayed under their feet.

'That boy!' Cassie complained.

'Perhaps he needs a father's hand,' her mother said softly.

Cassie's glance was sharp. 'And what do you mean by that?'

Her mother gave her one of those innocent 'Are you talking to me?' looks. 'Nothing. . . Nothing.'

'Oh, yes, you did! You think that just because Dan's handsome and rich I should try to get him to marry me, don't you?'

Joan shrugged. 'Well, he doesn't exactly fit the mental picture I've had of him over the years. I imagined him as a shaggy-haired painting bum, with a three-day growth on his chin and not a cent to his name. Let's face it, Cassie, the Dan McKay I saw this afternoon has a lot going for him.'

'Oh, Mum! So Dan's successful and spruced up now. So what? That's all surface gloss. Don't be taken in by it. And give me credit for some pride. You know how deeply he hurt me!'

'Yes, Cassie, I do, but that was a long time ago, love. People make mistakes and life goes on. Perhaps you——' She broke off and stopped abruptly. The bridge shuddered. 'Oh, dear. . . I just realised. . . I. . .I'd forgotten he was married.'

'His wife died a while back,' Cassie announced

bluntly. 'Not that that makes any difference. And before you ask. . .no, he hasn't any other children.'

'Gran! Mum! Come on!'

'Coming, Jason,' Cassie called, and they walked on in agitated silence.

'What do you think he's going to do about Jason?' Joan said at last. 'I mean. . .it's quite obvious that he guessed. And who wouldn't? Why didn't you ever tell me about the eyes? There I was thinking they were a throwback to old Uncle Bart.'

'Do we have to keep talking about this, Mum?' Cassie said impatiently. 'I'd like to forget it.'

'It's a bit hard to forget the man when he's going to be living next door.'

'This isn't the city,' Cassie argued hotly. 'It's not as though we're at leaning-over-the-fence distance from each other. He's a good mile away.'

'Don't be ridiculous, Cassie. You know full well he isn't going to forget *you*. Or Jason. I saw the way he was looking at the boy. Hungry, that man. Hungry for love. . .'

Cassie felt a sick pang in the pit of her stomach. There were many types of hunger, she wanted to say to her mother. And it certainly wasn't love on Dan's mind. Possession might be closer to the mark.

'I might let him see Jason occasionally, but he

needn't think he's going to tell all and sundry he's my son's father,' she said indignantly.

Her mother gave a dry laugh. 'And who's to stop him? Something tells me Dan McKay is not an easy man to handle. Once he's set his mind on something. . .'

Joan's words reminded Cassie of what Dan had said at the library door. . . 'I won't let it finish like this, Cassie.'

And that had been *before* he'd found out about his son! It was all too much for Cassie.

'Here, Mum,' she said, handing her mother the keys as they reached the other side of the river. 'You take the jeep and drive on up home with Jason. I want to see to the horses before it gets dark.'

'You and those horses!'

'I won't be long,' Cassie called as she walked away along the riverbank.

She dimly heard her mother grumble something about dying of starvation, but she kept walking. Actually, the horses didn't need attention. They'd been looked over, fed and watered that morning, but she desperately needed a few quiet moments away from her mother's probing, away from Jason's high-spirited chatter. And she needed time: time to soothe her chaotic nerves, time to think.

All the horses pricked up their ears at her coming, but only Rosie whinnied and trotted to the fence for a pat. The mare's unconditional affection tugged at Cassie's heart. If only people were like that.

Rosie had been eighteen years old, barren and in a deplorable condition when Cassie had saved her from the knacker's yard. People who saw her now could not believe she was the same bedraggled animal of eighteen months before. Not only was she blooming with health, but a foal was on the way.

'Hello, old thing,' Cassie said, running knowledgeable eyes over the mare's rump. There were no tell-tale hollows near the tail. 'No foal tonight, I see. That's good. You have to keep carrying that baby for another month, Rosie, so stick with it, my girl.'

Rosie nodded her head up and down as if in agreement.

Cassie sighed and curled an arm around the horse's neck. 'The man who gave me my baby has come back, Rosie. You don't know Dan. He was before your time. But I don't love him any more. In fact, I hate him! But that's not the problem. Or maybe it is. You see. . .'

She leant closer and pressed her cheek up against the warmth of the horse's mane. 'I have this ghastly confession to make,' Cassie whispered huskily. 'I detest myself for it, but. . .the truth is. . .when Dan kissed me in the library, for a moment I didn't want him to stop. After all this time. . .it felt the same. And how can that be? How can it, when I hate him so?'

As though sensing Cassie's distress, Rosie hung over the fence and nuzzled her mistress's hand. I'm here, the gesture seemed to say. Everything will be all right.

Cassie sighed and straightened. She gave the mare a farewell stroke then turned for the long walk home.

Half-way up the hill Cassie stopped and glanced over her shoulder. A lone figure was standing on the veranda of Strath-haven, and, though it was indiscernible from that distance and in the fading light, Cassie knew that it was Dan.

A shiver ran up her spine. He was watching her. Watching her and already planning his next move.

For, despite her warning him not to, Cassie knew that he *would* cross the river. He would come, if not for her then for his son. It was as inevitable as the sun setting that evening and rising the next morning.

The only question was. . .how soon?

CHAPTER FIVE

ROGER turned from the dining-room window, a glass of port in his hand. 'I hear your new neighbour is quite a man,' he directed at Cassie.

She glanced up from the table to look squarely at her boss. Though almost sixty years old, Roger was still dapper, with short grey hair, a neat moustache and an insatiable curiosity about people.

It was this last facet of his character that had Joan frowning madly at her daughter. Roger knew nothing of the circumstances of Jason's conception, though he'd been living in Riversbend at the time. No doubt he imagined – like everyone else – that some local lad had been responsible. The only people who could have guessed were the van Aarks, but they'd been rarely at Strath-haven and Cassie had kept out of their way after Dan had left. She doubted they'd ever known of Jason's existence.

'Actually, I know him,' she said, standing up to begin stacking the plates. They'd been relaxing with a port after a long Sunday lunch. 'Met him years ago.'

'Really?' Roger's clear grey eyes registered surprise. And interest. 'Do tell.'

'Nothing much to tell,' Cassie shrugged, and continued to gather the crockery. 'He was a visitor at Strath-haven once, a few years back. I ran into him one day when I took some eggs down to Mrs Rambler. If you remember, she used to cook for the van Aarks sometimes.'

'Hmm. . .' Roger turned back to stare through the window again, down at Strath-haven. 'McKay's his name, isn't it?'

'Yes, that's right.'

'Big businessman from Sydney.'

'So it seems.'

Roger turned with a cheeky smile. 'Unattached, too, from what I hear.'

Cassie gave him a sharp look. 'Now, Roger——'

He held up his hands in mock defence, spilling a few drops of port. 'Oops! Joan, love, I. . .er. . .'

Joan swooped with a serviette, quickly wiping the brown drops from the dusky pink carpet. 'Men!' she said, but indulgently.

When she stood up, Roger gave her a squeeze and a kiss. 'You couldn't manage without us, though, could you?'

Cassie turned away from their display of affection, an uncomfortable sensation twisting in her stomach.

'Mum! Mum!' Jason appeared in the doorway, his face bright with excitement. 'There's a red car coming up our drive. One of those with the top down. I think it's Dan driving it.'

'Dan?' Roger asked, puzzled. 'Who's Dan?'

Cassie did her best to ignore her thudding heart. 'He means Dan McKay, the man we were just talking about.'

Now Roger was frowning. 'And Jason calls him Dan?'

Cassie sighed and turned to her son. 'You go out and meet him, love. I'll be there in a moment.'

The boy ran off.

'Dan and I were having a chat after the auction yesterday when Mum and Jason turned up,' Cassie explained. 'Dan seemed to take to Jason and didn't want to be called Mr McKay, that's all. No big deal.'

'Hmm. . .'

Cassie didn't like the way Roger was looking at her. He was far too curious. And perceptive.

She produced a disarming smile. 'I'll just go and see what he wants. You stay here and finish your drink with Mum.'

Cassie hurried from the room before any more awkward questions could be asked.

But she didn't hurry to meet Dan. Once out of Roger's sight her legs ground to a halt, her whole being shaking with a thousand jangling nerves. She leant against the wall of the hallway and took several deep breaths. It was little use. She was still a mess. Yet she had known that Dan would come. . .eventually.

With a jolt she realised that she had sent her son out to be alone with his father. Dan could be saying *anything* to him!

It propelled her into action, and she raced along the hall, out on to the back porch, down the steps and literally into Dan's arms.

'My, my,' he drawled, reaching out to steady her. 'What a pleasant change to find you so anxious to see me.'

For a heart-stopping second, Cassie went totally blank. She stared down at the hands that were grasping her upper arms, then up into Dan's handsome, smiling face. With an inevitability that she found appalling, her body began to respond to his nearness, his touch. Heat suffused the surface of her skin as that insidious seed of suppressed longing burst into life once more.

How easy it would be to give in to it. So easy. . . All she had to do was sink against the hard broadness of his chest and lift her mouth to his.

Instead she wrenched out of his hold, angry more at herself than at Dan. But her tongue didn't seem to know the difference. 'Don't kid yourself!' she snapped. 'You're the last man on earth I want to see.'

'You mean this isn't for me?' he mocked, indicating her clothing.

Cassie looked down at the cream knitted suit which she had worn to church and kept on afterwards. It was the one time during her week that she discarded her jeans.

'You know very well that I wasn't expecting you today,' she flared, her fingers shaking as they nervously arranged the loose top over the matching skirt. Unfortunately, the smoothing down of the ribbed garment only emphasised the thrust of her full breasts, which at that moment felt embarrassingly swollen.

Dan's gaze followed her self-conscious actions. 'Weren't you?'

'Of course not!' Her cheeks flamed. 'We happen to have a visitor.'

His black eyes narrowed. 'Who?'

'My boss,' she informed, without thinking to add that he was shortly to be her stepfather as well. 'He came for Sunday lunch.'

'You must have a close working relationship to have your boss over during the weekend.'

Cassie thought she heard a nasty innuendo in the words. She gave a defiant toss of her head. 'Roger comes to lunch *every* Sunday! Not that that is any of your business, Dan McKay. What are you doing here, anyway? You weren't invited.'

His laugh was dry. 'Something told me not to wait for an invitation.'

She glared at him. 'I thought I told you to keep away from me.'

Anger, hot and strong, swept his features. 'Don't be such a little fool, Cassie!' he slammed back. 'You knew I wouldn't stay away. That's my son out there!' He indicated Jason with a sharp jerk of his head.

'For God's sake, Dan, be quiet...' Cassie darted a stricken look over his shoulder, relieved to see that Jason was fully occupied inspecting Dan's car. And what boy wouldn't be enthralled? Even Cassie could recognise a Mercedes sports coupé when she saw one.

Her eyes sliced back to Dan in agonised appeal. 'Please, Dan...'

He lifted a dark eyebrow. '*Please*, is it now? I thought from your attitude yesterday and just now that it was to be war between us!'

She groaned.

His face showed a guarded surprise. 'Not war?' he asked softly, almost seductively. His right hand lifted to lie gently against her cheek.

Instinctively she stiffened, her head jerking back, her nostrils flaring like those of a frightened horse.

His hand dropped, his mouth curling into a caustic grimace. 'I thought as much. I came here willing to be reasonable, willing to negotiate. But I'd be wasting my breath, wouldn't I, Cassie? You've got no intention of really sharing Jason with me. Your mind is firmly made up. I'm not to be trusted. I'm a bastard, through and through. And that's that!'

Dan's bitter resentment fuelled a similar emotion in Cassie. 'What the hell did you expect?' she muttered at him in a low, hoarse whisper. 'That you could come back after all these years and be welcomed with open arms? That you could wipe the slate clean with a few convenient half-truths?'

'I'll tell you what I expect,' he retorted. 'I expect you to at least have the decency to listen to me. I expect to be allowed a reasonable share of Jason's life, to have the opportunity to love him as a father has a right to love his son!'

Cassie could only stare at Dan in wide-eyed horror. The man was either mad or so consumed with his own importance that he couldn't recognise or appreciate the feelings of others. Didn't he have any concept of what he had done, seducing her with promises of love and marriage, then leaving her to find out after he had gone that he was a married man? Did he honestly think that she was going to expose her son to his brand of loving? What would happen when he tired of the experience, when he decided that being a father was hard work, when he took off back to the bright lights of Sydney?

'You have no rights, Dan McKay!' she spat at him. 'You gave away your rights nine years ago! And I warn you, if you hurt my son I'll——'

'*My*, son, too,' he broke in harshly.

'Only technically!'

He grabbed her. 'Is that my fault? How was I to know?'

'If you'd stayed around long enough, you would have found out, you. . .you. . .'

'Bastard?' Dan suggested.

'If the cap fits, wear it!'

His hands fell from her arms. He drew himself up, stiff and tall, his eyes frightening in their steel-edged resolve. 'You won't give an inch, will you?'

Cassie looked into Dan's eyes and knew instinctively, overwhelmingly that she had made a ghastly mistake. She should have been more conciliatory, more reasonable, regardless of the circumstances. Aggression only bred aggression, and Dan was a wealthy, powerful man – a man not used to being crossed. It came to her with shocking clarity that if she kept blocking access to his son he might actually steal the boy. She had heard of fathers kidnapping their children and fleeing overseas. The very thought made her feel ill.

'Now let me warn *you*, Cassie Palmer,' he ground out, his voice vibrating with deadly menace. 'If you thought I was a bastard before, that's nothing to the bastard I'm going to be. You don't want me to tell Jason I'm his father, do you?'

Cassie caught her breath, once again glancing

anxiously at her son. He was sitting behind the wheel of the sports car, making noises with his mouth, pretending to drive.

'But I will do exactly that if you don't do as I say. No one is going to keep me from my son, do you hear me? No one!'

And with that he spun round, striding away down the path. At the back gate, he whirled, setting incredibly cold eyes upon her. But when he spoke, his voice was amazingly normal. 'So glad you can drop in for a drink this evening, Cassie. . .I'll be looking forward to it. Say about eight? Your visitor should be gone by then. I know you won't be late. We have so much to talk about. . .' He cast a meaningful glance in Jason's direction, his threat quite clear.

Jason looked up, hearing Dan's last words. 'Can I come too, Dan?'

'Sorry, son,' he said gently. 'Only grown-ups allowed. Besides, don't you have to go to school tomorrow?'

Jason's face dropped. 'Yeah. . .' He climbed out of the car, eyes down.

'Don't you like school?'

'I s'pose it's all right.'

'You can come over to my place after school tomorrow, if you like.'

The boy's face brightened. 'That'll be super!' He ran to his mother. 'Can I, Mum?'

She looked over his head at Dan's uncompromising expression. 'As long as you're home before dark,' she managed to get out.

'Wow! Terrific!'

'I'll pick you up from school, Jason,' Dan suggested smoothly. He lifted an eyebrow at Cassie. 'I'm sure he'd like a ride in my car.'

Cassie's insides tightened. She didn't want her son left alone with Dan, but what else could she do? If she said no it might make the situation worse.

She glared at the man whom she had once loved. He was a stranger – a dark, malevolent stranger. Hatred welled up in frightening swirls. Bitter, hot hatred.

His mouth pulled back into a sardonic smile, terrifying her. For he had seen her hatred. And was unmoved by it.

'See you tonight, then,' he called nonchalantly. 'And tomorrow afternoon for you, my boy,' he added, ruffling Jason's hair before striding through the gate and round the nose of the car. He opened the driver's door, pausing to give Cassie a farewell salute before sliding behind the wheel.

It was a mocking, almost threatening gesture, impelling Cassie to place a protective arm around Jason's slender shoulders. The engine purred into life and Cassie caught a glimpse of a harsh glance before the red car disappeared.

Only then did she draw breath. How could she

still want such an individual? What devilish fate made her respond to his touch, and no other man's?

'Dan's real nice, isn't he, Mum?' Jason said with a happy, upturned face. 'I like him.'

Cassie's heart contracted. What an impossible situation she was caught in! 'He likes you, too, love,' she said truthfully.

'I can't wait till tomorrow. Hey, Gran!' He ran into the house, bursting with his news.

Cassie felt close to despair as she watched her son run off. Nine years she had spent making life happy and secure for her son. Nine long, hard years! It had not been easy being an unmarried mother in Riversbend; it had not been easy returning to university to finish her degree. But she had done it. She had got on with her life and made a success of it. She was a respected member of the community, and Jason was a happy, well-adjusted boy.

Dan was threatening everything she held dear.

And, much as she hated the man and what he was doing, she had handled him very poorly. Her blatant lack of co-operation had made him resort to a type of blackmail. Of course, she could go down to Strath-haven tonight and apologise profusely, then beg Dan to see things her way. But would he respond to such an appeal? He was angry. No. . .furious! He wasn't going to listen to her. She just knew it.

With a groan she turned round to walk back up the path, her mind still revolving. What weapon did she have, what argument could she use to sway this angry man?

And then it came to her...slowly... insidiously.

Cassie stopped at the base of the porch steps, her mouth suddenly dry. Could she do it? Dared she do it?

'Cassie...'

She blinked and looked up. Joan was frowning down at her, Roger at her elbow.

'Jason says he's going over to Dan's tomorrow after school,' Joan said. 'Is that right?'

Cassie swallowed. 'Yes, it is.'

'He also said something about you going down to Strath-haven tonight.'

Cassie could see that Roger was all ears. 'That's right. He's asked me down for a drink this evening,' she said truthfully.

'Well, well,' Roger beamed. 'And what did you say?'

'Yes, of course.'

If Cassie hadn't been so distracted she might have laughed at Roger's surprise, for it had been years since she'd accepted a date with a man.

CHAPTER SIX

CASSIE stepped over to the full-length mirror behind her bedroom door and stared into it. She turned sideways to inspect a rear view, and groaned.

'Dear God, I can't wear this,' she muttered. 'It's disgusting!'

She turned back to face the front, her eyes travelling once again over the figure-hugging red woollen sheath. It had been bought several years ago when she had been very thin, and the material now had to stretch to fit, so that, while the neck-to-knee, long-sleeved style was quite modest, the effect once it was moulded to her shapely body was suggestive in the extreme.

Cassie had merely wanted to look attractive, not like a scarlet woman. Her mother had suggested the dress, and the colour did look well on her, but its present effect was far too obvious, much too sexy!

But isn't that what you need to look like? an inner voice taunted.

A fluttering spasm claimed Cassie's stomach at the thought of trying to vamp Dan McKay. She hoped and prayed that such a drastic solution would not be ncessary. It worried her terribly what might happen to her if she did follow that course. What if things got out of hand? *She* might become the victim, not him, for much as she hated him she couldn't deny that she wanted him, too. And he made love so very very well. . .

Cassie spun away from the mirror and began to pace the room, talking to herself all the while. She would definitely try eating humble pie first. She would tell him that he could see Jason as much as he wished, provided he didn't reveal his parentage. She would explain the difference between life in a country area and the vast, impersonal nature of a city existence. The man was not heartless, surely? Even if he didn't give a damn for her feelings, he would probably listen to reason over matters relating to Jason.

She could point out how their son would be terribly hurt by the comments of unthinking people, not to mention those made by the other children at school. Kids could be very cruel.

Yes, she would try to reason with the man. . .at first.

And if that didn't work?

Cassie stopped pacing.

If reason didn't work, she decided with a surge of grim determination, she *would* try to capitalise on the sexual attraction between them. She didn't have to sleep with the man, merely string him along a little – anything to diffuse the situation, to give her some power over him, some weapon to wield. Maybe it was wrong to promise and then not deliver, but. . .

She firmly pushed aside any feelings of guilt. Dan should have known better than to threaten the security of her child. Cassie was prepared to do anything to protect Jason's happiness, even if it meant swallowing her pride, throwing away her personal dignity; even if it meant putting herself fairly and squarely into the lion's den.

A knock at her door interrupted the silent tirade of resolutions.

'Cassie? Can I come in?'

'Just a moment.' She pulled out a black thigh-length cardigan, dragging it over the sexy red dress. She didn't want her mother to jump to conclusions, even right ones. 'Come in,' she called, her heart racing.

'Cassie, I. . .' Her mother stopped and frowned. 'Won't you be hot in that cardigan?'

Cassie picked up a hairbrush and gave a good imitation of nonchalance, talking and brushing at the same time. 'It's going to be chilly in the jeep.' She flicked back her fringe and smoothed the rest into its natural pageboy style, deliberately not looking at her face. She didn't want her to see the over-bright blue eyes, or the parted lips, trembling in scarlet gloss. 'I'll take the cardigan off once I get there,' she added, swallowing a lump of panic at the thought.

Her mother was staring down at her stockinged feet. 'What shoes are you going to wear?'

Cassie had pulled out a pair of outrageously high red sandals which she'd bought one year at a sale. But after putting the dress on she'd changed her mind. 'My black flatties, I guess.'

'Your black flatties?' her mother repeated. 'In *that* dress?' She spied the red sandals near the bed and picked them up. 'What's wrong with these? I mean. . .it's not as if you're a tall girl, Cassie. Though it wouldn't matter next to a man like Dan.'

Cassie said nothing. But she knew better than to argue with her mother over matters of dress. She put down the hairbrush and reluctantly slipped on the shoes.

Joan smiled smugly at her daughter. 'You'll knock him dead, darling.'

Cassie's sigh betrayed her jagged nerves. 'Mum. . .you know I'm only going down to talk to the man.'

Her mother's face assumed one of her innocent expressions. 'Of course you are. . . Here. . .' And she picked up the bottle of Paradise perfume lying on the dressing-table, giving Cassie a liberal spray.

Cassie had to laugh. 'Mum, you are an incurable romantic.' And, curling an arm around her mother's elbow, Cassie shepherded her from the room.

'Thanks for looking after Jason for me,' she

said as they walked along the hallway. 'And don't let him talk you into letting him watch the Sunday movie.'

'Would I do that?'

'Yes! That boy can twist you around his little finger.'

Her mother's smile faded. 'You know, Cassie, I'm going to miss the little minx when Roger and I get married.'

'Now, Mum, don't start that. You know it's time you made a life for yourself. And it's not as if you're going to be far away. Riversbend town is less than three miles from here and you can come out any time. Besides, didn't we agree that Jason would go to your place in town after school each afternoon till I've finished work?'

'Yes. . .'

'Well, then, you'll still see plenty of each other.'

As the two women passed the lounge doorway, Cassie popped her head inside. Jason was watching *The Cosby Show* and laughing with the uninhibited joy of a child.

'I'm going now, Jason,' she called. 'Be a good boy for your Gran, and don't forget to clean your teeth.'

He swung round from where he was sitting cross-legged on the floor and smiled at her. Cassie's heart contracted at the sight of those dancing black eyes. Never had he looked so much like his father, and it was disturbing. How long would it be before some eagle-eyed gossip made the connection? Particularly if Dan started being seen in Jason's company in public.

The drive down to the suspension bridge gave her more time to think. And to worry.

Suddenly she wished she had not worn the red dress. It had been a stupid thing to do. And precipitate, being too blatantly sexy. How could she mediate the situation first with an ounce of dignity and common sense looking as she did?

The jeep reached the riverbank too quickly for Cassie's liking. She pulled up next to the bridge, sick with apprehension at what lay ahead. She prayed that Dan *would* be reasonable, for every tentacle of her intution was screaming that to invite Dan to make love to her in any way at all would be to invite disaster!

Extracting herself from behind the wheel in the ridiculously tight skirt proved difficult, though it made Cassie all the more determined to keep the cardigan on. She reassured herself as she struggled up the steps on to the moonlit bridge that a cardigan didn't look all that strange. The evening was clear and cool, a breeze coming off the river. Time enough to remove the covering garment later – if the need arose.

The house looked eerie in the moonlight, with only a few of the many windows showing a light. Cassie hesitated at the base of the stone steps, apprehension gnawing at her stomach. If it hadn't been for Jason she would have turned tail and run.

She put one nervous foot forward, then froze. A Dobermann, sleek and powerful, awaited her at the top of the stone steps, growling with teeth bared. She kept very still, her thudding heart appreciative of the breed's reputation, though she had never encountered one in all her years as a country vet.

She knew not to show fear with an animal, but the hairs on her neck were prickling ominously.

'Sit!' she tried in her most authoritative voice.

No change. If anything, the dracula-like teeth were bared even more.

Cassie swore under her breath. Where was Dan? He was expecting her, wasn't he? It was already ten past eight.

'Why don't you sit, you rotten dog?' she hissed. 'Or go away.'

'Maybe he justs wants to look at you.' A voice emerged from the blackness, along with its owner. 'Back, Hugo!' he commanded, and the dog disappeared.

Dan stood at the edge of the veranda, his impressively male body silhouetted against the rectangle of light falling from the open front door. Cassie caught her breath. He was as sleek and dark as the dog had been, yet infinitely more dangerous, his satanic image enhanced by the clothes he was wearing. Black shoes, black trousers, a black polo-necked sweater.

Cassie felt hopelessly intimidated, as well as a ghastly sexual awareness. Both reactions irritated her.

'Are you coming up?' Dan drawled. 'Or do we talk out here with the mosquitoes?'

'There are no mosquitoes in September,' she countered tartly.

He gave a mock salute. 'I bow to your judgement, Madam Vet.'

Cassie stiffened. 'How did you know I was a vet? Have you been questioning people about me?'

His sigh carried frustration. 'You really are paranoid, aren't you? Perhaps I just assumed it, my sweet. You told me nine years ago you were doing a veterinary science degree, don't you remember?'

Oh, yes... She remembered. She remembered *all* the things she had told him, all the intimate, loving, soul-destroying things!

A resurgence of bitterness had her glaring up at him, but he didn't appear to notice. Or maybe he couldn't see her properly in the shadows. Either way he ignored her angry look and stretched one hand towards her. 'Come. You're beginning to irritate me, standing down there like a reluctant virgin on her wedding night.'

Cassie clamped her teeth together, biting back a sharp retort. It was going to be hard to keep control of her temper, she realised with some dismay. She had to remember to be very pleasant.

Nevertheless, she ignored Dan's outstretched hand, negotiating the steps as carefully as possible in the ridiculously high heels. 'You'll have to do something about that dog of yours,' she said thoughtfully as she reached the veranda, 'if you expect me to let Jason come to visit.'

Dan's laughter chilled her soul. Cassie stared at him, unable to hide her alarm. 'Why are you laughing? I haven't said anything funny.'

His mouth snapped shut, then creased back in a humourless smile. 'It was the choice of the word "*let*" that I found amusing. Come. . .I'm tired of this stupid banter. We'll go into the library and get down to real business.'

With that he took her elbow, propelling her as he had the previous afternoon through the doorway, along the hall then into the library, his touch no less disturbing than on that occasion.

The door closed ominously behind them. Then, before Cassie could stop him, Dan slipped the black cardigan from her shoulders. 'You'll be too hot in this,' he pronounced.

She spun round, her cheeks reddening. But he hadn't noticed her dress yet. He was walking away from her to hang the garment over a chair near the door. Cassie glanced around the room, wondering where she could stand to make her choice of clothing less. . .obvious.

But there was nowhere.

She couldn't very well hide behind the heavy green curtains or the large walnut desk. Otherwise, the only furniture consisted of four deeply cushioned armchairs, whose backs were hard against the bookshelves. Even the drinks cabinet was built-in.

Stricken, she stared down at the pale gold carpet, which was thick and plush underfoot, trying desperately to find the courage to meet Dan's eyes. Once again she had underestimated something. This time her own pride. She knew – no matter what the motivation – that she could not belittle herself by trying to even mildly seduce this man. Yet he would be bound to suspect something, once he looked at her dress!

When she did finally glance up it was to find Dan staring at her, as she had expected. But not with a knowing leer. More a black, brooding anger.

'Going somewhere, Cassie?' he grated out. 'Or have you already been.'

Relief overwhelmed her. Here was the perfect excuse for her appearance, supplied by Dan himself.

'I have a late date' she returned, adopting a nonchalant manner. 'I didn't think I'd be here all that long.'

The black eyes blazed. Surely he couldn't be

jealous? she thought dazedly. The thought brought a swift, mad pang of pleasure.

'I suppose it's your boss again. What was his name? Roger? I do hope he's a patient man,' Dan added caustically. 'This might take some time.'

'He'll wait!' she snapped, perversely not telling him the truth. For some deep, dark reason that even Cassie didn't want to explore, she liked Dan sounding jealous.

'I dare say.' His eyes travelled over her body with insolent slowness, lingering first on her thighs, then drifting up to her full, taut breasts. 'A body like yours would be worth waiting for. From what I can see – which is ample – it's even better than I remembered.'

Cassie felt totally mortified. He might as well have touched her, so intense was her response to his scrutiny, his words. Heat suffused her skin. An unnerving excitement ran through her veins. 'I am more than a body, Dan McKay,' she protested, but far, far too shakily. 'I have a mind. And feelings!'

His laughter was mocking. 'I must apologise. It's hard to remember such esoteric matters when confronted by such a striking. . .dress.' His eyes slid down her legs to her feet. 'Not to mention the shoes.'

She assumed a stony mask, brilliantly covering up her fluster. 'I am not here to discuss my appearance. Or my love-life. I think we should get to the point.'

'Very well.' Dan turned abruptly and strode around behind the desk. He sat down in the leather swivel-chair, leaning back, elbows on the arms, fingers linked in front of his chest. His black gaze studied her mercilessly for several elongated seconds, making her feel lost and vulnerable.

'Do sit down, Cassie,' he said at last. 'If you can manage it.'

The prospect of sinking into one of the deep armchairs, her skin-tight skirt riding up danger-ously, rattled her. 'I'd rather not, thank you.'

'Suit yourself.'

She walked over to stand next to the long windows, staring blankly out on to the moonlit island. When her gaze landed on the outline of the river studio she closed her eyes. Tight.

'Remembering, Cassie?' Dan asked, in an oddly tender voice.

Her eyes flew open. 'Remembering what?' she snapped, whirling round to face him.

Undeterred by her sharp tone, he went on. 'What we once shared... Remember the time you came to me at the studio in the middle of the night, unable to sleep. How you slipped into my bed, naked and ready. How——'

'Stop it!' she lashed out, alarmed at the way his words were arousing her. 'I didn't come down here tonight to be tormented by you, Dan McKay.

I came here to discuss my. . .to discuss Jason. Nothing else. The last thing in the world I want is to be reminded of my stupid adolescent behaviour with you!'

She glared at him, her face coldly angry. But her hands were trembling, her pulse was pounding, her mind a chaotic mass of erotic memories. Memories of hot summer nights and moonlit swims, of hungry kisses and bodies blending, of passionate possession. . .and blissful surrender.

He stood up, and began walking around the desk, coming her way. Cassie froze. Dear God, don't let him touch me. . .

He didn't. Instead, he walked over to the cocktail cabinet and poured himself a drink. Straight Scotch, by the look of it. He didn't even bother to add any ice from the bucket resting at his elbow. Lifting the glass, he downed the amber-coloured liquid in one swallow, then turned to face her, eyes sardonic.

'Forgive my rudeness. I should have asked you what you were drinking these days.'

'I don't drink. You know that.'

One eyebrow lifted. 'All I know, my dear, is that you didn't drink once. But things have changed, haven't they? You've changed. The girl I remember would never have made a date with one man, intending to slink off afterwards to meet another.'

Cassie flinched inwardly, but refused to take

the bait. 'You call this. . .meeting. . .a date? Do I have to remind you that you blackmailed me into coming here tonight?'

Dan smiled coldly as he refilled the glass. 'All's fair in love and war,' he pronounced, then drained that drink as well.

He even poured a third. But this time he added ice and carried it back to the desk. His sigh was heavy as he slumped back in the chair. Cassie felt an unexpected and annoying wave of sympathy for him. He looked so bleak as he stared at her over the rim of the glass.

'Tell me, Cassie,' he said at last, 'what mischance caused you to fall pregnant with Jason in the first place? Did you forget to take the Pill one night? Was that it?'

Cassie sighed. She should have known that he would ask that. He was far too intelligent to forget. 'I wasn't on the Pill,' came the reluctant admission.

The glass of whisky hovered at his lips and he slowly lowered it to the desk. His eyes hardened. 'But you said you were?'

'No. . .I didn't.'

He leant forward. 'I remember – clearly – that first time. I asked if it was safe. You reassured me that it was perfectly safe. I assumed that meant that you were on the Pill as a general precaution.'

Cassie sighed. 'I realise that's what you thought. . .'

Silence descended.

Finally Dan spoke again, in a careful, almost wary tone. 'Were you deliberately trying to get pregnant, Cassie?'

Her eyes rounded. 'No!'

'Then why. . .why take such a risk?'

She shrugged despairingly. It would be useless to tell him how obsessive her feelings had become. How the first few times it *had* been relatively safe, but as the days had worn on and the risk had increased, she hadn't been thinking straight any more. She hadn't been able to help herself. All she'd been able to think of was Dan loving her, Dan possessing her, Dan. . . Dan. . . Dan. . .

'I was stupid,' she admitted grimly, and closed her eyes again, trying not to remember, but failing miserably.

A light touch on her cheek jerked her eyes open to find Dan standing in front of her. How had he moved so silently, so swiftly? She stared up into his face, taken aback that his expression mirrored an unexpected tenderness. 'No,' he said gently. 'Not stupid. . .just a woman in love.'

He was too close, Cassie thought breathlessly. Much too close. 'In love, Dan?' she scoffed, and took a step back. 'Hardly that, I think. Infatuated, perhaps. But not love. No. . .not love.'

Her cold denial affected him. She could see that. His nostrils flared wide. An angry muscle twitched along his jaw. 'And are you infatuated with this boss of yours?'

Cassie tossed off a careless laugh. 'For heaven's sake, Dan. I'm twenty-nine years old. Past the age of infatuation, surely?'

'It's just sex, then.' A statement. Not a question.

'Maybe I'm in love,' she tossed at him. Any thought of Jason had vanished. All Cassie wanted to do was lash out, to assuage some of her own personal pain and agony.

He grabbed her so quickly and so roughly that she gasped in pain. 'That's not true!' he ground out, his rasping breath only inches from her own. 'I know that for a fact. And do you know why? You're incapable of it! Your soul is so twisted and warped with bitterness, you've forgotten what love is. You're too full of hate!'

Suddenly his hands fell away from her arms, but a dangerous smouldering still remained in his gaze. It held Cassie, leaving her breathless and weak. When his right hand came up to cup her chin she did not pull away. She stared back at him, stunned into a dazed submission.

'Do let's be honest, my darling,' he drawled in a low, sensual voice. 'It's lust, not love, that drives you into that man's bed. You're a very sexy woman, Cassie Palmer – incredibly easy to turn on. Do you think I didn't notice the way you responded to me yesterday? Me. . .a man you despise. I dare say that if you hadn't remembered who was kissing you I could have taken you here, in this room, either on the desk or on the floor.'

His smile was cruelly knowing. 'That's lust, my lovely. And lust is a very transferable emotion. *Very* transferable!'

His hand slid down her throat, down over a single swollen breast, down over her ribs till it stopped on her quivering stomach.

Cassie sucked in a ragged breath through dry, parted lips. Why don't I do something? she asked herself dazedly. Why don't I stop him?

The hand moved again, this time sliding across then up over the curve of her hip to rest at her waist. 'You're trembling, Cassie,' he whispered harshly. 'Do you tremble for Roger so easily? Or is it only for me. . .?'

She almost said it, almost made her ghastly confession. Her lips actually opened, the words already forming. *Only for you. . . Only for you. . .*

His kiss smothered them totally, utterly, and, while Cassie's first instinct was to shut her mouth, to struggle, it was short-lived. From the moment his arms moved to enfold her close against him, the battle was lost. She groaned under his passionate onslaught, and slowly, inexorably, her lips parted, allowing his tongue the entry it so clearly desired. A sound growled deep in his throat, arousing her with its primitive, animal quality.

Her own tongue moved foward, quite instinctively, but when it slid into Dan's mouth she was not prepared for the explosion of passion she had so unwittingly unleashed.

His arms tightened around her till she could barely breathe, his tongue thrusting deep into her mouth in a savage, primitive rhythm. On and on went the kiss till Cassie's head was whirling, till her limbs were like jelly, till her body was a lifeless, malleable object moulded to Dan's in blatant sensuality. Chest was fused to chest, stomach to stomach, thigh to thigh.

Finally, he did take his mouth away, sliding swollen lips across her cheek till he found her ear. The tip of his tongue traced a wet path around the shell before dipping inside again and again, making Cassie shiver with sheer electric pleasure.

Her head fell backwards, offering up her throat to his ministrations, and when he took it, sucking the throbbing flesh at the base with hot, hungry lips, she groaned.

The sound brought his mouth back to hers in yet another kiss, this one even more feverish than the first. Blood began roaring in Cassie's ears. Liquid fire gushed along her veins. She was in another world, a crazy, ecstatic world where the senses swam, where time was suspended, where her only desire was to remain in Dan's arms.

She was dimly aware of his hands relaxing their

hold to run up and down her back, but when he began rubbing her softness against the hard muscle of his manhood Cassie's pleasure gradually changed to an aching, escalating tension. It wasn't enough to have his mouth fused to hers. It wasn't enough to have his hands on her. It wasn't nearly enough.

She wanted to feel him moving deep inside her. She wanted the release that only his total possession could give. And even as she wished it her own body started to move, writhing against him in an invitation as old as time.

Dan pulled back for a second, his eyes wide with passion and wonder, and then he was drawing her down on to the carpet, stretching out beside her. He kissed her again, one of his hands sliding down her taut, eager body, down to her knee then slowly up, up her softly trembling thigh.

She arched against him, tense, expectant, her whole being concentrating on his hand, which was moving inexorably closer to the hot, molten core of her desire.

The door of the library opened.

'Mr McKay, I knocked, but you didn't. . .'

Cassie almost died. She wrenched her mouth away and gaped over Dan's shoulder. The intruder was a complete stranger to her. He was no more than twenty-five and might have been good-looking under the red face. 'Hell! I. . .I'm terrible sorry, Mr McKay, I ——'

'Get out of here!' Dan growled, his stiffened body held rigidly above her. 'And close the bloody door on your way out!'

CHAPTER SEVEN

THE door shut with the force of an earth tremor.

Cassie's stricken gaze swung to Dan. But his eyes were squeezed tight, his face twisted in a type of anguish. He shuddered and expelled a long-held breath. 'God,' he muttered.

Cassie groaned as she thought of the picture they must have presented to their unexpected visitor. Another couple of seconds and Dan would have been. . .

Embarrassment brought a blast of heat into her cheeks. Upset and flustered, she tried to move.

Dan's hands whipped up to her shoulders and pinned her to the carpet. 'No!' he ground out, wild black eyes flying open.

She shook her head frantically and kept trying to escape, but her wriggling movements were futile. And their effect disastrous. Her swollen breasts accidentally rubbed against Dan's chest, rekindling the smouldering fire in his eyes. Seeing his reaction, she stupidly struggled harder, trying to slide away from under his hands, this tactic only serving to make her tight skirt ride dangerously high.

He swore under his breath, hot eyes fixed on

the tips of her breasts jutting provocatively against the thin woollen material. His breathing grew disconcertingly rapid, his chest rising and falling in a ragged rhythm.

'Dan. . .please. . .let me up,' she gasped.

His eyes snapped up to her face. 'Damn it all, Cassie, ignore that! He won't come back. He wouldn't dare! You can't want me to stop now. . .'

Cassie tried to speak, to object, but when his lips descended to devour the soft flesh of her throat her voice died. And when they moved down to a single swollen breast she could no longer even breathe.

His mouth opened and closed around its prey, the moist heat within quickly saturating the layers of material covering the nipple. She could feel his teeth against the sensitised peak, nipping it into even further arousal. More and more it responded to him, growing harder and larger, till the sensations became unbearable.

'No. . .' she objected. But feebly, without conviction.

'Yes,' he grated back.

Her wide blue eyes were drawn to the library door. She imagined that man, standing outside, listening, smiling, sniggering. 'No!' she screamed, and slapped Dan hard on the side of the head.

Glazed black eyes jerked up to stare at her.

'I said *no*!' she repeated, with gritted teeth this time.

Gradually, the almost incoherent quality in Dan's gaze faded, to be replaced by a brooding, barely controlled fury. He was still breathing hard and his hands were brutal in their hold around her hips.

For one terrifying moment Cassie feared that he would continue. And the horrible thing was, she knew that it would not be rape. Her body still wanted him, quite desperately. He only had to push the issue and she was his.

'Let me up,' she demanded. And held her breath.

After an excruciating couple of seconds, Dan shrugged and rolled away, a scornful smile curling his lips. 'It's a lady's privilege to change her mind,' he drawled as he got up. 'But you do realise, Cassie, that you're only delaying the inevitable.'

Cassie struggled to her feet. She was fiercely aware of the clammy material pressed against her breast, still wet where his mouth had been. Shame curled in her stomach. She had been so easy. . .

And while Dan's words had a ghastly ring of truth about them, they evoked a proud and defiant anger in her.

Her chin tilted upwards. 'Don't count your chickens, Dan. You're not dealing with the same silly naïve girl you seduced nine years ago.'

His face tightened. 'That much is obvious, my

dear. If I remember correctly, we had known each other. . .ten days, wasn't it?. . .before we became lovers. By your response tonight I think we'll be a lot quicker this time, don't you?'

His mocking disdain cut Cassie to the quick. Her only wish was to strike back, to hurt him as he was hurting her. 'Aren't you forgetting one small matter, Dan? I already have a lover – a lover who's waiting for me at this very moment, only too willing to meet my physical needs. I certainly don't need you!'

Cassie shrank back from the frightening force of his glare.

'You are not to go to this man tonight. Do you hear me, Cassie? Or any other night. I forbid it!'

Her laughter was almost hysterical. 'You forbid it? *You* forbid it? And who do you think you are, Dan McKay, forbidding me to do anything?'

He smiled.

Cassie rocked back. Never had she encountered a smile like it. Thin and cruel; edged in pure steel.

He turned and walked slowly round behind the desk, seating himself again and leaning back in the chair, looking up at her with cynically cold eyes. Cassie found his silence more threatening than the loudest tirade.

'I'll tell you who I am, Cassie Palmer,' he said at last. 'I am the father of your son. I am also an extremely rich man. But more than either of those things, I am a man who has had a gutful of sacrifices and compromises and considerations. I want my son. And, strange as it may seem, I still want you. . .' the corners of his mouth lifted in a dry, ironic smile '. . .even if you aren't the same girl I fell in love with. Nevertheless, you are a very desirable woman – a woman I have a mind to possess. Or should I say repossess? And before you tell me so, I'm well aware that you despise me now. Nevertheless, I am quite capable of living with that, as long as you give me what I want.'

Cassie's head was spinning. 'And what is that?' she asked shakily. 'Sex?'

His face remained stony. 'Among other things.'

'What other things?'

'My son, for starters. And not on any part-time, neighbourly basis. I want him here, in my home, all the time.'

'But I don't want——'

'I don't give a damn what you want!' he slammed at her, jumping to his feet and banging his fist down on the desk. 'You've lost all chance of my considering your wishes. I will not be treated like some vermin that's just crawled out from under a stone!'

Cassie quaked under the force of his fury. Dan had said he could be ruthless, but even she had not envisaged something like this.

'No matter what you thought of me,' he went on brutally, 'you should not have kept me in ignorance of my son. Maybe there was some excuse nine years ago, but yesterday, when I told you my wife was dead, when I showed I still cared about you, you should have told me the truth. That would have been the decent thing to do!'

'But, Dan, I —— '

'Enough! You wouldn't listen to my explanations then. I'm not interested in yours now.'

Cassie didn't know what to do, what to say. She was totally confused, frantically upset. 'I. . .I wanted to tell you,' she blurted out. 'When Jason was born it nearly killed me not to contact you.'

'Then why didn't you?' His voice was cold, unmoved. 'My name is listed in the phone book.'

'I. . .we. . . Mum and I hadn't told my father that you were responsible. He was so angry about my pregnancy. Mum thought it better he think it was some boy at a party one night. If he'd found out I'd had an affair with a. . .a married man. . .God knows what he would have done.'

'Come now, Cassie, you don't expect me to believe you were protecting *me* all this time?'

His derision brought utter frustration. 'No, of course not! It was to protect my father! He had a heart condition. Not that my keeping my affair with you a secret was any benefit in the end,' she said bitterly. 'Shortly after Jason was born Dad had an attack and died. And it was all my fault. Mine and yours! I hated you then, don't you see? And when you came back yesterday, smiling at me as though the past was nothing, I. . .I. . .' She fumbled for words. Everything was so mixed up in her head. She did still hate him, didn't she?

'You hated me even more,' Dan finished for her in a matter-of-fact tone. 'Yes, Cassie, I do see. Love turning to hate is a common enough occurrence. But it doesn't change a thing, because, love me or hate me, you're going to marry me.'

All the breath was punched from Cassie's body. 'Marry you?' she gasped.

Dan's smile was dry. 'I can see my proposal has come as a shock. Perhaps I should give you some time to consider it.'

Cassie swallowed. 'How. . .how much time?'

'Twenty-four hours.'

'Twenty-four hours?' she repeated blankly.

'Must you repeat everything I say?' Dan ground out irritably. 'When you come to pick Jason up tomorrow, you can give me your answer.' He sat back down, then glanced up, eyes and face hard. 'Of course, I should explain what will happen if you refuse.'

Cassie said nothing. She was incapable of speaking.

'Jason is my son. A simple DNA test will prove that. What's more, I am a father willing and able to support his son very well. Oddly enough, courts these days don't favour the woman in custody cases as much as they used to. I have no doubt that I will get a fair hearing, which is more than I got from you.'

'You'd try to take my son away from me?' Cassie cried in a choked voice. Her throat was dry, her heartbeat suspended from fear.

Was that a trace of pity she saw pass across his face?

'Only if you force me, Cassie,' he said evenly.

Cassie whirled away, her hands coming up to cradle her cheeks. 'If *I* force *you*?' she cried. 'Oh, God. . .'

She whirled back, tears pricking her eyes, but renewed defiance in her heart. She strode over to the desk and leant on it, her face flushed and angry. 'You would have to be the most heartless man in the world, Dan McKay, not to mention the most stupid! Do you honestly think any court in the world would award you custody of my son? Even if the unthinkable happened, even if you somehow bribed your way to a favourable decision, you wouldn't win in the end. Jason would hate you for taking his mother away from him. Hate you, do you hear me? Almost as much as I hate you!'

Dan's knuckles showed white as he clenched the edge of the desk and pushed himself slowly to his feet. He loomed over her, his face and stance intimidating, but Cassie was too angry to be afraid.

'I'll fight you, Dan,' she threatened, glaring up

into his blazing eyes. 'I'll fight you every inch of the way, with every weapon I have. Even if you get Jason, you won't win!'

An electric silence enveloped them as they glowered at each other.

Surprisingly Dan was the first to look away. He turned and walked over to the window where he stood and stared into the night, his shoulders stiff, his whole stance incredibly tense. After several excruciating seconds, he turned to face Cassie, the set of his mouth tight and grim. 'I take your point,' he conceded grudgingly. 'That is not what I want. Not at all. I want Jason to love me.'

Cassie was swamped by such a wave of relief that she had to clutch the edge of the desk to steady herself.

'You would make a good adversary in the boardroom, Cassie Palmer,' Dan admitted. 'But don't underestimate your opponent. You haven't won yet.'

Her chest tightened. She should have known that this wouldn't be the end of the matter. Dan was not a man willing to lose. In anything.

The possibility of his kidnapping Jason again crossed her mind. As melodramatic as such an event seemed, people did do dreadful things when desperate. Cassie had to stop the situation from deteriorating to that level.

'I'm prepared to be reasonable about access,' she offered tautly.

Dan's expression remained guarded. 'Oh? In what way? As friend, or father?'

Cassie bit her bottom lip. 'I. . .I don't think it's wise to tell him you're his father just yet.'

'And why not?' The black eyes glinted dangerously. 'He doesn't think I'm dead, does he?'

'No. . .'

'Well, what does he think? What have you told him about me?'

'I. . . Not much. I explained that I didn't want to marry his father as I was too young, and that you lived too far away to visit.'

'And he accepts that?'

She shrugged. 'Jason's only eight. Perhaps in time he'll want more.'

'Why do you object to my telling Jason I'm his father?'

'This isn't the city, Dan. People around here are shockable. And narrow-minded. Jason would be hurt by the gossip.'

'And you? Would you be hurt by the gossip?'

Cassie drew herself up straight. 'I'd survive.'

Dan's expression was hard to read. Was it admiration? Or derision. . . 'I've no doubt you would,' he mocked, answering the question for her.

'You won't tell him?' she swept on, chin still up.

His hesitation in answering made her stomach

churn. 'I can't promise that, Cassie,' he finally admitted.

She almost stamped her foot. 'Damn you, Dan! Didn't you listen to what I said?'

'I do not live my life according to the opinions of others,' he snarled.

Her laugh was scornful. 'As well I know.'

'I don't blame you totally for wanting to turn the screw, Cassie,' he said in a low, deadly voice, 'but I'm warning you, don't keep doing it too long.'

She was about to speak, to challenge him, but common sense made her hold her tongue. Push him too far and who knew what he might do? At least he seemed to have dropped his ridiculous marriage proposal.

'What about tomorrow afternoon?' she asked, deliberately changing the subject. 'Do you still intend picking Jason up from school?'

'Yes.'

'You won't drive fast?'

'Of course not.'

'And he'll be safe in the helicopter?'

'For God's sake, Cassie!' Dan exploded. 'He's my son, too. I wouldn't dream of putting him at risk.'

Cassie believed him. Whatever else, Dan seemed to care about the boy. 'I. . .I'll tell him to wait for you at the bus-stop outside the school.

Do you know where the Riversbend primary school is?'

'I'll find it.'

'It's down a side-street. It ——'

'I said I'd find it, Cassie. I've made my way successfully around the world several times. I don't need someone to hold my hand. Just you make sure you come personally to collect Jason, with your answer ready.'

'My answer? You mean. . .you still expect. . .?'

His expression was totally impassive. 'My proposal of marriage still stands, Cassie.'

'And if I say no?'

'I don't think you will, once you come to terms with the situation.'

Cassie gaped her astonishment.

'I'm sure you don't want Jason to be unhappy,' Dan went on, 'any more than I do.'

'How on earth can you ——?'

'Do let me finish, my dear,' he cut in coldly.

She sighed her frustration, but let him continue.

'You say that telling Jason I'm his father just now is not in his best interests. I challenge that. I think Jason needs me. And he needs me now! Not in six months' or six years' time. How do you think he'll feel if and when you finally reveal the truth? Do you think he'll appeciate your reasons for delaying? Or that he'll believe you were only protecting him from gossip? There's bound to be gossip no matter when we tell him. Of course, the gossip would quickly die down, if you married me. . .'

'But I can't marry you!' Cassie exclaimed, her glare hiding her underlying paniic. 'I won't!' My God, to be with him every day, to sleep with him every night. . .

Dan's returning glare held no compromise at all. 'Let me assure you, Cassie, I'm not going to go away. And I will eventually tell the boy the truth. It is his right, after all. I must admit, I don't envy your position when I do.'

'What. . .what do you mean?'

'I wouldn't like having to explain to Jason why you refused to marry his father, especially after I vow my undying love for you both!'

'You'd lie to him?' she husked.

His jaw clenched. 'About what?'

'You might love Jason, but you don't love *me*, Dan McKay. Don't you dare say that you do!'

He said nothing.

'Why are you doing this?' she threw at him. '*Why*?'

He didn't even flinch. 'I'm doing what's best for Jason,' he declared in merciless tones. 'I expect you to do the same. If you truly love him. . .'

Cassie's whole body slumped, her eyes dropping to the floor in a gesture of defeat. It was useless, absolutely useless. The man was too hard. And too clever. Appealing to her motherly love was the lowest tack.

But very successful.

She didn't even react when he moved to stand in front of her, when his hands reached out to close firmly over her shoulders. All defiance was dead.

'Cassie...I don't want to hurt you. I never wanted to hurt you... But I will have my son. Make no mistake about that.'

Her eyes lifted – sad, weary eyes. 'All right,' she sighed.

He frowned down at her, tension seeping into his fingers. The tips pressed harder into her flesh. 'All right? What do you mean by that?'

'I mean all right, Dan.' Her voice was dull, flat. 'I'll do what you want. And you don't have to wait till tomorrow for your answer.'

'You mean you agree to marry me?' he asked in a surprisingly shocked tone. 'Just like that?'

'Yes.' She felt tired. Terribly tired.

'Even though you hate me?'

A deep, dark pain jabbed at her conscience. It found relief in a final burst of spirit. 'Does it matter?' she flung at him. 'I will do what I have to do. You said it earlier. I'm only putting off the inevitable. Once you tell Jason he's your son, he'll wonder why he can't have a normal family life like other children. What answer could I give him? So you see, Dan? There's no need for any more threats or more blackmail. You've won.'

'What about us?' he demanded.

'What *about* us?' she shot back.

'Goddamn you, Cassie, you know what I mean. It's not just the boy I want.'

Cassie's heart stopped beating.

'Don't imagine that I'll settle for a marriage of convenience,' he went on fiercely. 'I want you in my bed every night. I want you, all of you, body and soul.'

His arrogant demands found an answering fire in Cassie. She glared up at him, blue eyes flashing. 'We can't always have what we want, Dan. Do you imagine I *want* to marry you?'

'You still want me to make love to you. That much I know.'

She kept her chin held high. 'If I do, then I despise myself for it!'

'Don't say that!'

'Why not? It's true. Every time you touch me, down deep inside I cringe. My body might look to yours for a temporary relief, but afterwards. . .afterwards, Dan, I will only feel revulsion.'

'No!' he cried as she tried to pull free of him. His arms swept around her, holding her close, lifting her on to tiptoes till his lips were touching hers. 'You're wrong, Cassie,' he whispered into her mouth. 'Wrong. . . Hate has warped your mind. It could be wonderful. . .perfect. . .as it was before——'

'No,' she denied, fiercely trying to ignore his

lips brushing against hers. 'It will never be the same. Never! We don't love each other any more. When we go to bed now it will be having sex, not making love.'

'Call it anything you like!' he rasped, his fingers digging into her back. 'But don't delude yourself that it will be anything like the sex you've been having. Even now your body cries out instinctively for mine. You're trembling, Cassie. You want me. I was your first lover, your first real love. Nothing will change that, no matter how many men you've slept with since, no matter what that twisted soul of yours pretends. You were totally mine once and you will be again.'

'Never!' Cassie shook her head violently from side to side, all the while knowing that Dan was right. She might despise him as a person, but sexually she was still under his spell.

Quite abruptly he let her go, almost throwing her aside, stalking back over to the window and glaring through it in brooding silence.

When he whirled back to face her, Cassie was shocked by the raw, naked pain on his face. 'Well? What are you waiting for? Get out! Go to your blasted lover, for all I care! But understand this, Cassie Palmer. No wife of mine will lie in another man's bed. So you make it clear to your darling boss tonight that your affair is over! Terminated!' His eyes narrowed. 'If I ever find out differently. . .'

Cassie swallowed. An undercurrent of sexual revenge smouldered through Dan, making her fearful, yet at the same time disturbingly aroused.

'What. . .what about Jason?' she asked in a husky whisper. 'Do. . .do you still want me to pick him up from Strath-haven tomorrow? I could come after work, about five-thirty.'

'Do whatever you like,' he growled and spun away. 'Just get out of my sight.'

Cassie stared at the grim figure, a strange compassion stirring inside her. Dan was hurting, really hurting. It didn't matter to her that his jealousy came from a bruised ego, not true feeling. She wanted to go to him, to hold him, to tell him that there was no lover. But before she could even begin to move he rounded on her again, his face hard once more.

'Are you still here? What's the problem? Won't darling Roger have waited this long for you?' His mouth creased back into a cruel, taunting smile. 'Perhaps you've changed your mind, is that it? You want me to give your body that temporary release you spoke of. . .'

Cassie backed away, her eyes wide. When he took a step towards her she grabbed her cardigan and fled, Dan's wild, harsh laughter echoing in her ears.

CHAPTER EIGHT

CASSIE spent a terrible Monday. On the surface she functioned normally, going to work, operating all morning, making calls all afternoon, smiling and talking as though nothing was different. Underneath, she was a seething mass of confusion and fears. How could she have been so stupid as to agree to marry Dan? Whatever had possessed her?

The ever-observant Roger had frowned at her more than once, finally asking what was wrong, but she made some excuse about not sleeping well. He believed her because insomnia had been a recurring problem of Cassie's over the years.

Her mother had not been as easy to put off that morning at breakfast. She had been bursting with curiosity, wanting to know what had transpired with Dan. Cassie had no intention of telling her mother the blunt and embarrassing details of the entire evening. And Jason's presence at the breakfast table had precluded any open discussion about his father.

Cassie had, however, confessed reluctantly to her mother that Dan had asked her to marry him, not adding that she had already been emotionally blackmailed into saying 'yes'. She had let her mother think that the matter was yet to be decided. And, as far as Cassie was concerned in the cold light of day, that was so!

Joan had been astonished, then delighted, expressing the opinion that she was sure it would be for the best. 'After all, you've never really got over the man, have you?' she'd said perceptively. 'And I'm sure he must still care for you if he wants to marry you. Men these days don't marry merely because of an illegitimate child.'

Cassie did not have the heart to disillusion her. Jason was without doubt Dan's main motive for proposing marriage.

But he definitely did not care for her any more. He openly disliked the woman she'd become. Though for some perverse reason he still wanted her. His vow to reduce her to some sort of sexual slave was obsessive in its intensity, fuelled perhaps by a desire for revenge. Dan bitterly resented Jason's existence having been kept from him.

What terrified her most was how easily Dan would achieve his objective if she married him. And he expected her answer that afternoon!

By the time Cassie climbed into her jeep at the end of the day, she was emotionally exhausted. Quite automatically she turned on to the road for home instead of taking the highway which led to Strath-haven, and was half-way there before she realised her mistake. Shrugging wearily, she continued on, thinking to herself that it was just as well. She really couldn't face Dan looking as she did.

When she brought the jeep to a halt in front of the old farmhouse, Cassie was about to climb out from behind the wheel when she stopped. Why should she go inside and change? It was better that Dan saw her exactly as she was attired every workday. White overalls, no make-up, hair scraped back into a functional pony-tail. Maybe he would change his mind about marrying her, she thought wryly, if he saw her at her least attractive.

Cassie restarted the engine and drove down the hill towards the suspension bridge, detouring slightly to skirt Rosie's paddock. No untoward developments there, she thought with relief as she saw the mare actually cantering. Not that there should be. Foals rarely came early, but Rosie was getting on in years, which could make things slightly unpredictable. If anything went wrong at this late stage, Cassie worried. . .

I'm getting paranoid, she thought irritably. Rosie's as healthy as a horse! She laughed at her own pun and turned the jeep for the short run down to the river.

Jason must have been watching for her, for he raced to meet her as she stepped off the bridge, throwing his arms around her waist in an un-characteristic hug. 'Gee, you're late. We thought you weren't coming. Dan was going to ring up Gran to find out what had happened to you, but I told him you'd make it sooner or later. I said you probably had a 'mergency with a cow or something.'

Cassie smiled down at her bright-eyed son as he skipped along the gravel path ahead of her, back-wards, marvelling at his energy and thinking to herself that his happiness was really worth any sacrifice. But surely he could be happy, she frowned, without his mother making such a disas-trous marriage?

'And guess what?' he was saying. 'I had three rides in the helicopter. But it's gone now, see?' he pointed to the spot on the front lawn where the machine usually stood. 'Dan sent it back to Sydney.'

Cassie glanced up then, having for some time been half-aware of Dan watching them from the veranda. Perhaps he was ensuring that she made no retreat now that she'd arrived.

'And which did you enjoy most?' she asked Jason, trying to keep her voice normal as they approached the front steps. 'The sports car?' She nodded towards the shining red Mercedes parked nearby. 'Or the helicopter?'

Jason said, 'The car was terrific, but the helicop-ter was super!'

Cassie's head snapped up to see Dan striding down the front steps of the house. Her breath caught in her throat seeing him at such close quarters, his very male frame dressed in blue jeans and a maroon shirt, the casual attire far more reminiscent of the Dan she had first met.

Made of faded denim, the jeans were tightly fitted, moulding his slim hips and powerful thighs. The long sleeves of the shirt were rolled up, the collar open at the neck. No watch or jewellery adorned his smooth, tanned flesh which drew Cassie's gaze like a magnet. Her insides tightened as she remembered how she used to run her hands over his hairless chest, loving the velvet feel of him.

Cassie blinked. What had Dan just said? She couldn't think.

Unnerved, she turned to her son. 'Ready to go home, Jason?' Even as the words popped out of her mouth she knew that she was acting like a fool. Dan would not let her go so easily. But the blistering sexual awareness he always evoked in her made Cassie want to run.

'Mrs Bertram is making us coffee,' Dan said smoothly. 'We can have it on the veranda and talk while Jason plays with Hugo.'

The enormous black dog must have heard his name, for he bounded around the corner. Cassie stiffened. 'Are you sure he ——'

Her protest was cut off by the sight of her son

hugging the slavering Dobermann around the neck. The animal's huge tongue slurped up Jason's face, bringing squeals of objection. 'Oh, yuk! You sloppy old thing. Come on. . . Let's play fetch.' And the happy pair ran off.

'Don't concern yourself,' Dan reassured in a soft, kind voice. 'Once Hugo has been introduced to a person as a friend, he is devoted. He would protect Jason with his life now.'

Cassie could not help being surprised by Dan's pleasant manner. Where was the mocking devil of last night? 'Have. . .have you had the dog long?' she asked.

'Five years. Since he was a pup.'

'He's certainly a beautiful animal.' She kept watching the dog in the distance. It was safer than looking at Dan.

'He was Roberta's dog.'

Cassie's heart stopped. 'Roberta?'

Her eyes turned slowly to see Dan observing her closely. 'My wife,' he said evenly.

'Oh. . .' A chill came over Cassie. She didn't want to hear about Dan's wife. She couldn't bear to think that he had belonged to another woman all the time he'd been having an affair with her. A woman he had returned to and stayed with despite his talk about separation and divorce.

Mrs Betram's arrival with the coffee was timely.

She was a slim, efficient-looking woman of about fifty. Not a local. Cassie allowed Dan to take her elbow and lead her silently up the steps and over to the table set up on the veranda. The coffee-service was exquisite – made of the finest cream pottery. A selection of delicate pastries rested on a serving plate.

Mrs Betram smiled at Cassie. 'And you'd be Jason's mother?' the woman asked.

Dan stepped in and effected a proper introduction. Cassie could not help noticing the woman's open curiosity about her. Or was it astonishment that her boss was interested in such a country bumpkin? She wished now that she had stopped to improve her appearance.

'That's a lively lad you've got there,' Mrs Betram commented as she poured the coffee.

Cassie chewed her bottom lip. 'He hasn't been any trouble, has he?'

'Oh, good heavens, no!'

'He's had a whale of a time,' Dan added with a laugh. 'But I think Paul was glad to go back to Sydney.'

'Paul?' Cassie repeated enquiringly.

'My pilot.' Dan's eyes rested on Cassie in dry amusement. 'You almost met him last night. Thank you, Mrs Bertram, we can manage now. Cream and sugar, Cassie?'

Cassie was glad of the woman's departure, for a fierce blush was creeping up her neck. How could Dan refer to such an embarrassing encounter so. . . so casually? It was tactless. And tasteless. And there she'd been thinking he'd turned over a new leaf!

'Yes, please,' she said stiffly. Then added, 'Mrs Bertram seems a nice person.'

'She is,' Dan agreed. 'Not that I've known her all that long. She's only been my housekeeper since Roberta died. Prior to that——'

'Do you have to keep referring to your first marriage?' Cassie flared.

Dan replaced the cream-jug with a sigh. 'Cassie. . .I want to explain. . .about Roberta——'

'But I don't want to hear,' she retorted wildly, knowing she was over-reacting, but finding it impossible to stop. 'I never want to hear about her. Never! Not if you want me to marry you!'

She raised furious eyes to his, almost daring him to continue, to ruin what he so obviously wanted. He glared back at her, his mouth setting into a thin, angry line.

'Right,' he bit out, and, with an abrupt movement, stood up and strode inside, returning shortly with a wad of papers and a biro. He pushed the coffee-cups aside and spread the sheets out on the table before her. 'You have to sign here.' He jabbed at some blank spaces on the forms. 'And here. This last one is an authority for my solicitor to pick up a copy of your birth certificate. Marriage licences require paperwork. And a special licence requires even more.'

She gulped, her earlier anger fading with the growing reality of the situation. This was not the past. This was here and now!

'We will be married on Sunday,' Dan was saying, 'here, in the garden. I'm flying in a celebrant from Sydney. There will be no guests other than your immediate family. Mine will not be attending. They all live in Perth. Too far to come at short notice. Here...' He picked up the biro and held it out for her.

Cassie took it with a trembling hand, then stared blankly down at the forms. Dan kept on talking in a rather cold, formal voice. At some stage he had sat down again.

'I imagine Mrs Bertram will be concerned about her position here when I inform her of our coming marriage. Shall I tell her she can stay, or do you prefer to run the house on your own? It's entirely up to you. Though I do strongly suggest that you consider keeping the staff on. They're reliable and discreet, and you'll need help when we entertain. As well as Mrs Bertram, I have employed a local couple to do all the cleaning and gardening.'

Cassie sat like a stone. Housekeeper... staff...entertain...

It suddenly hit her what marriage to this man would entail. She had not even considered his position – that as a successful businessman Dan would lead a full social life. His wife would be expected to play the role of hostess. The prospect was daunting. And rather ironic, with Cassie dressed as she was today. It brought home the folly of going ahead with the idea.

She lifted panicky eyes. 'Dan, I... Are you absolutely sure you want this...this marriage?'

His face tightened. 'I thought that that matter was settled,' he stated in clipped tones.

'Yes...well...I mean...'

Cassie's stomach was tied up in knots. So, it seemed, was her tongue. She scooped in a calming breath and tried again. 'Look, Dan,' she said in a conciliatory tone, 'I've been thinking. It's still too soon to tell Jason you're his father. Give him a little more time to get to know you...'

He slanted her a sharp look. 'Bargaining time again, is it? I thought everything was settled last night, Cassie. You agreed to marry me.'

'But, Dan, I...I hadn't realised what was entailed. I mean...I'm a vet, a simple, no-nonsense country vet. I'm not used to the high life. Dinner-parties and such aren't my style. You must understand that if I married you I would not give up my profession to play a social butterfly.'

'*When* you marry me, my dear,' he corrected. 'Not *if*.' He gave her the oddest look. It was almost warm. 'I don't mind if you work after we're married. Be assured, I bought this place so that I can live a quieter existence. I may have to fly away on business sometimes, and no doubt I'll invite the occasional couple up for the weekend, but other than that I want to be a simple family man. Speaking of which, will you still want to work after you fall pregnant?'

'Pregnant?'

'I want us to have more children, Cassie. You must agree that Jason deserves a brother or a sister. You were the one who said you wanted him to have a normal family life.'

Cassie stared at Dan, an appalling thought catapulting into her brain. If she had not stopped him last night she might have already conceived a baby.

One hand fluttered up to her temple. The blood was pounding horribly in her head. She felt dazed. And ill. It felt like a ghastly replay of the past.

'This is all too fast for me,' she rasped. 'Please, Dan, give me more time.' She lifted beseeching eyes to him.

His face grew cold. 'More time for what? To run away? To thwart me further? You've already deprived me of eight years of my son's life. I have no intention of risking any more.'

'I won't run away,' she assured him desperately. 'But you can't expect me to marry you and have a baby just like that. I have other responsibilities, other obligations.'

'Such as?'

'My mother——'

'Your mother is getting married in less than a

fortnight,' Dan interrupted bluntly. 'To dear Roger, no less.'

Cassie's mouth fell open.

'Jason is very talkative,' Dan explained drily. 'He told me all about his Gran and your boss. Since even I don't believe that you would be double-crossing your mother with a man of nearly sixty, I can only assume that you lied to me last night. Why, Cassie? Why did you want me to think your boss was your lover?'

Cassie looked away from his probing eyes and said nothing.

'Who are you sleeping with that you have to have a cover for him? Is he married? Is that it?'

Hurt eyes sliced back to him. 'I've only ever slept with one married man, Dan McKay, and that was in ignorance. I don't happen to have a lover. . .at the moment,' she added when she saw a triumphant light flash into Dan's eyes.

He totally ignored her last words. 'So. . . You weren't on your way to a romantic rendezvous last night. Then the red dress was for me, after all, wasn't it?'

Cassie panicked at the smug way Dan was looking at her. 'Of course.' Her sarcastic tone brought a wariness to his eyes. 'But don't flatter yourself. I came down to Strath-haven last night planning to seduce you.'

'You *what*?'

'You heard me. I was going to use your. . .your

lust for me to get you to do what I wanted. But I couldn't go through with it. Even with my son's happiness at stake, I couldn't sink as low as that!'

Silence descended on the pair of them. As the fires of temper cooled Cassie began to regret her nasty words. What was to be gained by these continual slanging matches? It was better that she try to bring some civility at least into their relationship.

She sighed. 'I'm sorry, Dan. I...I shouldn't have said that.'

'Why not...? If it's true.' His voice was bitter.

She gave him a truly apologetic look. 'If you insist on going through with this marriage, then I think we should try to be friends. How can Jason be happy with parents who are always fighting?'

That undermining warmth crept back into Dan's gaze. 'I don't want to fight with you, Cassie,' he said softly. 'I've never wanted to...'

Cassie struggled to stay unaffected. Dan was looking at her as though he almost loved her, and it was hard, so hard not to respond. She reminded herself that he was clever at doing that – projecting something that wasn't real. He simply wanted her co-operation, and he meant to get it one way or another.

'Sign, Cassie,' he urged.

Her gaze dropped to the forms. She felt like she was on a roller-coaster ride, being swept along with no control, no real say. If she signed, she would be signing her life away, putting her future happiness into Dan's hands in more ways than one. She hesitated, her heart pounding, her head whirling.

'*Sign!*'

She glanced up into his stubborn face again, knowing that it was useless to appeal to him. She was trapped, as much by her own dark desires as anything.

She signed.

The biro dropped from nerveless fingers to clatter on to the table.

Dan stood up and began to gather the papers. 'Drink your coffee,' he said in a gentler tone. 'You look pale.'

The cup rattled in the saucer as she picked it up.

The brew was rich and hot, but Cassie scarcely noticed. She drank like a robot, all feeling stunned by the enormity of what she had just done.

'You won't regret it, Cassie,' he reassured her.

She stared up at him, long and hard. She saw an incredibly handsome man with striking dark eyes and a sensual face; a powerfully built man, with broad shoulders, a flat stomach and long, athletic legs.

She saw a stranger.

CHAPTER NINE

'DARLING, you look lovely!'

Cassie gave her mother a stiff smile before returning to glance in her dressing-table mirror. She fiddled with her hair for the umpteenth time, poking some escaping tendrils up under the wide picture hat. 'I wish I hadn't let you talk me into wearing white,' she frowned. 'Or this hat!'

'But it suits you! And what's a bride, without a veil or a hat?'

Cassie glared ruefully at her bridal outfit once more. The dress was made of lace, with a fitted bodice, long sleeves and a straight slim skirt, finishing just below the knee. The silk lining was strapless, Cassie's faintly tanned skin showing through the lace on the shoulders and arms. A hint of cleavage was visible on second glance. Despite the colour, the gown did not exude a virginal quality.

Cassie breathed deeply in and out, trying to calm herself. But nothing was going to shift the knots in her stomach. Today was her wedding day. Tonight would be her wedding night. . .

'I can't tell you,' her mother was saying, 'how happy I am about this marriage. It's like a miracle.

Roger and I can live here on the farm instead of moving into his small unit in town, and you and Jason will be just across the bridge. Speaking of Jason...I'll never forget the look on that boy's face when Dan told him he was his father. Never! It brought tears to my eyes. And if you noticed, Dan was not without a tear himself. One has to give credit where credit is due, Cassie. No matter what the man was like nine years ago, he's different now. You couldn't ask for a more loving and devoted father.'

Cassie could not agree more. Dan was there every afternoon, picking Jason up from school, keeping him company till Cassie finished work. Jason came home smelling decidedly doggy, but with tales of fun times and computer games, Dan having bought him a whole computer system to make up for eight missed birthdays and Christmases.

But that was all he had bought Jason, which rather surprised Cassie. She had feared that Dan would lavish gifts on his son, spoiling him rotten in an attempt to win the boy's affection. It seemed that that wasn't necessary. Jason was already besotted, talking about his new dad non-stop.

Cassie had also been surprised by local reaction to her coming marriage. Dan had accompanied her and Jason to the cricket game the day before, and once Jason had announced to all and sundry that this was his dad, who was marrying his mum

the next day, they had been swamped with con-
gratulations. The obvious sincerity of the good
wishes had brought a lump to her throat.

Of course, in public Dan conducted himself like
a loving fiancé, holding her hand and smiling,
even putting an arm around her shoulder occasionally. Cassie had found it hard not to flinch
away from his show of false affection. As it was,
she did hold herself stiff and tense when he
touched her. It was all a strain, and on the rare
occasions when they had found themselves alone,
Dan had been silent and grim. Only once had he
spoken, and that had been to ask her to hold out
her finger so that he could check its size for her
wedding ring.

'Hey, come on, you two,' Roger called through
the doorway. 'The wedding chariot awaits.'

Cassie steeled herself and turned towards him.
'Do I look all right, boss?' she asked, a slight
catch in her voice.

Roger whistled. 'If I wasn't already mad about
the mother I'd give our lad across the river a run
for his money.'

Cassie laughed. When she'd first told Roger
about her coming marriage and the reason behind
it, he had been slightly piqued.

'But why didn't you tell me before?' he'd
chided, then added grumpily, 'It all seems
unnecessarily rushed.'

Somewhere along the line, though, he had been

won over to the idea. Perhaps, Cassie thought with dry amusement, it was after Dan had joined them for dinner on Friday night and told Roger about his planned wine cellar.

Cassie's gaze swept over her mother and Roger, who were both looking at her with expectant faces. While she'd lain in bed the previous night, taut and sleepless, Cassie had determined to go through the ceremony showing not the slightest doubt, even going so far as to feign complete happiness. She didn't want her family to worry about her. But it was going to be tougher than she'd thought.

Still. . .

Her lips pulled back into a wide smile. 'Well, folks? What are we waiting for?'

Roger's white station-wagon looked magnificent. The enamel gleamed with polish, the grey upholstery was freshly shampooed. But Cassie almost cried when she saw the bride doll resting on the bonnet, secured there with traditional ribbons. It seemed to represent all that was sweet and loving in a wedding, all that would be missing from her own.

Jason was already in the car, bouncing up and down on the back seat. 'Come on, Mum. We don't want to be late.'

'Brides are supposed to be late,' his Gran remarked as they all climbed in.

'Why?'

Roger laughed. 'So that when she shows up the poor bridegroom is so relieved that he forgets what a damned fool thing he's just about to do!'

'Roger Nolan!' Joan reprimanded. 'If that's the way you think about it, you can——'

Roger silenced her with a quick kiss before accelerating off.

'Oh, yuk!' Jason squirmed. 'I hope you and Dad aren't going to be mushy like that, Mum.'

Cassie's butterflies churned again, but she managed to give her son a reassuring smile. 'I don't think so, Jason,' she murmured.

'That's good! One of the boys at school said you would be kissing all the time, but I told him you wouldn't. He didn't believe me, but he doesn't know you like I do, does he, Mum?'

Cassie's stomach turned over. Out of the mouths of babes. . .

'When are you going to be back from Sydney, Mum?'

'Friday,' she supplied. 'Don't forget your gran is getting married next Saturday.'

'You mean I've got to wear these horrible clothes again?' Jason wailed.

'I'm afraid so.'

'By the way, Cassie,' Roger joined in. 'I've hired a young chap straight out of university to help while you're gone. He can stay on while I'm away too. I might even keep him on permanently if he works out. The practice is big enough, and who knows what might happen in the near future?'

He gave her a look in the rear-view mirror and Cassie knew exactly what he was thinking. She might get pregnant. Thinking about such matters did little for her strained state. It reminded her that in a matter of hours her marriage to Dan would be consummated. She found the prospect terrifying yet insidiously exciting. Nine years... Would it be as she remembered? Would the lack of love make a difference?

'Here we are!' Jason squealed, bringing Cassie back to the present. 'Look, there's Dad coming down the steps. Doesn't he look terrific?'

Yes...doesn't he? Cassie thought with a jolt. He was dressed in a dark grey suit and white silk shirt, the red tie and handkerchief providing a startling splash of colour. His hair was slicked back from his face in controlled waves, the style bringing attention to his strong, handsome face. His mouth, however, was set tightly in a clenched jaw. His eyes weren't happy. He appeared tense as he strode stiffly across the driveway to their car.

'Our bridegroom looks jittery,' Roger laughed softly.

'Hush, Roger,' Joan hissed.

Cassie swallowed nervously. Jittery was exactly how she was feling, but she doubted that nerves were the cause of Dan's formidable expression.

Maybe he was beginning to doubt the wisdom of marrying a woman he didn't love. Maybe his egotistical and possibly vengeful wish to have her in his bed was on the wane.

Cassie did not look up at Dan when he opened her door and stretched out his hand. She took it, and as he drew her to his feet she finally lifted her eyes. She was taken aback when he smiled at her. 'You look very beautiful,' came his softly spoken compliment.

For a long moment they stared at each other, silent and still, and Cassie felt an overwhelming rush of emotion. It filled her soul, pierced her heart. It was blinding in its intensity.

I love him, came the awful realisation. I've always loved him.

She shrank from the admission, her blood going cold, her hand pulling away from his.

Dan turned away from her, but not before she saw the renewed tightening of his features.

'Come on, everyone,' he said with perfect control. 'The celebrant is waiting for us in the gazebo. Come, Cassie. . .' He turned back and took her hand without really looking at her and the group moved off.

Somehow Cassie made it through the ceremony. She spoke when she had to speak, smiled when she had to smile, kissed when she had to kiss.

Nothing much registered. She felt numb. All she could think was why...why...why...?

He didn't deserve her love. He'd tried neither to win it nor to earn it. Nine years ago he had taken all she had to offer, then deserted her. Now he had swept back into her life, ridden roughshod over her emotions, then forced her to marry him. Even his love for Jason could not justify his selfishness. Cassie felt crushed by the unfairness of it all. Crushed and close to despair.

'You look tired, darling,' her mother said afterwards as they stood sipping champagne on the veranda. Roger and Dan were talking to one side; Jason was playing with Hugo, despire dire warnings about his new suit; the celebrant had departed in the helicopter.

'What was that, Mum?' Cassie said, her manner distracted.

Joan was frowning at her. 'Everything is all right between you and Dan, isn't it, Cassie?'

Cassie pulled herself together. Her mother deserved better than to be forever weighed down with her grown-up daughter's problems. As a parent she had been wonderfully supportive, even renting out her home for some years to go to Sydney to help mind Jason while Cassie went to university.

'Of course, Mum. Don't go imagining things. I'm just tired. You know what a rush it's been this week, shopping for these clothes, packing and moving things over to Strath-haven, organising things for Jason.'

Joan nodded in agreement. 'Yes... You'll be glad of a holiday. Just as well you're not leaving till tomorrow, though. Where will you be staying in Sydney? I might need to ring you.'

'To tell the truth, I don't have any idea where we'll be staying. Dan wants it to be a surprise.' Which was a lie. Cassie and Dan had not communicated on a private level at all during the past week. Except for the ring. She glanced down at the wide gold band, truly aware of it for the first time.

Married, she thought shakily. For better for worse, for richer for poorer... She looked around. Well, it was certainly for richer, came the ironic thought.

'I'll give you a call in the morning, Mum,' she said, 'and tell you where we'll be.'

'I think it's time we made tracks, love,' Roger called to Joan. 'You know how short these days are. It'll be dark soon.'

Cassie turned to Roger. 'You won't forget to check on Rosie, will you?' she asked, unable to keep the anxiety from her voice.

Roger came over with a big smile on his face and hugged her. 'Now don't you worry your pretty head about that horse of yours, my dear. I wouldn't miss an excuse to come out and visit your mother, now, would I?'

'Is there some problem with a horse?' Dan asked. 'Cassie?' His face was faintly reproachful.

Cassie stiffened instantly, causing Roger to give her a puzzled look. She made a conscious effort to relax and smile. 'Not really. I'm just an old worry-wart. Like Mum. Come on, you two, off you go. I know you have things to do. Jason! Time to go!'

Her mother became tearful now that the time had come to say goodbye. Even Jason seemed subdued. Cassie bent down and gave him a big hug and a kiss. For once he didn't complain about her being mushy. He hung on tightly. 'You're to be a good boy for Gran,' she said, her voice thick, 'and when Daddy and I get back we'll come and get you.'

'Straight away? You promise?'

'I promise.' He sounded so young, Cassie thought, with a clutch at her heartstrings. She gave him another squeeze, shutting her eyes tight to stop her own tears from spilling over. When she opened them to look over Jason's shoulder, she saw that Dan was watching her. His face was totally unreadable.

'Got a hug for me, too, son?' he asked.

For some unaccountable reason, Jason did not answer. Or turn around. He buried his face in his mother's neck, almost knocking her hat off.

Dan knelt down close. 'I'm not taking your Mummy away for long, Jason,' he reassured him gently. 'We'll ring you every night. And next year we'll all go on holidays together. To anywhere you'd like to go.'

Jason glanced over his shoulder, his eyes brightening through the wet lashes. 'To Disneyland?'

'Disneyland it is!'

Jason threw himself into his father's arms with a tiny sob. Tears trickled down Cassie's cheeks, making her turn away.

By the time the small group departed Cassie was feeling like a wrung-out dishcloth. She stood, mournfully watching the station-wagon disappear in the distance, her whole body sagging with exhaustion.

'Come, Cassie. . .'

She did not resist when Dan took her elbow.

'It's bedtime for you,' he said as he took her inside the front door.

She stopped and looked up at him. 'Bed?' she repeated shakily.

'Yes.'

A tremor ran through her. Couldn't he even wait till it was decently dark? A lone tear trickled down her cheek, but she had no energy left to fight him. And he had won, hadn't he? She had never really stopped loving him, no matter what he had done, or what he did now.

He led her upstairs like a child, turning her into the first bedroom on the right. Cassie had been in the room the day before, unpacking her meagre things, only half filling the expansive walk-in wardrobe. At the time she had gazed around the large, almost empty room, pretending all the while to be considering what sort of furniture would suit.

But her eyes and mind had been mainly focusing on the king-sized brass bed, her imagination projecting her forward to this moment in time. Her mental fantasy had been filled with desire and passion, hearts pounding and naked flesh burning. Even after she had gone home the thought of Dan finally making love to her had kept her awake most of the night.

Now her eyes were dull. Her mind blank. Her heart heavy.

She stared down at her marriage bed, and all she longed to do was sink into the downy white quilt, to lay her head on the pillows, to escape into the oblivion of sleep. No desire heated her veins. No passion pricked her senses. She felt listless and defeated – a rag doll.

'Here. . . Let me help you.' Dan removed her hat, throwing it on to a nearby chair. Her hair began to tumble down, but she made no move to fix it. She stood woodenly while he moved behind her and undid the hook at her neck. She remained totally unaffected.

The zip presented little problem for Dan's skilful hands, and once the dress was slipped from her shoulders and off her arms it puddled to the floor. He took her hand and stepped her out of it.

Cassie dimly heard him catch his breath. She had been wearing a white strapless bra and half-slip under her dress, the garments chosen for necessity of style rather than eroticism. But both were made of fine silk, and did little to hide her womanly curves.

She was mildly surprised when Dan took her hand and led her over to the side of the bed, making her sit down. But she showed no resistance, going along with whatever he wanted in a numbed, robotic trance.

Yet when he knelt and gently removed one of her shoes her own breath suddenly stuck in her throat. His touch was infinitely light along her ankle, a seductive feather-caress on her flesh. And when he moved to pick up her other foot she actually flinched, her eyes widening.

His head snapped up to stare at her, his gaze frowning and thoughtful before returning to his task.

Cassie pushed clenched fists down into the mattress at her sides, fighting the unexpected sensations his touch was creating inside her. No... She didn't want to feel that... Not now! If anything, she wanted to hate him for making her love him.

But what had lain dormant, suppressed by

nerves, dulled by weariness, dampened by champagne, was slowly, inexorably stirring into life.

'Lie back,' he ordered, his voice husky.

She swallowed, but did as he asked, tension gripping her insides. When his hands slid up under her slip to peel back her stockings a sliver of intense excitement shot up her spine. Shaken, she levered herself up on one elbow to watch the stockings join the hat in the corner.

When Dan took hold of both her hands and pulled her to her feet she stared up at him, the battle for control still written on her face. His gaze was intent as his right hand came up to push the hair back behind her ear. It lingered on her neck, the thumb rubbing the sensitive skin at the base of her throat in slow circular movements.

For a moment Cassie relaxed, seduced into compliancy by the mesmerising touch. She closed her eyes, the darkness making her even more aware of Dan's hand. It was delicate and sensual. And arousing. Every nerve in Cassie's body started screaming for him to do so much more. She wanted both his hands on her body. She wanted them on her breasts, her stomach, her thighs. She wanted them to search and invade, to bring her to that excruciating edge when——

The shocking wantonness of her thoughts jerked Cassie's head away from his hand. Her eyes flew open in a type of stunned horror.

Dan glared at her, then swore under his breath.

Clearly angry, he turned away to yank down the quilt. 'Get into bed, Cassie,' came the gruff order.

She hesitated, but slowly climbed in, frowning when he pulled the quilt back up around her shoulders. 'But I thought you——'

'Go to sleep, Cassie!' he snapped. 'Even I'm not so much a bastard as to take you when you're dead on your feet. And so clearly unwilling.'

'But, Dan, I——' She stopped. He was already walking from the room. To call after him, to explain that he had misunderstood her reactions, to beg him to come back was impossible. She had some pride left.

She stared after him, willing him to turn around. But he kept on going. And when the door actually shut, Cassie had no option but to accept that her marriage was not to be consummated that night.

She groaned and threw herself into the pillow, disappointment an acute pain in her heart. And while she supposed that Dan's leaving had been considerate and uncharacteristically sensitive, she couldn't get rid of the feeling that, when the moment had finally come, he hadn't wanted her all that much. The Dan of old would not have walked away, *could* not have walked away. But then, the Dan of old had loved her. . .in a fashion.

Sobs welled up inside Cassie till she could no longer hold them back. She cried and she cried. And when at last she fell asleep, clutching the pillow, she wasn't to know that Dan did come back, some time later.

He stood at the side of the bed, staring down at her, his eyes narrowing when he saw the tear-streaks on her cheeks. He dragged in a deep, unsteady breath, then turned, snapping off the light before leaving the room.

CHAPTER TEN

CASSIE woke to semi-darkness, jerking upright in the bed. It was several seconds before she realised where she was. And that she was still alone.

She sank back down on the pillow and let out a trembling sigh, then reached over to switch on the bedside lamp. She glanced at her watch. Ten-past six. She had been asleep for over ten hours!

Her eyes darted to the door which was slightly ajar. Had Dan come back during the night? If so, why hadn't he come to bed? Why had he left her alone when he'd been so adamant all along that he wanted her?

The more Cassie thought about Dan's actions the night before, the more confused she became. Nothing made sense. Unless. . .

Could it be possible that he really did care about her, that his feelings encompassed more than a wish to possess her physically? It would explain his kind consideration in letting her sleep alone.

Or was it that his desire for her had waned now that he had won his objective? Maybe all he'd really wanted was his ring on her finger and Jason under his roof.

125

Dismay curled in her stomach. Oh, God...
What if he never wanted to make love to her?
What if he had tricked her into a ghastly shell of a
marriage? What if...?

Cassie groaned. This was ridiculous! She was
letting her mind run away with her. Dan wouldn't
be so cruel, so ruthless! He wouldn't!

Would he?

She threw back the covers and leapt from the
bed, refusing to allow herself to lie there and
wallow in such imaginings. That was all they were,
she berated herself savagely. Silly, stupid, sick
imaginings!

She dragged in a deep breath and determined
to do something. Anything to stop her mind
churning away!

A walk! That was it! She would get dressed and
go for a walk. That should clear her head. She
would go down to the river and watch the sun
rise. She might even wander over and take a last
look at Rosie. It wouldn't take long, and at least
it would eliminate that worry for the rest of the
day.

Ten minutes later Cassie was showered and
dressed in jeans and sloppy Joe. She made the
bed then tiptoed downstairs to the kitchen. There
she quietly got herself a glass of milk and was
about to leave when she spied a notice-board on
the wall near the back door. She hesitated, then

dashed off a quick message, telling Dan where she'd gone.

The sun had already risen by the time she reached the centre of the bridge, splashing a red gold into the grey waters. But it was cold just standing there, so Cassie kept on walking across, her eyes automatically scanning the horse paddocks in the distance. As her gaze swept over Rosie's field, a prickle of fear clutched at her heart. She couldn't see Rosie. Of course, she could be resting in the shed, but. . .

Cassie quickened her step, almost stumbling down the steps on to the far riverbank. She broke into a run, covering the distance along the path to the makeshift stables in record time, launching herself on to the fence surrounding Rosie's paddock. Where *was* she? Cassie's head swivelled this way and that. The paddock looked empty.

Suddenly Cassie saw her, lying prone in the far corner beneath the old fig tree.

Never had Cassie felt such panic. It tore into her belly, churning, painful, blinding. Oh, dear God, she prayed, pulse pounding, tears threatening. Don't let anything happen to my Rosie!

Cassie was through the fence and at the distressed animal's side in a flash.

'There, there, Rosie,' she cried, sinking down into the dirt on trembling knees and stroking the horse's quivering flanks. 'I'm here, old love. I'm here. Everything will be all right.'

But everything was not all right. The foal was not turned right in the birth canal, and Cassie needed all of her skill and patience to rectify the matter. By the time she had, Rosie seemed almost exhausted. The horse was old and tiring quickly. Cassie felt helpless, but she kept the growing panic out of her voice and talked to Rosie in calm, reassuring tones. 'You're doing splendidly, old girl. Have a rest for a while.' Cassie cradled the horse's head in her lap, letting her long, stroking hands and soothing words give the mare a much needed respite.

Another contraction started. Rosie stiffened. Her head jerked up in pain before wearily dropping back. Cassie felt like crying, but she didn't. Yet the effort to stay calm and supportive was tremendous.

Time ticked away and Cassie's worry increased. She wished she had her bag with her. An injection to strengthen the contractions might have helped. But there again, maybe not. Rosie was not young. Cassie resumed praying.

'Come on, old love,' she encouraged verbally. 'You can do it. Now here comes another contraction. Push!'

And to her surprise Rosie responded magnificently. She gave a great heave, then another and another. And out popped a slithering mass, the protective bag peeling back to reveal a healthy, though very messy foal.

'Fantastic!' Cassie praised, tears of relief and joy finally gushing over. With the pain gone Rosie was a different horse, scrambling to her feet and immediately attending to her foal. It had been many years since the old mare had given birth, but animals never forgot. Her long motherly tongue began the tedious task of cleaning and drying without any hesitation.

Cassie retreated to the fence, climbing through to wash her hands under the tank tap, then returning to lean against the railings and watch Rosie's meticulous work. The mare did not stop till her baby's coat was dry, after which she began the even slower job of nudging the foal up on to unsteady feet. When finally the filly – Cassie had craned her neck like a rubber man to acquire this knowledge – made it up on to those spindly long limbs, Rosie began directing her gently towards her teat, swinging her rump around every time her wayward charge headed in the wrong direction. It was a slow, frustrating process, but Rosie was patient and kept repeating the manoeuvre. Success was difficult because the foal, being a fraction premature, was frailer than some and kept falling over.

Cassie clapped her hands when the filly finally remained standing long enough to clamp on and suck. Her chest felt like it would burst with pride. For this was her triumph as well as Rosie's. She had single-handedly brought the mare back from certain death to this miraculous moment. More tears poured from her eyes as another well of emotion spilled over.

'So there you are!'

Cassie swung round to see Dan striding angrily towards her. He ground to a halt beside her, his anger disintegrating into exasperation when he looked into her eyes. 'Oh, God, no,' he muttered, 'not tears again.' His head shook from side to side in utter frustration. His sigh was weary. 'Even I can't cope with this.'

Taken aback, Cassie blinked up at him.

'And I certainly can't cope with any more of those goddamned confused innocent looks!' he exploded. 'You agreed to this marriage, Cassie. Admittedly, I forced your hand, but you know it's for Jason's good. You could at least give it a chance instead of. . . Oh, hell!' He ran an agitated hand through his hair and his eyes mirrored a type of desperation. 'What else could I do?' he cried in anguish.

Cassie was stunned by his tortured outburst, but the implications of the emotional words slowly penetrated. Could this be a ruthless man talking? A man without feeling. . .cold and callous? Impossible!

'Goddamn it, Cassie,' he burst out again, 'I'm not a saint and my patience is fast drawing to an end. I tried to be a considerate husband last night, didn't I? I put your feelings first, though, damn it

all, walking away from you was the hardest thing
I have ever done.'

Cassie's heart contracted. He *had* wanted her.
He had!

'And what happens?' he raged on, grabbing her
by the shoulders and shaking her. 'I get up this
morning, only to find your bed neatly made and
you gone! I've been looking for you for over an
hour. . .worrying. . .not knowing. . . And when I
find you, you're in tears again. What am I supposed to do, dammit? Or don't you care what I
do——?'

'Oh, Dan,' she broke in breathlessly, 'I'm so
sorry. . . I. . . Didn't you see my note?'

His hands dropped to his side in surprise.
'Note?'

'I left a message in the kitchen telling you I was
walking over to check on Rosie. . . Obviously you
didn't see it. And my crying has nothing to do
with you or our marriage. I was crying from
happiness.'

She grabbed his arm and turned his stiff, resist-
ant body towards the fence. 'See? Rosie's had her
foal. A lovely filly. . . That's why I was so long.
She was in labour when I arrived and she needed
some help. . .'

Cassie pointed to the mare and foal, who were
obviously doing well, the filly standing content-
edly in her mother's shadow, Rosie continually
checking to see if her little miracle was still there.

'See?' Cassie looked up at Dan, her eyes shining with tears. 'See?' she repeated anxiously when he again said nothing.

He looked long and hard at her. 'I see,' he said at last in a thick voice.

A surge of intense relief swamped Cassie. He understood. . . She had reached him.

'Thank God,' she sighed.

Cassie knew now, beyond any shadow of doubt, that she wanted Dan as her husband – on any terms. She loved him to distraction. And now that he'd shown that his consideration had been based on true caring, that he genuinely wanted their marriage to work. . . Well. . . Cassie was prepared to more than meet him half-way.

'So you weren't thinking of leaving me?' he asked, still frowning.

'No!'

His face remained guarded. 'The tears were really for the horse?'

'I swear.'

Gradually the tautness left his features, but he did not smile. His eyes flicked over Rosie's way. 'This horse – Rosie. . . She means a lot to you?'

'Oh, yes.'

'Why is she so special?'

Cassie proceeded to tell him all about Rosie, talking with the enthusiasm of a true animal lover. 'I couldn't let her become dog food, could I?' she finished, flushed with pleasure at Dan's showing interest.

He gave her a slightly sardonic look. 'No. . .of course not. What about all these other horses?' he went on, dry amusement settling on his face. 'Are they refugees as well?'

'Most of them. But Rosie's special. The others I will sell or give away once they're in good condition. Rosie I could never part with.'

They had begun walking along the path as they talked.

'Why don't you move them over to the island?' Dan suggested. 'There's plenty of good pasture.'

'That would be wonderful, but. . .'

'But what?'

'They'd have to have stables, or a barn. It gets pretty nippy up here in the winter. And they like shelter when it rains.'

'Stables it is, then.'

Cassie frowned. 'Good stables run into a lot of money. Perhaps——'

'Cassie!' Dan stopped. He took her by the shoulders and turned her to face him. 'I can afford stables. I can afford anything you want. Anything! All you have to do is ask and I'll buy it for you.'

Cassie's heart squeezed tight as she stared up into his beautiful, serious face. You can't buy me what I want most, Dan, came the destructive thought, but she firmly pushed it aside. He was trying hard to please her. And he did care. Maybe it was just for Jason's sake, but why quibble about that? Everything was looking a lot brighter than it had when she'd woken up that morning.

She smiled. A marriage where only one partner loved would always be a lop-sided compromise. Better that she begin compromising right now. 'I might take you up on that,' she said with feigned lightness.

'Just name it!'

Cassie could see that he wanted to buy her something, *needed* to buy her something. Perhaps it was his way of making up for forcing her into the marriage. But really, she didn't need anything, and had to rack her brains to come up with a suggestion.

'I...I could do with some new tyres on my jeep.'

'Tyres?' He grimaced. 'I offer my new bride anything she wants in the world and she says *tyres*!'

Cassie could see that he was really quite pleased.

'Dan,' she murmured, her voice catching in her throat.

'Yes?' Wariness again showed in his eyes.

'Good morning,' she said. And kissed him.

There was no doubting that she shocked him. He jerked back from her lips as though they were coated in poison. 'And what was that for?' he said, after regathering his composure.

'Nothing. I just felt like doing it.'

He lifted a single eyebrow. 'Did you, now?'

'Yes.'

'Impulsive, are you?'

'Sometimes. . .'

He gave her the oddest look, part sensual, part sad. 'You know. . . I've been thinking. . . We don't know each other very well, do we?'

Cassie stiffened, then turned to walk on. Dan moved with her. She hoped his remark wasn't another lead into his telling her about his previous marriage. Perhaps it was irrational, but she still didn't want to know the whys and wherefores of the relationship that had drawn Dan away from her. Maybe at the back of her mind a few questions niggled. Maybe she would like to know what kind of woman Roberta had been, whether she'd been wealthy or beautiful, and how she had died. And maybe in time she would ask. . . But not now! Her sense of compromise did not extend that far as yet.

'We know enough,' she said tautly.

She kept on walking, but she could feel him looking at her. 'That's a matter of opinion,' he said quietly, but the words carried hurt.

Cassie's regret was instant. They had actually been breaking down the barriers between them. Now, with her stupid jealousy, she had sent them back to square one.

'I'll have to ring Roger later,' she went on,

changing the subject in an effort to smooth over the sudden tension. 'He'll need to check on Rosie and the foal while I'm away. I hope nothing goes wrong.' Her eyebrows scrunched up in a burst of new worry. 'Perhaps we could. . .?' She turned sharply towards Dan.

'No, Cassie,' he said firmly, taking her elbow as they began climbing the steps up on to the suspension bridge. 'We can't. We are going to Sydney this afternoon and that's that. Roger will look after the foal. We need time alone together, away from here, away from everyone. We need privacy.'

Privacy. . . A knot formed in Cassie's stomach as she dwelt on that word and all its connotations. Privacy. . . As they crossed the bridge she darted a surreptitious glance down the river to the point, and the studio. Privacy with Dan meant only one thing. . .

Cassie stopped abruptly in the centre of the bridge. 'Dan. . .'

'Yes, Cassie?'

'Do you still paint?' she blurted out.

'No.'

She frowned.

Dan's mouth curved back into an ironic smile. 'I don't mind telling you why not,' he said, answering her unspoken question. 'Truth is, I haven't had much time for painting over the last few years. I've been too busy making money.'

'Oh.'

'You know, you've never even asked me what business I'm in. I could very well be a drug smuggler, for all you know.'

Cassie was taken aback by Dan's remark, more because of her reaction than the comment itself. She instinctively and immediately rejected any possibility of his being a criminal. Dan might be a typically selfish male, he might even have been an unfaithful husband, but he was basically good. Despite what had happened between them, she felt sure that he didn't deliberately set out to hurt people. He did seem to have a conscience. Somewhere. And criminals didn't.

'I wouldn't believe that for a second,' she stated truthfully.

'That's a relief to know.' His voice was dry. 'I thought you'd believe anything of me.'

'Of course I wouldn't.' She turned smiling eyes up to him and took pleasure in his surprise. 'Well? Are you going to tell me what business you're in, or do I have to drag it out of you?'

He laughed, then frowned. 'It's not that easy to explain.'

'See? Now you know why I didn't ask.'

He laughed again. Cassie liked the sound. In fact, she liked this relaxed, smiling Dan a lot. He seemed so different from the man who had callously told her that he didn't give a damn for her feelings. This was more like the warm, loving Dan of nine years ago, a Dan she could live with.

'How about import and export, property development, rental properties and blue-chip stocks?'

She pursed her lips. 'Sounds impressive.'

'And are you?'

'Am I what?'

'Impressed.'

It was her turn to laugh. 'Sorry. Money's not my thing.'

He sighed, but not unhappily so. 'I guessed as much. By the way, why did you ask me about my painting?'

Cassie swallowed and thought quickly. 'I...er...was just wondering what you intend doing with the studio,' she improvised, nodding down the river. Initially she had wanted to ask him about her portrait. Whether he had finished it or thrown it away. It had been only half-done when he'd left. But once again such a question felt too close to the bone for their fragile relationship. Better to keep the conversation light. She could handle that.

Dan stared down at the studio. Cassie was perturbed to see his features tighten. 'I intend doing nothing!' His tone was brusque.

'Nothing?'

'That's right. It's there and it can stay there. But I don't plan on using it. Come along.' He took Cassie's arm and propelled her forwards.

'Mrs Bertram always cooks breakfast for eight o'clock and there's nothing she hates more than cooking for absent mouths. She'll be having a pink fit.'

Mrs Bertram was doing no such thing. She was a very efficient woman and had everything under control. Cassie and Dan settled down in the morning-room to a delicious breakfast of freshly blended fruit juices, potato cakes and cheese-flavoured scrambled eggs, along with toast and coffee.

'This is simply delicious,' Cassie complimented, and the housekeeper beamed. 'I think I'm going to become very spoilt.'

'You'll have to tell me what Jason likes to eat, Mrs McKay,' the other woman said. 'Perhaps you could make a list and I can get in supplies while you're away.'

Dan looked up from where he'd been sitting, silently forking eggs into his mouth. Cassie was aware that his mood had changed since she'd mentioned the studio, and, while it bothered her underneath, she was determined to ignore it.

'You don't let Jason eat junk food, do you, Cassie?' Dan said. 'I don't agree with children eating rubbish all the time.'

Cassie prickled with resentment at what seemed like Dan interfering before she remembered her resolution. Compromise was the name of the game. 'Jason has always had a healthy, balanced diet, Dan, but the occasional ice-cream and sweet doesn't do any harm, does it, Mrs Bertram?'

'Of course not! Life would be pretty boring without some luxuries.'

A dry smile pulled at Dan's mouth. 'That's what I keep telling my wife... Speaking of diet, Mrs B., you won't forget to feed Hugo, will you?'

'Forget to feed that animal?' The housekeeper made a horrified sound. 'If I did I might end up on the menu myself. That dog eats like a lion!'

'Hugo's a lamb,' Dan countered in mock disagreement.

'More like a wolf in sheep's clothing,' Cassie joined in.

Mrs Bertram cackled. 'Oh, I like that one!'

'Are you women ganging up on me already? Watch it, Mrs B. – I could always hire a male housekeeper.'

Mrs Bertram laughed some more. 'I don't think you will, Mr McKay,' she said, glancing back at Cassie as she walked from the room. 'Not with that lovely bride of yours.'

Cassie blushed as Dan's eyes swung on to hers, their black depths engulfing her with a sudden, hot intimacy. 'She might be right there,' he drawled. 'Maybe I should even hire a woman pilot. What do you think?'

'Your bride might object to that,' Cassie retorted without thinking.

'Would she?' Dan murmured, holding her eyes,

probing, as if wondering whether she cared enough to be jealous. . .or possessive.

Mrs Bertram popped her head inside the door. 'Anyone for more coffee?'

They both declined, but the intimate moment was broken.

'I have to make a few business calls after breakfast,' Dan explained once Mrs Bertram had gone. 'I'm sorry to leave you alone, but I don't want to be bothered with anything while we're away. The helicopter will be here around eleven, and we should be at the Regent in time for lunch.'

Cassie's heart skipped a beat. 'The Regent? Is that where we're staying?'

'Yes. . . Didn't I tell you before? Sorry. I've been staying there occasionally since——' He broke off, his jaw clenched down hard, his chest rising and falling in an impatient sigh.

Since. . .? Since when? Cassie worried. What was Dan thinking about to give him that strained look?

He looked up at her, his expression now one of schooled blandness. 'It's a very good hotel. You'll like it, I'm sure.'

Her palms were clammy where they gripped the cutlery. 'What. . .what should I pack? Clothes-wise. . .'

Dan picked up his coffee-cup and drained it. 'What? Oh, yes. . .clothes. . .' Without batting an eyelid he said, 'As little as possible.'

Her blush was instantaneous. Dan frowned, then laughed. But it was not a light laugh. It had a harsh edge. 'Sorry. I wasn't trying to embarrass you. The helicopter has a weight problem when it carries two passengers. Not only that...' He hesitated.

'What?'

'I couldn't help noticing when you brought over your clothes that you don't own much in the way of feminine finery. I'll take you shopping this afternoon. I know you don't care for extravagances, but I have a mind to see my wife in designer labels.' He smiled, and again the gesture did not carry much warmth.

Cassie's whole insides tightened. 'If that's what you want...'

His black eyes swept over her, and he muttered something under his breath. There was a slight shake of his head as he got to his feet, as if he were annoyed with himself, but when he looked up at her next his smile was quite charming. 'Haven't you got some phone calls to make as well?' he asked. 'I heard you tell your mother you would ring and let her know where we'd be staying. And I suppose you'll want to ring Roger about the horse.'

Cassie nodded.

'Better get a move on, then. It's nearly ten already.'

He turned away from the table and strode from

the room, leaving Cassie to sit alone and worry. Why had Dan's moods changed so? First when she'd mentioned the studio, then later, when he'd been telling her about the Regent.

What had he been going to say about the hotel? Probably that he'd stayed there on and off since Roberta died, she decided.

Cassie vividly remembered his pained look, and the way he'd had to choke off his words. Had he loved his wife that much?

Cassie blocked out the surge of jealousy and tried to face facts. What *was* the truth about their affair all those years ago? Had Dan really been getting a divorce, or had his marriage just been going through a bad patch, with his finding comfort in Cassie's arms, only to race back to his wife as soon as she needed him?

In the light of Dan's new and kinder manner, Cassie now wanted to know, really know, for it was impossible to found a marriage on misunderstandings and lies. Better she know the truth too, no matter how it hurt.

Had he somehow loved them both, she mused, but had ultimately chosen the woman he'd felt he owed the most allegiance to?

Cassie clung to this most hopeful of the possibilities, reassuring herself that, while Dan had chosen his wife, he had at least tried to let *her* down as lightly as possible. Under those circumstances, he wouldn't have mentioned his wife in that letter he'd written. Neither would he have dreamt of Cassie getting pregnant. That had been *her* stupidity!

No. . .to be fair, Dan was not as black a character as she had believed all these years, Cassie now decided generously.

But, given this line of thought, why *had* he been annoyed when she'd mentioned the studio?

Cassie sighed. She was doing it again, going round and round in circles. And all because they had never really talked, never opened up to each other. There had been too much hurt, too much bitterness, on both sides. They had both been at fault, because they had both felt betrayed; she by Dan's abandonment, he by her keeping him in ignorance of Jason.

So, where do you go from here, Cassie? an inner voice challenged.

She stood up, lifted her chin and squared her shoulders.

To Sydney, came the answer.

To the Regent.

And privacy.

CHAPTER ELEVEN

THE trip to Sydney was nerve-racking. At the beginning the pilot, Paul, kept sliding curious glances her way, making Cassie blush. She imagined that he was vividly recalling the scene he had encountered in the library, which did nothing for her composure.

Dan was broodingly silent for the entire flight, which didn't exactly help. He sat there, in his formidable pin-striped suit, thinking about God knew what, and precluding any attempt on Cassie's part for conversation.

On top of that, Cassie was terrified that they might crash. She hadn't realised she would be afraid, having flown a few times before in her university days. But this was so different. Before she had been in a regular-sized plane. The helicopter seemed too small. And too flimsy! Jason would certainly not be allowed to go up in it again!

She was so uptight, she couldn't even appreciate the aerial view of Sydney as they came in to land. Cassie just stared steadfastly forwards, gripping the sides of her seat with knuckle-whitening force. When the helicopter hovered to a halt on the helipad, her attempt to suppress a sob of relief was without success. Dan darted her a sharp look.

He sighed, but from that moment was solicitous and caring of her needs. He helped her alight and led her numbed body across the cement roof, then held her arm all the way down on the lift ride before propelling her through a busy foyer out into a waiting taxi.

Cassie climbed over into the far corner of the back seat, huddling into it like a frightened animal. Dan gave her another of his exasperated looks before putting an arm around her shoulder and firmly pulling her close.

Cassie slanted him a surprised look, but when she met a stubborn glare in return she gave in gracefully and settled into the crook of his arm. It was really a very pleasant and relaxing position, for his body made a warm haven against the surprisingly chilly Sydney air. Cassie had dressed in a green linen jumpsuit and had thought the long-sleeved style a good choice for a mild spring day, but the clouds had gathered over Sydney and a brisk wind was blowing.

Cassie gradually grew aware of much more than Dan's warmth. His taut thigh was pressed against hers, and she could hear his heart beating. It was going faster, she thought, than his outwardly bland appearance warranted, and making her fertile imagination hurtle forward to the moment when they would finally be alone, when he would take her in his arms and make love to her.

Dan's desire for her was the one thing she no longer sought to question in her mind. No matter how he felt in his heart, he did want her. That, she was sure of.

The Regent was all and more than she had thought it would be. No hotel gained such an international reputation lightly. But it was the service afforded Dan that impressed Cassie the most. It was 'Good afternoon, Mr McKay', 'Lovely to see you again, Mr McKay', 'Of course, Mr McKay', every step of the way. When he casually mentioned that he would like a salad lunch served in his suite the meal practically preceded them, wheeled in on an elegant trolley within seconds of their walking into their rooms.

Cassie was speechless for a second at the sheer extravagance of their accommodation. Dan's wealth came home to her with a jolt as her eyes took in the massive bedroom and sitting-room, and the exquisite marble bathroom, not to mention the spectacular view. This must have cost a fortune, she thought dazedly, and wandered over to stand gazing at the water and the Harbour bridge.

'It's even better at night,' Dan said, coming up behind Cassie to place curving hands over her shoulders. She forced herself to relax back against him, but her nerves were at screaming point.

What now? she worried. A chatty lunch, then a long shopping expedition, with her stomach in knots all the while? Oh, God, she couldn't eat a thing, and she no more wanted to go shopping than fly to the moon.

When an involuntary sigh puffed from her lips he turned her to face him. 'You're not tired, are you?'

She looked up into his tense face, and for the first time appreciated that Dan was under strain as well. His emotions were probably as confused as hers, she realised. Perhaps he thought, as he had the previous night, that she was unwilling. Maybe if she. . .

A nervous spasm claimed her insides, but a mad recklessness drove her to slide her arms up around his neck and lift herself up on tiptoe, her lips hovering just beneath his. 'Make love to me, Dan,' she whispered shakily. 'Now. . . Please. . .'

A frown gathered on his handsome face. 'Now?'

Her heart was thudding in her ears. 'Yes,' she whispered.

His face contorted in almost violent rejection as he wrenched her arms down and whirled away, stalking over to the corner of the room. He stood with feet apart, glaring fiercely through the window down at the traffic below, the rigid shoulders and clenched fists telegraphing his inner upheaval.

For her part, Cassie was totally shattered. Had

she been so wrong? 'Don't. . .don't you want to make love to me, Dan?' she managed to choke out, feeling more wretchedly vulnerable than she ever had in her life. She had bared her heart to him, given up her defences. . .

He turned with grinding slowness to face her, his expression bitter. 'You know I do. But not like this. Not to get it over with because. . .' His hands lifted and fell in a helpless, tormented frustration. 'I don't want you as some sort of maternal sacrifice, Cassie. When I take you to bed, I want you to want me – as a woman wants a man.'

The searing need in his voice forced Cassie to answer with her own. 'I do want you, Dan.'

He made a harsh, guttural sound.

'I do!' she insisted vehemently, taking a tentative step towards him as she searched desperately for words to convince him. The truth now – nothing but the truth would bridge this terrible chasm of misunderstanding. 'I. . .I wanted you last night, too. . .'

Disbelief shot into his black gaze. 'You shrank away from me last night, Cassie,' he accused. 'I didn't imagine that. You hated my touching you. God knows, you warned me. . .that you'd despise me for it. . .but. . .'

She came another step closer. 'No! You misunderstood.' Her voice was urgent, frantic. 'Perhaps at first. . . I wanted to hate you because I. . . Oh,

Dan, don't you see? When you kept touching me, in the end I couldn't help myself. I. . .' The words trailed away as she saw his mouth twist with bitter distaste.

'Couldn't help yourself, Cassie? God, you don't leave a man much pride, do you? Telling me that you're so starved of sex that you'd even tolerate a partner you despise in order to gain satisfaction.'

'That's not what I meant!' she cried. With mounting horror, Cassie began to see what she had wrought with her own stupidly proud words that night in the library – her crazed defiance of his accusations – and all because she had wanted him – only him! 'I don't despise you, Dan, I. . .' She stopped, realising suddenly and shockingly that if she said she loved him, he wouldn't believe her.

'You what? Love me?' He gave a brutal little laugh. 'I'm not a dreamer, Cassie. I've had to face too many harsh realities in my life, and one more is that underneath all your brave little gestures you detest me! Don't bother denying it. I've seen it often enough in your eyes.' One hand shot out to clasp her chin. He lifted her face with cruel fingers. 'You have very expressive eyes, Cassie,' he ground out. 'They don't lie. . .'

His own eyes darkened and narrowed, frightening her for a moment. Then suddenly his hand gentled, his expression becoming heart-meltingly tender. 'Lovely eyes,' he murmured thickly.

'Lovely eyes... Lovely mouth...' His thumb rubbed over her lips. 'Lovely body...' His hands grazed down over her breasts.

He shut his eyes and groaned. His anguish tore at her heart, compelling her to comfort him. Quite instinctively she wrapped her arms around his waist, hugging him to her. 'Oh, Dan...don't... Please, don't... You must listen to me.——'

'Listen to what now?' he snarled, pulling back from her. 'More lies?'

Cassie gazed up at him.

His eyes were open, and the hardness had returned.

'I don't want to listen any more,' he grated out. 'I'm tired of it all. So tired... Perhaps you're right. Perhaps I should stop fighting myself and just take what you keep offering. Maybe all we'll ever have together is this!'

She had no time to say anything before he jerked her back into his arms, bending his mouth to hers, obliterating the light, obliterating the world, obliterating everything but Cassie's awareness of him, his mouth, his arms, every inch of his body. And after a while it didn't seem to matter if he took her in anger. So long as he took her!

With a low moan she gave herself up to the lips that were devouring hers, to the hands that even now were moulding her body to his with such devastating intimacy. His tongue plunged deep in her mouth again and again till the thudding in her temples reached a blinding crescendo.

Finally she had to gasp away to catch her breath.

'No!' he growled, cupping her face with brutal hands, glowering down at her with those hot, black pools. 'Don't do that... You asked for this, and you will do it my way... Give me your mouth... Breathe my breath if you have to...I want some part of you joined to me while I undress you...'

The erotic power of Dan's words blasted a searing heat into Cassie's body. Her cheeks flamed. Her limbs melted.

'Open your mouth, Cassie,' he ordered thickly, groaning when she offered her parted lips once more.

She knew that with her silent submission to his request she had surrendered more to him than her mouth. More than her body. This was what he had once vowed he'd wanted. Her very soul! But she no longer cared. Let him do with her as he willed.

His hands were on her clothes, undoing the buttons on her jumpsuit, dragging it across her shoulders and down her arms, letting it fall to the floor around her feet. He stepped her out of her shoes. Yet all the while their mouths were as one. The blood was pounding in Cassie's head. Her whole insides were twisted in a knot of yearning. Every nerve-ending was jangling.

Her heart stopped as she felt his fingers on the clasp of her bra, and then her breasts were free, falling unfettered into his hands. She moaned softly into his mouth as he caressed her. Her legs began to quiver.

His kiss kept her from sinking floorwards. His kiss and his hands. Suddenly they weren't gentle on her flesh, but she didn't mind. She was as wild with passion as he seemed to be. She wanted him to be rough with her breasts, to lift the swollen mounds, to torment them, to feed this mad, fomenting need inside her. And he did, ravaging the tender flesh mercilessly, rubbing the sensitive, aching peaks till she whimpered in her pained pleasure.

He stopped kissing her, sliding his hot, moist mouth down the throbbing column of her neck, all the while murmuring her name. Over and over he said it. 'Cassie. . . Cassie. . .'

Then abruptly he scooped her up into his arms and laid her across the bottom corner of the bed, letting her head drop over the side, her soft hair falling floorwards from her neck. He took her arms and pushed them back on either side of her head, the position lifting her breasts to his quest-ing lips. Cassie arched upwards, and as he drew one ripe, aroused nipple into the hot cavern of his mouth an animal sound husked from her parted lips. She found herself staring up at the windows, blindly gazing at the upside-down view.

Cassie's head was spinning. The room was spinning. Dazedly she grew aware that Dan had abandoned her flesh, that he was stripping off his clothes. And then he was back, lifting her head gently on to the bed, running his hands lightly down her body, peeling off the last scrap of clothing between them.

'So beautiful,' he murmured.

She was like liquid, her limbs heavy, her body consumed with a strange, drugging heat. She shut her eyes, making herself more aware of Dan's exploratory touch. His hands skimmed over her flesh, grazing her nipples, circling into her navel, then gently dipping between her thighs.

Her legs parted of their own accord, opening her body to his touch. She became languorous in his caresses, murmuring his name. His mouth replaced his hands, kissing her everywhere. More and more she opened to him. More and more.

She gasped when his lips moved intimately against her, but the pleasure was shockingly addictive. Electric jolts shivered along her veins. A mounting tension claimed her insides.

'Don't stop, don't stop,' came her impassioned, shivering words when he suddenly abandoned her.

His laugh had a harsh, triumphant sound to it. But he bent his head once more, repeating the blissful torture, taking her once again to the exciting edge of the abyss. It was ecstasy and agony. Heaven and hell. 'Oh, God!' she cried, her head threshing from side to side as the excruciating, nerve-tingling, irresistible pleasure was snatched from her once more. 'Please. . .oh, please,' she begged, squeezing her eyes tightly shut.

'Look at me, Cassie,' he growled. 'Open your eyes and look at me!'

She moaned and her eyes fluttered open to gaze pleadingly up at him. He was standing at the foot of the bed, his hair dishevelled, his breathing ragged, magnificent and virile in his nakedness.

'Now tell me you want me!' he ground out.

She opened dry lips. 'I want you ──'

'I want you, Dan. Say it!'

'I want you, Dan,' she sobbed.

Never had she seen such a look. So triumphant, yet so ghastly. Every muscle in his face was drawn tight, his eyes glittering like those of a madman. He made a hoarse sound, then stepped forward to abruptly slide his hands under her buttocks. She suddenly felt like a dissociated object, stretched out before him on the quilt, he still standing beside the bed.

'Dan. . . No. . . Not like this. . .'

But he ignored her, his face contorted as he plunged into her, groaning as he wrapped her legs tightly around him, then grasped her hips in a vice-like grip. She had no leverage to struggle against him, and in truth she no longer wanted to struggle. Her body had surged with an indescribable sensation at his forceful possession. Nothing, she thought, could be more right than to be joined like this to the man she loved.

A trembling sigh quivered from her lips. Dan's eyes snapped up to hers. They were half shut in their passion, but they were watching her. His hands reached to cup her breasts, and his palms grazed the tips. Her lips parted with a soft moan.

'It has to be like this, Cassie,' he muttered thickly. 'I have to see your face... See your pleasure... Don't close your eyes, Cassie. Look at me.'

She did. And found it the most unbelievably arousing experience. Black lights danced in his eyes every time she made a sound, and when she moistened dry lips with her tongue she could see the flames of desire leap in his gaze.

'Your body and mine are one now, Cassie,' he rasped as he ground slowly into her. 'This is how it's going to be from now on. No other men... You will know only me!'

Cassie knew nothing. All she knew was sensation. Pleasure. And a blindly escalating tension. It was gripping her thighs, her insides, making her muscles tighten around him. She had to move.

'No!' he gasped. 'Keep still!'

She held herself back for as long as she could, trying to be patient. But, inevitably, her control slipped. Her body began to rock, moving with him, urging him on. Her hands gripped on to the quilt at her sides, her fingers tightening and releasing in time with the primitive rhythm. Her breathing quickened further, as did her movements, and finally he could no longer resist her urgings.

Cassie's body convulsed, her lips parting wide in her gasps of uncontrollable pleasure. And while her body was still shuddering in ecstasy Dan climaxed. Then slowly, exhaustedly, his spent body collapsed on top of her.

For several stunned seconds all Cassie was aware of was Dan's weight on her, then gradually, dreamily, the aftermath of their lovemaking took hold. All her limbs flooded with a heavy languor. A blissful peace seeped into her mind. And in this moment of satiation and contentment, her arms slipped around him, her palms sliding over the warm, damp skin on his back. He had denied her this contact, and now she wanted to revel in it. Love ran from her heart down her arms, through to her fingertips. She caressed his skin, stroked and touched him with the intensity of a woman starved of affection. This was Dan, her man, her love. She hugged him close.

When he suddenly began to roll away she cried, 'Don't go!' and clung on.

For a second he hesitated, then he sank back. Her arms crept back around him in a tightly possessive clasp.

'Oh, Dan,' she choked out. 'My darling, my love. . .'

His body froze above her. Then with a stiff, jerky movement, he withdrew. He spun away and sat on the side of the bed, his shoulders shaking.

'Goddamn you, Cassie,' he hissed. 'Goddamn you!'

Cassie shot upright, stunned by his unexpected desertion, his savage words. 'Dan. . .' Her hand gingerly touched his shoulder. 'What's wrong? What have I said? Done?'

He rounded on her, black eyes flashing, his expression one of disgust. 'Is that all it takes with you, Cassie? One good lay and you love me? Or do you love every man who satisfies you?'

She shrank back from him in horror, but he swept on, his voice full of derision. 'Let's at least have some honesty in this marriage! So the sex is good between us. More than good. Great! Well, I'm not surprised. It always was. But, for pity's sake, I don't need it served up with false platitudes. OK? Keep the my darlings and loves to yourself!'

Cassie's face began to crumple. She couldn't believe this man. . . He was either incredibly stupid, or heartless! For nine years she had bottled up her love for him. Nine years! And here she was at last, dying to give him every last scrap of it, offering her heart as well as her body on a silver platter. And what had he done with it? Thrown it back in her face!

Appalled, she stared into his flushed, arrogant face and fought her tears, fought them for all she was worth. Her earlier intentions of asking him about his marriage, then explaining everything she had said and done since his return, flew out of the window. She got to her feet, making no attempt to hide her nudity. She drew herself up straight and glared down at him, face proud, eyes chilling with enforced steel.

'Very well, Dan,' she said in clipped tones. 'If you'll excuse me, I am going to have a shower. You said something about taking me shopping afterwards? Forget it! I'm not in the mood. How's that for honesty?'

She spun away and marched over to the bathroom door, where she whirled to face him once more. 'And speaking of honesty, I have one more thing to say. You can stop throwing other men up in my face. There have been no other men. None at all. I lied. You were my first and only lover, Dan. *First and only*!'

Forcing her chin up in crumbling defiance, she threw herself into the bathroom, slamming and locking the door behind her. But as she leant, heaving against the door, the silence from the room outside rushed to haunt her. He hadn't come after her, wasn't banging on the door, didn't beg her forgiveness. She bit her lip and stumbled over to the shower, snapping on the water just in time to let the sound of the teeming jets drown out her sobs.

CHAPTER TWELVE

CASSIE stayed in the shower for ages, unwilling in her misery to face Dan once more. But at long last her water-wrinkled skin forced her to turn off the taps and emerge. She dried herself and dragged on one of the towelling bathrobes supplied by the hotel.

This marriage was impossible, she decided bleakly as she ran her fingers through her damp hair. She couldn't bear to live with Dan every day, sleep in his bed every night, having to keep herself in check, never able to tell him that she loved him. And any hope that in time he might come to love her as she did him was sheer fantasy!

A shudder ran through her at the memory of the way he'd turned on her, so soon after they'd been bound together in what she'd imagined, however stupidly, was a loving union. But it had only been sex on Dan's part. A mere indulging of his carnal desires. On a personal level, he was as cold and ruthless as he'd once declared.

Why had she deluded herself into believing differently – that he was capable of true feeling for her? He'd spelled it out clearly enough for her that night in the library. His one desire had been to secure his son in his life. That was the only reason he had married Cassie. Sex with her was merely a coincidental bonus. Nothing else. For some ghastly, perverse reason she still aroused him – as she had nine years before. If he appeared softer and more considerate occasionally it was only because it suited his purpose at the time. No man wanted a difficult wife. Or an unwilling bed-partner. He'd spelled that out as well.

But love? No... He didn't want her love. Didn't want it, didn't need it, couldn't accept it.

Cassie could no longer hide from the obvious truth. Dan had only ever loved one woman. And that woman was dead...

Desolation crashed through her, draining the blood from her face, making her lean weakly against the bathroom vanity unit. What on earth was she going to do? How could she cope?

She stared at herself in the vanity mirror, at the puffy red eyes, the swollen lips, the pale, ravaged face.

But you have to cope, her reflection told her. There is Jason to think of, your mother, Roger... You knew this marriage wouldn't be easy. You can't run away at the first hurdle even if it's a seemingly insurmountable one. You just have to grit your teeth and bear it.

Gathering herself, she moved over to the door and turned the knob. She felt sick at heart as she stepped out into the bedroom, the prospect of facing Dan again making her stomach churn.

The bedroom was empty.

Cassie raced into the adjoining sitting-room. It, too, was empty. Dan had gone.

Panic set in till she took a hold of herself.

So he's stepped out for a while, she reasoned. He'll come back. . .eventually. And when he does I'll smile and tell him I'm sorry, that in future I'll be a good, quiet little girl, that he can make love to me any time he wishes and I'll. . .

With a sob Cassie sank down on to the sofa and buried her face in her hands. But she didn't cry. She refused to. She steadied her breathing, hardened her resolve, and when her eyes finally lifted they were dry. The years of wretched emptiness had schooled her well.

I will survive, Cassie drilled herself. I will lock my love away, as I did before. It will not be easy, but I will do it. I have to!

Steady blue eyes swept the room, landing on the untouched tray.

Eat! her mind ordered.

Cassie ate. But she didn't really taste a thing. Then she dressed, slowly, back into her lime jumpsuit.

Still Dan had not returned. The light was beginning to fade as the sun sank behind the tall city buildings. Cassie firmly squashed any renewed sense of painc and proceeded to the bathroom, making up her face with relative composure, combing her hair into place. Still no Dan. Her watch showed just after five.

The sound of the telephone ringing jarred into the silence. Cassie raced over to snatch up the receiver from the bedside table. 'Yes?'

'Cassie?'

'Roger?' Surprise lifted her voice.

'Yes. . .'

Roger's heavy acknowledgement and subsequent silence sent a shiver of alarm up Cassie's spine.

'Cassie, I. . .' He sighed and again fell silent. Cassie could hear someone sobbing in the background. It was a woman.

'Oh, my God!' she cried. 'Jason. . . Something's happened to Jason!' She cradled the receiver in both hands to stop herself from dropping it.

'Now don't panic, Cassie. He's all right. I mean. . .well, he's still alive. . . Shh, Joan! He. . .er, was hit in the temple with a cricket ball at practice this afternoon. He's at the district hospital and they say it might only be a concussion, but——'

'Is he conscious?' she broke in frantically.

There was a telling silence before Roger said, 'No.'

'Oh, God,' she groaned.

'The resident here's been trying to contact a

Sydney specialist who's the best, but he's in theatre. It appears that there may be some pressure forming inside Jason's brain which will have to be alleviated. He——'

The bedroom door opened and Dan walked in.

'Just. . .just a moment, Roger,' Cassie rasped.

She lifted stricken eyes towards her husband, who froze on the spot. 'Dan, it's. . .it's. . .' Her voice was choked off by the enormous lump in her throat. A strangled sob escaped her lips.

'What is it?' he demanded thickly. 'What's happened?'

'There's been an accident,' she croaked. 'Jason. . .'

For a moment she thought he hadn't heard her. His face went totally blank. Cassie stared at him, only then noticing his oddly dishevelled state.

Suddenly Dan's face sagged. 'Oh, God, no!' he moaned. 'Not Jason. . . Not him, too. . .'

'Cassie? Cassie, are you there?' came the voice down the line.

'Yes, Roger, I'm here.' She glanced worriedly over at Dan, who looked as if he was going to collapse. 'Yes. . .yes, I'm listening. . . What's that?' Her attention was now all on what Roger was telling her. 'Of course I could. Give me the name of this doctor Jason needs, and I'll keep on trying till——'

The phone was swept out of her hands. 'Roger? Dan McKay speaking. What's this about a doctor?

Fill me in, will you?' His voice was astonishingly steady and firm, as was the hand that pushed Cassie's shoulder down till she was sitting on the bed. Only then did she realise how much she was shaking.

'I see... Yes... I don't need to write it down. I'll remember... I'll let you know when we'll be arriving... If I don't get him, I'll get someone else... What? No. No, of course I don't blame anyone. Accidents happen... Yes, I'll be in touch soon.'

He hung up, but was instantly punching out other buttons, making calls, giving orders. Cassie was dazed by the astonishing change in Dan's manner. What kind of man was this she was married to? One moment totally stricken, the next, a powerhouse of decision-making.

Yet she was immensely grateful for his taking charge, only now fully aware of how close to breaking down she was.

'Come, Cassie,' he grabbed her elbow, lifting her forcibly to her feet. 'We have things to do. Quickly. No, leave our luggage...'

There was no time for tears, no time for talk, no time to give in to the sickening lump of fear growing inside her. Cassie was whizzed across the city into the emergency section of St Vincent's Hospital, where she stayed in the taxi while Dan literally ran inside. The minutes passed – precious, life-ebbing minutes. She kept thinking of her little boy lying in a hospital bed, fluid building up on his brain, building, building till something burst. . .

She prayed crazy, bribing prayers. Please, God, if you spare him, I won't ask that Dan ever love me. Let him hate me if it will make any difference! I'll do anything. . .anything. . . Only let my son live!

Suddenly Dan was back, a big, brusque man in a white coat accompanying him, who looked quite disgruntled. 'This is highly irregular,' he was muttering. 'Highly irregular. . .'

Dan glared at the doctor, who glared back before looking over at Cassie's startled, strained face. Her eyes clung to him, appealingly, desperately. 'Oh, please,' she begged.

His face gentled. 'Right!' he gruffed. 'We're on our way.'

The two men climbed in, the doctor in front, Dan beside Cassie. The taxi lurched off, but they had now caught the peak hour and were often held up for minutes at a time without moving. No one spoke. Cassie found the delays and the silence unnerving. She started to talk, more to herself, than anyone.

'Strange how things turn out. There I was on my way to Sydney thinking that I would never let Jason go up in that helicopter again. I was worried about it crashing. And what happens? He gets hurt at cricket. Cricket. . .' She let out a ragged, trembling sigh. 'You worry and worry, trying to keep them safe, trying to foresee the dangers. But sometimes, no matter how hard you try, no matter what you do, things happen——'

Her head snapped round at the sound Dan made. It was ghastly. Tormented.

'Yes,' he rasped. 'But do they have to keep happening? First——' He stopped, bruising her heart with a brief, haunted look before he wrenched his eyes away. 'And now Jason,' he said raggedly as he stared steadfastly through the side window.

Cassie's heart went out to him. To lose a wife, then to be in fear of losing a son was surely more than any man could bear. Her hand slipped along the margin of seat between them. She picked up his hand and pressed it gently.

Dan's eyes jerked across. He glared first at her, then down at their linked hands.

'He'll be all right,' she whispered soothingly. 'He has to be.'

He looked at her with eyes that were in hell. 'You don't know, or understand, Cassie. But if I lose Jason too. . .' He closed his eyes, his whole body slumping, his hand cold and lifeless within hers.

Cassie's spirits sank to rock-bottom and silent tears began to fall. Dan was right. She didn't know. They might already be too late.

It was half-past seven by the time the two

helicopters reached the Northern Rivers District Hospital. They landed in the car park, the doctor sprinting ahead into the hospital. Dan and Cassie climbed out and walked together in a tense black silence across the bitumen, up the wide steps and into the lighted foyer.

'Cassie!'

She looked up to see her mother and Roger hurrying towards them. 'Cassie, darling, thank God you're here. Jason's holding on, but——' Joan threw her arms around her daughter and burst into tears.

It was a long night. After examining Jason the doctor ordered immediate surgery to relieve the build-up of cranial pressure, and, despite Roger's suggestion they would be better off waiting at home, all four of them remained in the hospital waiting-room into the small hours of the morning. The tension between the group was so high that neither Roger nor Joan seemed to notice Dan's odd behaviour. He made no attempt to be with his new wife as he either paced the floor or sat in grim silence in one of the chairs. He refused all offers of coffee and had visibly aged ten years.

Cassie wanted to go to him, wanted to do something to comfort him. But she too was hurting. She too was afraid. And it all seemed so hopeless. Family crises either brought people together again, or drove a deeper wedge between them. Theirs appeared to be doing the latter.

Everyone snapped to attention when the doctor suddenly appeared in the doorway. He was smiling. 'The danger's over now, Mr and Mrs McKay. Jason will be just fine.'

An audible sigh of relief reverberated through the room.

Someone breathed, 'Thank God!'

Which Cassie did, fervently, before rushing forward to take the doctor's hands. 'However can we thank you, Doctor?' she cried.

'To see you smile like that goes a long way, Mrs McKay.'

'Can we see him now?' she asked.

'If you like. He's back in his room, but he's still asleep from the anaesthetic.' He glanced over Cassie's shoulder at Dan. 'Well, Mr McKay? Is that helicopter of yours all tanked up and ready to go?'

Dan nodded slowly, apparently too full of emotion to speak.

'Then I must run. I have theatre in the morning, and even geniuses like myself need some sleep.' He grinned and left.

Cassie hugged her mother before turning to Roger. 'You must take her home to bed. . . You, too. . . You've both been under a terrible strain, but Jason is all right now. Dan and I will stay with him.'

When they hesitated, she practically pushed the pair of them from the room. Then with a deep, steadying breath she turned to face her husband. This was no time for personal problems. It was a time for rejoicing. Their son was alive!

'Dan?' Quite determinedly she walked over and curled an arm around one of his. 'Shall we go and see Jason?'

Dan looked rigidly down at her, but his eyes didn't seem to register. They seemed to be in some far off place, where he was enduring his own private agony. 'Cassie... I want you to know...to understand... I have to tell you. You *must* listen!'

She raised startled eyes at the vehemence in his voice. He hesitated, his eyes searching hers as though seeking some sort of reassurance, but suddenly a bleakness invaded his face and he shook his head, expelling a shuddering breath. 'What's the use? It won't make any difference. At least we have Jason... All right. Let's go and see him.' He grasped her elbow and propelled her from the room.

Cassie allowed herself to be bustled down the corridor, half wishing she could stop and ask Dan what it was that she should know and understand. In the back of her mind she knew that it had something to do with his wife, but how could she think of such things when her mind and heart were full of Jason and his recovery? And, as Dan said, what difference could it make now?

A pretty young nurse was sitting beside Jason's bed in the small, private room. She stood up and smiled when Dan and Cassie came in. 'I'll be outside if you need me,' she said quietly.

Cassie took one look at the tiny white figure in the bed, his head swathed in bandages, and almost burst into tears again. She clung on to Dan's arm.

'He looks so small, so defenceless,' she cried with a tiny sob.

'So lifeless,' Dan murmured. 'Just like. . .'

Dan groaned and tried to twist away from her, but Cassie clutched his arms. It struck her forcibly as she looked up into his contorted face that, if she truly loved Dan and wanted to make her peace with him, she had to face Roberta's ghost.

'Dan. . . What is it? Tell me!'

He shook his head.

'Is it. . .something to do with Roberta?' she persisted. 'Is that it? If it is, then I want to know.'

Again he shook his head. 'No, you don't. You never wanted to know. Not that I blame you. I've done it all wrong. . .grabbing at you. . .grabbing at Jason. I wanted you both. . .so desperately.' Tears glittered into his eyes. 'All these years of——' His mouth clamped tightly shut and he closed his eyes. 'You'd never understand. . .'

'Dan, please. . .give me the chance,' she

pleaded. 'I. . .I didn't want to know about Roberta before because I was jealous. . .and I couldn't bear to hear about the wife you had loved. . .more than me. . .'

He opened eyes that had known a hell which she could not even guess at. 'I didn't love Roberta, Cassie. And there were times when I hated her from the depths of my soul for keeping me tied to her side. But she had no one else. No one. . .'

'Tell me about it,' Cassie urged, slipping her arms around his waist. She lifted loving, reassuring eyes. 'Tell me everything.'

He stared at her as though he couldn't believe the words he was hearing, or the way she was looking at him. 'It isn't a pretty story, Cassie.'

She swallowed. 'I can take it.'

'Yes, no doubt you can,' he sighed. 'You're remarkably tough.'

Cassie flinched and looked away.

He swung her chin back with a tender fingertip. 'Don't think I meant that unkindly, Cassie. I admire you. I really do. You're strong and independent, and underneath. . .underneath there lies a heart any man would give his life to capture.'

He gazed down into her startled face and gave a sad little shake of his head. 'It was the blackest day of my life when I had to write that letter to you. . .letting you go. . .' He dragged in a deep, trembling breath then led her over to a visitor's chair at the foot of Jason's bed. 'Better sit down,' he explained. 'This could take some time.'

Cassie sank down in the chair in something of a daze, unsure of grasping on to the hope that was surging into her heart. Dared she believe that Dan had really loved her? That he might still? Yet something – possibly the bleakness on his face – warned her to be careful, to keep her vulnerability in check.

Dan wandered over to stare through the window into the night, his words floating across the room in an oddly detached fashion. 'I was twenty-six when I met Roberta, a qualified accountant with a flourishing business and a flair for finance – well on my way to making my first million. But I was lonely. I wanted to get married, start a family of my own. My only sister had moved to Perth when she married, and taken my widowed mother to live with her. I missed them. . .'

Dan turned and began to pace the room. His voice grew more emotional. Strained. 'Roberta was bright and lovely – fun to be with. A little immature, perhaps, but——' He stopped and slanted Cassie a rueful look. 'I was very arrogant in those days, so sure of myself and of making the future work for me. It didn't seem important at the time that I wasn't madly in love. I'd always believed being madly in love to be a passing illusion and not a good basis for marriage.'

He sighed, and resumed pacing. 'The honey-moon didn't last very long. Roberta was only happy when we were either giving parties or going to them, which wasn't my idea of marriage. I pressed her to have a baby, but she wanted to wait a few more years, have more fun before being tied down with children. Our lives seemed empty and meaningless to me, and our relation-ship deteriorated. Eventually she did become pregnant. . .'

Cassie bit her bottom lip to keep from making a sound. She looked up to see Dan grimacing with remembered frustration.

'. . .but only by sheer accident. I practically had to bribe her to have the child, promising to hire a full-time nurse so that she could continue her socialising.'

Dan's mouth softened into a sad smile. 'But it was worth it. Her name was Maree. . . She was such a beautiful little girl. She —— ' He broke off and cleared his throat. 'She drowned when she was two years old.'

Cassie's heart squeezed tight, a moan of com-passion escaping from her lips. To lose a child. . . Dear heaven! If she had lost Jason tonight. . .

She lifted agonised eyes to Dan, who was staring at his son, as if reassuring himself that Jason was still alive. Yet when Dan saw Cassie looking at him he turned away and walked stiffly back over to the window, his back towards her.

'Roberta was on the phone when it happened,' he went on in a thick voice. 'She had a charity luncheon to attend and was trying to arrange a baby-sitter after Maree's nanny had fallen ill. Maree must have wandered out on to the patio and fallen in the pool. Somehow the gate had been left unlatched... Roberta had had a swim that morning...'

'Oh, Dan!' Cassie cried. 'How horrible for you.'

Dan spun round and for a split second Cassie saw the horror of his pain. It was a tangible thing, festering on his face like an open wound. 'I've never known such despair,' he said hoarsely. 'Such misery.'

He sucked in a ragged breath. 'Grief nearly drove me mad. I...' He shook his head, struggling for composure. 'Roberta, though, seemed strangely unaffected. If anything her social life increased. She was out practically every night, not returning till dawn. I tried ignoring the evidence of her infidelity at first, but in the end I confronted her. She admitted that there'd been other men. Dozens of them. I don't remember being shattered. Just empty. And sad. But I did begin divorce proceedings and then leave.'

Cassie rose unsteadily to her feet. 'And was this when you came to the island?' she asked huskily.

'Yes... My work had been affected by the strain I was under. A business partner of mine was a friend of the van Aarks and he arranged for me to stay there for a holiday. He knew I liked somewhere quiet to paint. . .'

He walked towards her then, and looked her straight in the eyes. 'I loved you, Cassie. You have to believe that. And I needed your love quite desperately. It was something I'd never had before – never believed existed – and I was so greedy for it after losing Maree that I couldn't wait until I was entirely free of Roberta. I had to have you. And I meant to marry you.'

He ran an agitated hand through his hair. 'But then the call came through about the accident. Apparently Roberta had been seeing some chap who owned a motorbike. They'd been drinking heavily and went out for a ride. The bike went out of control on a corner and hit a power pole. Roberta's lover was killed. She was a mess, but alive. Her father rang me from the hospital, begging me to come. He was terribly distressed. He was a widower, you see, Roberta his only child. I couldn't refuse. But it was the middle of the night. . .too late to call you. . .'

Dan's sigh carried an ocean of regret. 'I meant to contact you first thing in the morning, but all hell broke loose. When the doctor came with the news that Roberta would be a paraplegic for life, her father collapsed and died. A stroke. . . brought on by shock. Roberta kept asking for him. God, it was ghastly. I didn't know what to tell her, what to do. Whenever I tried to leave the room she became hysterical. I had her crying and doctors pleading with me to keep her calm.'

Dan lifted tormented eyes to Cassie. 'In the end I had to tell her the truth. It seemed kinder than letting her lie there in a torment of worry and doubt. Oh, Cassie. . .no matter what she'd done in the past, no one deserves to have to suffer that much. When she looked up at me from her hospital bed. . .so helpless. . .so distraught. . .so utterly, utterly alone. . .I knew that I couldn't leave her.'

His sigh was filled with pain. 'So I sat down and wrote you that letter – that rotten, soul-destroying letter.' Dan looked down at Cassie, his eyes flooding. 'Forgive me,' he rasped.

She pulled him close. 'Oh, Dan. . .darling. . .'

There was a moment when he resisted her embrace, then his arms swept around her, hugging her even more tightly than she was hugging him.

Tears flooded into Cassie's eyes as she finally accepted the truth of Dan's love, and the awful tragedy that had shaped his life. She could see now why he had acted as he had when he'd found out about Jason. First when he'd discovered his existence, and then today. . . My God! The control the man must have exercised over himself as he'd frantically gone through the motions of trying to save his son's life.

'I. . .I did my best to make life bearable for

her, Cassie,' he murmured brokenly. 'She. . .died peacefully. . . Some type of embolism.'

'Hush, my love. No more.' She looked up at him, her heart overflowing with love and compassion. She laid a gentle, reassuring hand on his cheek. 'You did everything you could do.'

His hand came up to cover hers and he turned his face into the palm, kissing the warm, soft flesh. A shudder ran through him. 'Tell me you still love me,' he rasped. 'For pity's sake, just tell me that.'

Her eyes swam. 'Don't you know, my darling?' she whispered softly. 'I've always loved you. I'll never stop loving you.'

With a groan, he crushed her to him, his hands cradling the back of her head into the warmth of his neck. 'Oh, Cassie. . . Cassie. . . I love you so much. I thought I'd lost you today, really lost you.'

'Never.'

'But I was stupid, hateful, cruel. . . I thought. . .I couldn't believe——'

'Hush. . . Tell me you love me again,' she murmured.

'I love you,' he said.

'Kiss me.'

He did.

'Mum? Dad?'

They spun out of their embrace and raced to

the bed, hand in hand. Both of them had tears streaming down their faces.

Jason frowned with his one exposed eye. 'Oh, yuk,' he pronounced weakly. 'Sammy Johnson was right. You are going to be mushy all the time.'

CHAPTER THIRTEEN

A PALE pre-dawn grey blanketed the island, a fine mist rising from the river. The helicopter came in low over the tree-tops to be landed with considerable expertise barely twenty metres from the front steps of Strath-haven.

'Home,' Cassie whispered.

Dan gave her a squeeze. 'Home,' he repeated, and kissed her lightly on the forehead.

'You'd better get this machine back to Sydney, Paul,' Dan informed the pilot as they alighted. 'Sorry about the long night.'

'That's all right, Mr McKay. Glad to hear that your boy's going to be all right.'

They watched from the veranda as the helicopter took off, disappearing quicky into the distance.

Dan had his arm around Cassie's shoulders, holding her close against him. She felt wonderfully warm and content. She sighed.

'Tired, Mrs McKay?'

'Oddly enough, not in the least.' She smiled up at him. 'Maybe I'm overtired. In a few hours I'll probably crash.'

'Fancy a walk?'

'A walk? Where?'

She saw his eyes drift down the hill towards the studio, and her stomach automatically contracted. A silly reaction, really. He loved her, didn't he? What was she afraid of now?

But the feeling would not pass. It held an insecurity, a fear of finding out some last hidden factor that might even now spoil her happiness. Life had taught her to be wary.

'OK,' she said, bravely keeping any fears to herself.

'You're very quiet,' Dan noted as they approached the small wooden cottage. 'Are you sure you're not tired? We can go back if you are.'

'No, no, I'm fine. A little cold.' She shivered, but more from nerves than the chill of the coming dawn.

He quickly took off his jacket and placed it round her shoulders. 'Better?'

She nodded, but the feeling of foreboding continued. 'Dan. . . Have you any special reason for wanting to come here?' She hoped that she didn't sound as nervous as she felt.

'In a way.'

'Oh?' She looked up at him, but he said nothing, merely smiled an enigmatic smile. Not even the most suspicious person could have found anything ominous in that smile. But still, Cassie's chest tightened.

They stopped before the front door, its white

panels looking much the worse for wear. Dan stretched out his hand towards the door-knob.

'Maybe it's locked,' Cassie suggested, hoping the ridiculous hope that it was.

'It's not,' came his reply, just before his hand connected.

'How do you know?' she practically accused.

He swung a puzzled face around. 'What?' He turned fully to grip her upper arms. 'My God, Cassie, you look sick. What's wrong?'

'I. . .I don't want to go in there,' she cried, her deep concerns bursting into words. 'I don't want anything to happen. . .to spoil things between us.'

His frown dissolved into a look of such tender understanding that Cassie almost burst into tears. 'Oh, Cassie.' He enfolded her into his arms, cradling her head into his chest. 'My poor love. . .so brave. . .so fine. . . Do you think I would ever do anything to hurt you again?'

He drew back, his eyes soothing her. 'There's nothing to worry about in there. Nothing. This is a very special place, a place where all our memories are good.'

'But I thought you hated it,' she choked out.

'Hate it? Now why would you think. . .? Oh, yes, I remember. . . The other morning on the bridge. You silly ninny,' he whispered, wiping her brimming eyes with soft fingertips. 'I couldn't bear to think about the studio then because it represented everything I'd had once but which I

thought I'd never have again. I was certain you'd
never love me, no matter what you said and did. I
thought your turn-around was all for Jason.
Nothing more. The way you looked at me sometimes... It was so different from...' He hesitated. 'Come inside, I have something to show
you.'

The studio was exactly as she remembered. One
large room with a fireplace at the southern end, in
front of which stretched a deeply piled brown rug
and an old flowered divan. Around the walls stood
a variety of furniture: book-cases, cabinets, a
table and chairs, an ancient refrigerator. A general air of disuse hung over the whole place,
despite its having been recently cleaned.

Dan took her hand, leading her over and settling her on the divan before turning to stride
across the rug towards an old sideboard in the
corner. Cassie watched, puzzled, as he opened
one section, but when he pulled out a rectangular-
shaped object wrapped in a red felt cloth she
knew instantly what it was...

Her throat grew dry as he removed the cover
and placed it on the mantelpiece.

He stared at it for a few seconds, then took
several slow steps backwards. Finally he turned,
as though reluctantly, to face her. 'This is how I
remembered you,' he said.

She stood up and walked towards her portrait,
her mind marvelling at Dan's skill, her heart

hating it at the same time. It was too good, too clear, too telling. . .

'I finished it after I left,' he was saying, 'from memory.'

It made Cassie remember, too. And the memory was unexpectedly painful.

Two big blue eyes looked out at her from the canvas. They were the eyes of a girl in love, deeply in love, blindly in love – the eyes of a girl who would ask no questions, expect no answers, who would give and give without any thought of self. A girl such as she could never be again. If Dan was waiting for her to look at him like this, she thought wretchedly, he would wait forever.

He moved to stand beside her. 'I used to get it out occasionally. Mostly when I'd had a drink or two. And I'd gaze at it for hours.' He let out a ragged sigh. 'You had Jason, Cassie. I had this.'

Cassie turned slowly to face Dan, a dreadful empty feeling in the pit of her stomach. Was this what Dan still loved? she agonised. This fantasy? Was this why he'd come back to Strath-haven – to try to bring the portrait to life?

Dan had told her at the hospital, as they'd sat with a sleeping Jason, the circumstances of his return. He'd found out that the island was on the market quite by accident, months after Roberta had died, ages after he'd given up hope of ever seeing Cassie again. Too long had passed, he reasoned, for her not to be married.

But once he'd heard about the island he'd been compelled to find out. He'd made enquiries at the register of marriages, found no record of a marriage, then looked up the electoral roll to see if she was still registered locally. It seemed impossible that she wouldn't be involved with someone else, but still he had bought Strath-haven and come back, hoping.

Hoping for what? Cassie frowned.

'Dan. . . This isn't me. . .I'm not *her* any more.'

His hand reached out to smooth her wrinkled brow. 'Yes, you are. You're still my darling girl. . .' His expression became glazed, as though he was a long way away. Nine years away. . .

Dismay rolled over her heart.

He must have seen her reaction, for suddenly his face cleared to show a spark of anxiety. 'What is it, Cassie? What have I said?' He grabbed her arms, his sudden movement making the jacket slip from her shoulders. Both of them ignored it as it fell to the floor. He stared down at her, his alarm growing with each second.

Her eyes slid inexorably towards the portrait.

'Oh, Cassie,' Dan sighed. 'Don't go thinking things like that. I haven't shown you the painting to make you feel insecure. I merely wanted to explain that when I met you again, and found you so mature and assured, it came as a shock. I guess for me it was as though you had been frozen in time, and it took a while for my thinking to readjust. You'd grown up. Truly grown up. But once I'd got over the shock I found that you appealed to me even more so. You are a woman such as Roberta never was, or ever could be. Strong and brave. Good and kind. But you are still in essence the girl I painted, with the same sweet, generous heart. You can't imagine how I felt tonight when you told me that you loved me, had never stopped loving me. I thought my heart would burst with emotion. All I can say in return is that I'll try to be worthy of your love. And that I will love you till the day I die.'

Tears shimmered into Cassie's eyes, tears of true joy. 'Oh, Dan. . .'

He bent to kiss her lightly. 'Don't cry,' he murmured. 'I can't bear to see you cry.'

'Even with happiness?' she managed to get out.

'Even that.' One finger traced her lips. 'From now on, all I want to see is laughter in your eyes, smiles on your mouth. Except, of course. . .' his expression carried a warm mischief '. . .when I don't want to see your mouth at all.'

His own mouth descended slowly, giving her time to be ready for him, capturing her parted lips in a heady explosion of passion.

Cassie remembered dimly having wondered if sex would be different without love. Yes, she realised dazedly. Yes, it must be. . . For this was the ultimate, this was insurpassable, this was making *love*.

It wasn't just that his touch pleasured her, nor that his mouth matched hers perfectly. There was an inner joy as he kissed her, an almost miraculous blending of the physical and emotional.

He undressed her quickly, yet with infinite tenderness. Each caress, while tinged with impatience, carried the most undeniable respect.

He said nothing, but his silence was loving, an intense showing of his feeling for her. Nothing was too much trouble. He stroked her body, stroked and kissed her till she was a furnace of longing. And when he came to her she was filled with the sweetest bliss, his possession taking her swiftly along the crescendo of sensation till everything burst around her, showing her ecstasy as overwhelming as the man who had created it.

And as she lay in replete contentment on the rug, her arms around Dan, Cassie realised that they had come full circle. This was where it had all begun. This was where Jason had been conceived.

The thought claimed her quite clearly, with a certainty that would not be denied. A child would spring from this union, a brother or a sister for Jason. This was a new beginning, a going forward. There would be no more looking back.

A long time afterwards, Dan lifted himself from her and brought a hand to touch her face. This he did wondrously, gently, as though in awe of his own feelings.

She looked up at him, not knowing that at that moment, with all her defences down, with her body and soul finally at peace, her eyes were exactly the same as those of the girl in the portrait. Clear and trusting and oh, so full of love.

'Will I never get tired of you, my darling girl?' he murmured thickly.

She smiled. And said one word, a word that carried the total message of their love for each other.

'Never.'

Diana Hamilton is a true romantic and fell in love with her husband at first sight. They still live in the fairytale Tudor house where they raised their three children. Now the idyll is shared with eight rescued cats and a puppy. But despite an often chaotic lifestyle, ever since she learned to read and write Diana has had her nose in a book – either reading or writing one – and plans to go on doing just that for a very long time to come.

A HUSBAND'S PRICE
by
Diana Hamilton

A HUSBAND'S PRICE

Diana Hamilton

CHAPTER ONE

CLAUDIA passed an uncertain hand over the photograph album. She hadn't looked at it in years; hadn't wanted to set eyes on it even. She tried to walk away and out of the room but somehow couldn't, then, her teeth biting into the warm flesh of her full lower lip, she gave into temptation and knew she'd regret it.

Sitting abruptly at the table beneath the library's stone mullioned window, she hooked a strand of soft brown, deadly straight, shoulder-length hair behind one ear and tentatively opened the album. Here they all were. All the people; all the memories. All the shattered dreams and broken trust.

Her fingertips shakily grazed the glossy surface of the prints. She had put the album away on the top shelf out of sight a long time ago. Her father must have glanced through it then abandoned it here on the library table. Had he, in his grief, been searching for that lost summer, desperately straining to catch an echo of vanished, happier times?

And here he was. Guy Sullivan, her father. Six years ago, he would have been fifty-two, a big man, in his prime then, his arm around his blonde and beautiful bride of three months. Her stepmother, Helen.

Twenty years her father's junior, recently divorced, the sizzling blonde could have turned into the stepmother from hell, but hadn't. From the day Helen had applied for the position as a relief receptionist here at Farthings Hall, Claudia had seen how attracted her father was. Guy Sullivan had been a widower for eight years, Claudia's mother dying of a rare viral infection when her only child was ten years old.

Three months after their first meeting, Guy and Helen had married. Claudia had been happy for them both; her initial fears that Helen might resent her, or that she might resent the woman who had taken her mother's place in her father's affections, had been unfounded. Helen couldn't have tried harder to charm her new stepdaughter.

And here she herself was: the Claudia of six years ago. Hair much longer then—almost reaching down to her waist—her curves lusher, her smile wide, open, untouched in those long-gone innocent days by the betrayal that was to come later.

Her eyes misted as she looked at the photograph. She'd been eighteen years old and happy to be spending the summer at home before going to teacher training college. She'd been glad to help out around Farthings Hall, the exclusive country house hotel and restaurant that was both home and livelihood not only for her father now, but for his father before him.

And there in the background, prophetically perhaps, Tony Favel had been caught by the camera leaning against the stone parapet that bordered the terrace that ran along the west façade of the wonderful old Tudor house.

Tony Favel, her father's accountant, the man who had brought Helen into their lives, introducing her as some kind of distant cousin, keen to make a new life for herself after a messy divorce. Even now she could hear the echo of his following words. 'And haven't you said, Guy, you're looking for a part-time receptionist for when Sandy packs it in to have that baby she's expecting?'

Tony Favel. At the time the photograph had been taken, he would have been thirty. Even then, his lint-blond hair was beginning to recede, his waistline to thicken. Claudia swallowed hard, her vivid blue eyes clouding as they rested on the grainy, slightly out-of-focus image of her husband. Tony Favel, whom she had married at the end of that summer six years ago.

Slowly, not wanting to, yet driven by something too dark for her to understand, Claudia turned the page and found what she had known she would find. And feared. All those pictures of Adam.

At the end of that summer, she'd vowed to destroy every last one of them, to rip them to shreds and burn them. But, when it had come down to it, she hadn't been able to bring herself to touch them. Or, at least, that was what she had told herself at the time. Love and hate: different sides of the same coin. She had told herself she hated him but obviously she must have still been in love with him. Why else would she have found it impossible to destroy his likenesses?

She had taken all but one of the photographs of Adam herself and, looking at them now, she couldn't deny that fatal male beauty. Or deny that those smoky grey eyes, that rumpled, over-long black hair, those pagan-god good looks and body to match hid a black, black heart.

The odd picture out was the one of her and Adam together. Adam's arm was placed possessively around her waist, pulling her close into the side of his lithely powerful body, and she was gazing adoringly up into his face. So there they were, the two of them, eternally smiling, caught for posterity looking as if they were walking confidently through the best, the most bliss-fully happy, the most wonderful summer of their lives...

She never looked back into the past because it hurt too much, but now she couldn't seem to help herself and the memories came crowding in. She could clearly see her younger self running lightly down the service stairs on that sunny, early summer day six years ago.

She'd spent the best part of the morning helping the housekeeper, Amy, to ready the guest suites. There were only four of them; by country house hotel standards Farthings Hall was small. But very, very exclusive. There was a waiting list as long as your arm both for accommodation and for the restaurant tables.

And, after all that hoovering, polishing and dusting, she'd been good and ready for a dose of that glorious sunshine she'd only so far yearned for through the spotless, glittering upstairs windows. She'd been just eighteen years old, was at the very beginning of the long summer holiday, had done her duty by helping Amy and now smelt freedom.

'Oops!' She skidded to an abrupt halt before she knocked her new stepmother to kingdom come. 'Sorry—didn't see you!'

Small and willowy with hair like spun sunlight, Helen always made Claudia feel large and clumsy and, just recently, awkward and a bit in the way. Oh, Helen had never, ever, given her an unkind word or look either before her marriage to Guy or after, but for the past few days there'd been an edginess about her, a brittleness that went hand in hand with discontent.

But thankfully not today. Claudia felt her muscles relax as Helen's narrow green eyes gleamed at her. 'Such energy! Oh, to be young and full of bounce again!'

'You're not old.' Claudia grinned, falling in step beside her stepmother who was heading down the passage to the courtyard entrance. At eighteen, just, she regarded the thirties—even the early thirties as she knew Helen to be—as knocking on the door of middle age. But there was something timeless about Helen's sexy little body, golden hair and perfect features.

'Thanks.' Helen's voice was dry. She reached the door first and pushed it open. The sunlight streamed through and made her a dazzling, glittering figure in her lemon-yellow sheath dress and all that chunky gold jewellery she seemed to favour. 'Coming?'

Claudia had promised herself a walk to the rocky little cove that could only be reached via the deep valley that bisected the Hall's extensive grounds, but if Helen wanted her company she would gladly tag along. She usually fell in with other people's wishes because she liked those around her to be happy and, perhaps just as importantly, she liked people to be pleased with her.

Like a big, exuberant puppy, she thought with wry, self-mocking humour. She could almost hear herself panting, feel her tongue hanging out!

'Sure. Where to?'

'To find Old Ron. He hasn't sent the fruit and veg up to the kitchens yet. Chef's furious. Lunches will be starting in an hour. I said I'd chase him up. Besides—' green eyes gleamed up into the speedwell-blue of Claudia's '—Guy hired a dogsbody to help Ron through the summer.' Her sudden giggle was infectious. 'He may be some kind of a drop-out of no fixed abode, but he sure is gorgeous! Worth the trek down to the kitchen gardens any time of the day!' She paused significantly. 'Or night!'

Claudia giggled right back. She knew Helen didn't mean it; she had been married only for a couple of months or so, and she wouldn't have eyes for any other man. 'I didn't know Dad had been hiring,' she commented, striding along the raked gravel path.

She wasn't surprised that this was the first she'd heard of a new employee. Recently she'd overheard her father and his new wife tersely arguing over Helen's apparently sudden decision to give up her post. She had seemed to be saying that now she was married to the owner she shouldn't have to work like a hired skivvy—though she would be happy to continue to do the flowers. Claudia had kept well out of the way of both of them, waiting until they'd sorted out their differences. She could imagine only one thing more embarrassing than overhearing them squabbling and that would be overhearing them making love.

Firmly squashing that thought, she asked, 'So when did Adonis join the crew? Is he really a homeless drop-out?' Claudia knew she was very lucky to have somewhere like Farthings Hall to call home. She couldn't imagine what it would be like to have nowhere.

Helen shrugged slim, lightly tanned shoulders. 'Goodness knows. He turned up on a clapped-out old motorbike a couple of days ago, looking for work. He admitted he was ''just drifting'' and apparently seemed happy enough to have the use of that old caravan at the back of the glasshouses for the summer, plus his food and pin money, in exchange for helping Old Rob around the grounds. His name's Adam, by the way. Adam Weston.'

But Claudia wasn't really listening as she followed Helen through into the walled kitchen garden, her thoughts exclusively for Old Ron now. The ancient groundsman couldn't cope. Everyone knew it except him, which was obviously why her father had decided to hire someone to help out for the summer. How would Old Ron feel when he had to make way permanently for someone fit and young, someone who could actually walk faster than a snail?

Old Ron had worked here forever. Her grandfather had hired him initially, before Farthings Hall had been converted into the now exclusive country house hotel with what was reputed to be the best restaurant in Cornwall. He'd been here ever since, never marrying, inhabiting a flat conversion above the old stable block. Of course, Dad would never ask him to vacate his home, or pay rent, and, knowing her father, he would probably find him a token something or other to do, just so the old man wouldn't feel entirely useless...

Then, for the second time in thirty minutes, Claudia almost ran her stepmother down. Helen had stopped without warning in the centre of the path, just inside the arched doorway in the high, ivy-clad, red-brick wall—the heated summer air was suddenly and unexpectedly thrumming with a tension so sharply intense that Claudia found herself instinctively holding her breath.

She expelled it slowly when she saw what Helen was staring at, her stepmother's green eyes laughing, maybe even teasing just a little.

The new hired help was enough to bring a smile of glowing pleasure to any woman's eyes.

Adam Weston was just as magnificent as Helen had implied, only more so. Leaning against a garden fork, dressed only in frayed denim cut-offs and scuffed working boots, he blew Claudia's mind.

The breadth of his rangy shoulders was, she admitted admiringly, deeply impressive, accentuating the narrowness of his hips, the length of his leanly muscular legs. The tan of his skin was slicked with sweat and his forehead, beneath the soft fall of rumpled dark hair, was beaded with it. And his eyes, an intriguing smoky grey, narrowed now in overt male appraisal, were firmly fixed on the slender, golden figure of her stepmother.

Claudia shivered. It was a brilliant day, the hottest this summer so far. Yet she shivered right down to the soles of her grungy canvas shoes. She stepped forward, out of the shadows, uselessly regretting her faded, a-bit-baggy old jeans, the washed-out old shirt she wore for house-cleaning.

Her movement broke the spell. Whatever had been here, shimmering and stinging in the scented summer air, had gone. Helen said, her musical voice low and quite definitely husky, 'Adam, meet your employer's solitary offspring and pride of his life—Claudia. Dearest, say hello to Adam. And then, perhaps, he can run along and find Old Ron before Chef arrives with his cleaver!'

'Hi there—' Adam Weston brushed the wayward hank of soft dark hair out of his eyes and stepped forward, extending a strong, long-boned hand. And smiled.

And Claudia, for the first, and very probably the last, time in her life, fell deeply, shatteringly and quite, quite helplessly in love...

'So there you are.' The mesmeric spell of the past was broken as Guy Sullivan walked slowly into the book-lined room leaning on his ebony-handled cane, a little of the strain leaving his eyes when he saw his daughter. 'Amy's just got back from collecting Rosie from school. They were looking for you.' His eyes fell on the album and he shook his head slightly, admitting, 'I can't think why I wanted to look at that. No good looking into the past—you can't bring it back. Neither of us can.'

Claudia got to her feet and resolutely stuffed the album back in its former hiding place, aware of her father's eyes on her, the rough compassion in his voice. Six weeks ago, his wife and her husband had been killed when the car they were in was mown down on a blind bend on a steep hill by an articulated lorry that had lost its brakes.

Just over a week later, they had discovered that Helen and Tony had been lovers. Their affair had been on and off, but mostly on, since before Tony had introduced the glamorous divorcée and suggested that Guy consider her for the post of relief receptionist.

Her father had made that discovery when he had been going through his dead wife's effects and had happened across diaries and some highly explicit love letters. It had devastated him. Coming on top of the shock of the fatal accident, it had brought about his third heart attack in six years.

It hadn't been anything like as severe as the one he'd had, right out of the blue, at the end of the summer six years ago but, nevertheless, it had weakened him still further and it would be a long time before she could stop worrying about him.

And how she was going to be able to break the other piece of shattering news she couldn't imagine. The thought of what it could do to him terrified her.

'Did you mention the possibility of the loan we need to refurbish the guest suites?' Guy sat on the chair Claudia had vacated and leaned his cane against the table.

His once strong features were now gaunt and grey and Claudia would have done anything to spare him from this final horror. But the best she could do was prevaricate, just for now, delay the inevitable for as long as she possibly could.

Ask the bank manager for a loan? As if!

Her discussion with the manager this afternoon had been on a different topic entirely. Their business was as good as bankrupt, their financial difficulties severe—so severe that selling up was the only option. It was something her father was going to have to be told about. But not now.

Now she asked, changing the subject, 'Where's Rosie?' As a rule she collected her small daughter from school every day, but because of her appointment at the bank she'd had to ask Amy to do it. She didn't know what they would do without the grey-haired, rosy-cheeked dumpling who had been at Farthings Hall as long as Claudia could remember. Amy had done her best to do what she could to fill the gap when Claudia, as a ten-year-old, had been left motherless.

'Amy took her through to the kitchens for some juice. Oh, I forgot to mention it, but Jenny can't come in this evening—summer flu, or some such excuse.' Guy Sullivan got slowly to his feet. 'Look, I can help Amy out round the kitchens—we can take the trickier stuff off the menu—and free you up to take Jenny's place, wait on tables.'

'No, Dad.' Claudia automatically declined the offer. Her father was physically and emotionally frail, and still in need of all the rest he could get. 'Amy and I can manage.'

Ever since Tony had had a falling-out with Chef six months ago—and Claudia had never got to find out what it had been about—she and Amy, with Jenny's help, had been keeping the restaurant going on a reduced and simplified menu. Tony had been reluctant to hire a replacement chef and now Claudia knew why. Tomorrow she would have to cancel the advertisements for the new and experienced staff she'd decided had to be hired if the hotel and restaurant were to continue. There was no point now. The business, their home, was to be sold over their heads.

'Why don't you sit outside, Dad? It's a glorious day; let's make the most of it.' She almost added, While we can, but managed to stop herself in time. 'I'll fetch Rosie and we'll all have tea on the terrace.'

Ten days later, Amy asked rhetorically, 'I guess you can't have told your father the bad news yet?' She filled a mug with strong black coffee and held it out. 'He looked happy, almost back to his old self, when his friend collected him this morning, so he can't know that his home's about to be sold from over his head.'

'I'm a coward,' Claudia admitted wearily, taking the mug of steaming coffee. 'But every day he gets that little bit stronger. And the stronger he gets, the more able he'll be to cope with yet another blow.'

'And what about you?' Amy demanded. 'The blows fell on your head, too. Your husband died; he'd been playing around with that madam, Helen, his own stepmother-in-law, would you believe? And yes—' her round face went scarlet '—I know we're not supposed to speak ill of the dead—but really! So you've had blows, just the same, so why should you have to carry this other load on your own?'

'Because I haven't had three heart attacks in half a

dozen years and because I didn't love Tony, and Dad adored Helen.' Claudia looked at the mug in her hands, and frowned just slightly. 'I really haven't got time to drink this.'

'Of course you have,' Amy asserted firmly. 'This Hallam man won't be looking under beds for fluff or running his fingers round picture frames looking for dust. You've been running around like a scalded cat ever since you got back from taking Rosie to school. So drink your coffee and try to relax. You've got time for that before you need to get changed. And, no matter what anyone else believed, where you're concerned, nobody can pull the wool over my eyes. Like my own daughter, you are. I knew your marriage to Tony Favel wasn't a love match. When you married him you were still hankering after Adam—and don't pop your eyes at me—I knew how you were feeling when he just upped and disappeared. But, like I said, you and Tony rubbed along; you didn't hate him, so what happened must still have been a dreadful shock.'

Claudia eyed her old friend over the rim of her mug as she sipped the hot liquid. What else did Amy suspect? Know?

She didn't want to think about that. She put her mug down on the work surface, changing the subject. 'How many tables are booked for this evening?'

'All of them.' Amy collected the used mugs and up-ended them in the commercial-size dishwasher. 'I dare say we do have to keep going as best we can so it can be sold as a going concern. But thank heaven we're at the end of the season, that's all I can say.'

Casting her eyes over the spotlessly gleaming

kitchen, Claudia nodded her heartfelt agreement. It was early October now and hotel bookings ceased at the end of September, so they didn't have that aspect to worry about. They didn't do lunches, either—they wouldn't start up again until Easter—but evening meals went on right through the year. So yes, that was something they could give thanks for.

And there were other things, too, she admitted as she lay in the warm bath water ten minutes later. Life wasn't all bad; there were tiny glimmers of good luck if you looked hard enough.

The bank manager wasn't exactly an ogre. He had shown considerable if understated compassion at that meeting she'd had with him ten days ago. After painting his pitch-black picture and explaining that Farthings Hall would have to be sold, and preferably as a going concern, to cover those terrifying debts, he had advised, 'Before you have to advertise the property for sale I suggest you contact the Hallam Group—you've heard of them?'

Claudia had nodded. Who hadn't? No one remotely connected to the hotel and leisure industry could be ignorant of that huge and exclusive outfit.

She'd felt suddenly nauseous. One shock too many, she supposed. The bank manager had used the intercom to ask someone called Joyce to bring through a tray of tea, leaning back in his chair then, steepling his fingers as he had continued—just as if she'd denied any knowledge of the Hallam Group—'Quality hotels and leisure complexes; they don't touch anything that's run-of-the-mill or even marginally second-rate. It's mainly a family-run company, as you probably know, and Harold Hallam was the majority shareholder. He died, oh, it must be a good twelve months ago and rumour has it his heir is about to expand, acquire new properties.'

He had paused when the tea was brought through and poured, then had suggested, 'If you could interest them in Farthings Hall and effect a quick sale, it would be better all round—a quick takeover by the Hallam Group would mean less time for the type of speculation that could agitate your father. I suggest you ask your solicitor to get in touch with them.'

Useful advice, because only yesterday her solicitor had phoned to say that someone from the Hallam Group would be coming out to Farthings Hall to meet her this morning to discuss the possibility of a private sale.

'Don't commit yourself to anything. This new chief executive might be trying to show his board of directors what a smart operator he is. Remember, this will be an exploratory meeting only. The legal people can be brought in after the initial informal discussion between the principles. That's the general idea, I believe.'

That suited Claudia. And what suited her even more was David Ingram's invitation to her father. They were near neighbours, had been friends since boyhood, and David had wanted to know how Guy felt about being picked up the next morning. After lunch, they could have a game of chess.

Claudia had breathed a huge sigh of cowardly relief when her father had accepted the invitation. She could have her meeting with the Hallam man with her father none the wiser. Every day that passed without him having to learn the miserable truth was a bonus.

And Rosie was out of the way, too, safely at school. Had she been at home, she would have wanted to be with her mummy, even though she loved Amy to pieces. Serious conversation with a bubbly, demanding five-and-a-bit-year-old was problematical to say the least.

The trouble was, since the death of her daddy and Steppie—as Helen, her stepgrandmother, had preferred to be called—Rosie had become very clingy. Not that either of them had spent much time with the little girl, and both of them had developed the habit of absenting themselves if Rosie had been ill or just plain tiresome.

Their deaths must have left a hole in the little girl's life; one day they'd been around—in the background, but around—and the next they'd been blown away. But possibly the most traumatic thing had been her beloved grandpa's illness and his subsequent need for lots of rest and quiet. Rosie probably couldn't understand why her grandpa could no longer play those boisterous games she enjoyed or read to her for hours on end.

Claudia sighed and heaved herself out of the bath. The Hallam man would be arriving in half an hour. She couldn't remember if the solicitor had actually said his name. But it would be Mr Hallam. She definitely recalled him saying that her visitor was the deceased Harold Hallam's heir. It would be his son. Her solicitor would surely have said, had the new chief executive gone under a name other than the family one.

And what to wear? A simple grey linen suit with a cream silk blouse. Cool, businesslike, entirely suitable for a young widow.

Her soft brown hair caught back into the nape of her neck with a mock-tortoiseshell clip, and with the merest suggestion of make-up, her mind played truant, sliding back to those photographs she'd been looking at on her return from her traumatic meeting with her bank manager. Particularly, the one of her.

How she had changed. Still five feet seven inches, of course, but she'd lost all those lavish curves. After Rosie's birth she'd fined down but now, since the traumas of the last few weeks, she looked positively scrawny. The Claudia in that old photograph had been a cheerful optimist, with laughing eyes and a beaming, open smile.

The mirror image she scrutinised now was older, wiser, a bit of a cynic with an overlay of composure, a strength of will that practically defied anyone to mess with her. She was through with being anyone's eager little doormat. She was twenty-four years old, the age Adam Weston had been when they'd first met. She looked and felt a great deal older.

And another difference: the woman in the mirror was as good as bankrupt. The girl in the photograph had been quite a considerable heiress.

And therein had lain the attraction, of course.

She remembered with absolute and still painful clarity exactly how, over six years ago now, she had discovered that particular home truth.

Helen had told her. Helen had been sitting on the edge of her bed, clad in brief scarlet satin panties and bra, looking absolutely furious, yet finding compassion as she grabbed Claudia's hand and squeezed it.

'And you know what that slimeball Adam Toerag Weston had the gall to say? I can still hardly believe it! He actually told me not to be miffed because he'd been messing about—as he so chivalrously put it—with you! Miffed—I ask you! As if I'd be interested in a loser like him! As if I'd have some furtive, sleazy affair with a jobless, homeless, penniless layabout when I'm married to a lovely, lovely man like your father! But this is the point, dearest—'

Helen had released her hand with a final squeeze, reached for a scarlet satin robe and wrapped it around her body. 'He actually said that he'd played up to you because you were quite an heiress. You'd agreed to marry him, or so he claimed, and, as his darling daughter's husband, Guy wouldn't object to keeping him in the manner to which he had always wanted to become accustomed—not if he didn't want to alienate his darling daughter. I only hope, dearest, that you haven't let him go too far with you, that you haven't actually fallen for him, or anything stupid like that...'

Claudia had closed her eyes to stop the hurt from showing. She had wanted to scream that it wasn't true, that Adam loved her, loved her for herself, that he didn't care about her father's wealth, Farthings Hall, the land, all that stuff. But she had never lied to herself. And if the evidence of her own eyes hadn't been enough there had been that conversation on the first date they'd ever had.

It hadn't been an accident that had found her in the vicinity of the old caravan at the back of the glass-houses about seven hours after she'd first been introduced to Adam. Or an accident that she had been wearing a pair of very brief shorts and her best sleeveless T-shirt. The crisp white garments had shown off her long and shapely legs and accentuated the honey-gold tan she'd managed to acquire.

Her heart had been fluttering wildly as she'd approached the open caravan door, but she'd told herself not to be stupid. She, as his employer's daughter, had the perfect excuse for being here.

She could hear him moving about, whistling tunelessly beneath his breath, and before she could knock or call out he had appeared in the doorway, still wearing nothing but those threadbare cut-offs, a towel slung over one shoulder. Instead of the heavy working boots, he'd been sporting a pair of beat-up trainers.

'Hello again.' He'd smiled that smile. For several seconds Claudia hadn't been able to speak. She'd felt her face go fiery red and had hoped quite desperately that he'd put it down to the heat, to the sun glinting off the roofs of the glasshouses, boiling down from a cloudless blue sky.

'I...' Agitatedly, she had pulled in a deep, deep breath. A huge mistake. Just looking at him, being on the receiving end of that deeply sexy smile, had made her legs go weak, made her breasts feel hot and full and tingly. And dragging air into her lungs that way had made them push against the soft white cloth of her top, and she'd known he'd noticed because his gaze had dropped, fastened there, right there, his lids heavy, thick dark lashes veiling his expression.

So she had begun again, gabbling now. 'I wondered if you have everything you need? The caravan hasn't been used in ages, not since—'

'It's fine. That nice housekeeper of yours—Amy?—supplied me with a bundle of bed- and bath-room linen, food supplies—and the place is clean, sweet as a nut.'

He had loped down the steps, pulling the van door to behind him. Claudia had swallowed a huge lump of disappointment. She'd hoped he'd invite her inside to see for herself. But what he had said was even better, more than she'd hoped for. 'I'm told there's a path through the valley leading down to a cove. I fancied a swim. Coming?'

Was she ever! She'd gone back to the house to get her swimming costume and met him back at the caravan. And it had been lovely, that walk. They'd talked a lot; well, he had, mostly. She'd asked him questions about himself but he'd skirted them, telling her to talk about herself, but she hadn't been able to; there hadn't been much to say. So it had ended up with him asking questions, making comments.

'This is a fantastic place. Magical. How does it make you feel, knowing it will all be yours one day? Not yet, of course, but some time in the future. Will you keep it on? Does the responsibility worry you? Uneasy lies the head that wears the crown—and all that.'

They'd been sitting in the soft golden sand by then, the sun dipping down towards the sea. He hadn't seemed to need an answer; he could almost have been talking to himself. He'd leaned forward, softly tracing the outline of her mouth with the tip of a forefinger. 'You are very lovely.'

And after that everything else had been simple. He'd gone out of his way to confirm his deductions that the land, the house, the business would all be hers in the fullness of time, and had gone ahead and trapped her with the honey-sweet bait of great sex and her own foolish notions of undying romantic love...

Claudia blinked, shaking her head, annoyed with herself, pushing the unwanted memories away. She couldn't remember now what had made her think back to all of that. Adam. Betrayal. Loss.

She pulled herself together and swiftly left the room, heading down the stairs for the library. She'd asked Amy to bring Mr Hallam there when he arrived at eleven-thirty. Then bring coffee through.

She glanced at her watch and groaned. Eleven thirty-five. He might already be here. Unforgivable of her to have gone off into that backward-looking trance, wasting time.

'He's arrived!' Amy appeared at the foot of the stairs, her voice low and urgent. 'I put him in the library and said you wouldn't be a minute. I was on my way to warn you.'

'Yes, I'm sorry to be late.' Claudia gave Amy a reassuring smile. She should have been there to greet the man, of course, but she was only late by a few minutes, not long enough to warrant Amy's obvious anxiety.

'Wait.' Amy caught her arm before she could hurry through. 'You don't understand. It's not a Mr Hallam, like you said. It's—'

'Remember me?'

The library door now stood open, framing the impressive, immaculately suited figure of Adam Weston.

'Because I remember you.' He moved forward, eyes fixed on Claudia's speechless lips, then they lifted to clash with hers. 'How could I possibly forget?'

He smiled, a sensual movement of that wickedly crafted mouth. It was sexier than ever. But his eyes didn't smile; didn't come near it. 'Might I ask you to bring us some coffee, Amy?' he asked the stunned-seeming housekeeper. 'Mrs Favel and I have a great deal to talk through.'

CHAPTER TWO

SILENCE. Shock clamped Claudia into a small, dark, very tight corner. Clamped her in so tightly she could barely breathe, let alone speak.

How dared he show his face here? Oh, how dared he?

Then the thick silence eased just a little, slowly nudged away by the inevitable impingement of ordinary, everyday sounds. The sonorous, echoey ticking of the longcase clock; the stutter and grumble of machinery from directly outside as Bill, the new groundsman, tried to start the ride-on mower; Amy's voice—the sound of the words she spoke as they fell on the still air, but not the sense of them—and the sound of the housekeeper's feet on the polished wood floor blocks as she walked away; the thump of her own, wild heartbeats.

He'd changed, and yet he hadn't. That was the first coherent thought she had. Though how a thought could be coherent and contradictory was a total mystery.

At thirty, Adam Weston was a spectacularly attractive man. The once over-long, soft black hair was expertly cut and those pagan-god features were tougher now, more forceful than they'd been six years ago. That superbly fit body was clothed in a silky dark grey suit, crafted by a master tailor, instead of the scruffy

cut-offs and washed-out T-shirts that had been his ha-
bitual wear during that long, hot summer when she
had loved him so.

A man with those looks, that kind of honed physique, would always land on his feet, especially if he
still possessed that laid-back, lazy charm, the charm
that had had her swooning at his feet from that first
unforgettable smile.

Obviously, he'd finally married an heiress. Well,
bully for him! she thought cynically, wondering if
he'd come here to gloat because he'd done very well,
thank you, for himself and she was practically bankrupt.

'What do you want, Adam?' Her voice was tight,
quaky, like an old woman's. And she knew she didn't
look anything like the lushly curvaceous, fresh-faced
and dewy-eyed eighteen-year-old he'd sweet-talked
into his bed all those years ago. She didn't need that
look of distaste he was giving her to tell her that,
while he'd been able to bring himself to the point of
actually making love to her six years ago, he found
her a total turn-off now.

Claudia lifted her chin and told herself she didn't
care, in either event. 'I'm expecting someone. Can
you see yourself out?'

She knew she sounded like a snob of the first water,
the lady of the manor ordering the boot boy out of
her rarefied presence, and saw his eyes narrow and
harden. Those smoky grey eyes that didn't smile any
more.

'You're expecting *me*, Mrs Favel.' His voice was
clipped. Hard. As hard as his eyes. 'The Hallam

Group,' he reminded her, as if, Claudia thought resentfully, he thought she was completely stupid.

But hadn't he always thought that? That she had rampaging hormones where other people had brains. That she'd be a pushover, blindly and ecstatically rushing into marriage with a drifter who was only interested in getting his hands on her assets, which, in those days, had been considerable.

Within a few short weeks he'd had her besotted, head over heels in love and so eager to accept his proposal of marriage she'd practically fallen over herself. And the only thing that had stopped her dragging him down the aisle had been the evidence of her own eyes...

Adam walking out of Helen's bedroom, his face tight and furious. He'd been so furious he hadn't seen her at the top of the service stairs, her arms full of freshly laundered bed-linen.

Helen. Helen sitting on the edge of her bed, clad only in those wisps of underwear. Furious, too, spitting out that poison about him only being interested in her, Claudia's future financial prospects, ramming home the final nail in the coffin of her love for him with, 'He must have seen me come up here—he knows your father's out. I was getting ready to have a shower before changing. He just walked in and started on about the way he'd always fancied me. He said we could have fun—adult fun. He was sick of playing with a child, only the child, as it happened, would one day come into a fortune. He meant you, my poor sweet! And then...heaven help me...I told him to pack his bags and get off Farthings Hall property. I said if he was still around when your father got back he'd regret it.'

'I was told to expect the late Mr Hallam's heir,' she said now, her voice stiff with remembered outrage and pain. Then added insultingly, 'Not the tea boy.'

His smile was wintry. 'And I always thought you had such lovely manners.' He turned, walked away, moving over the huge, raftered hall back towards the library. 'Harold Hallam was my mother's brother. He didn't marry and, as far as anyone knows, he had no issue. I inherited his holding in the Group. Perhaps now we might begin our discussions, provided you're satisfied with my credentials. Unless, of course, you're no longer interested in any offer my company might be prepared to come up with.'

Disorientated, Claudia stared at his retreating back. Such wide, spare shoulders tapering down to that narrow, flat waist, such long, long legs, and all of him so elegantly packaged in a suit so beautifully cut it could only have come from Savile Row.

'So you finally fell on your feet.' She truly hadn't realised she'd spoken the thought aloud until he turned at the door to the library, grey eyes chilling, that utterly sensual, boldly defined mouth contemptuous.

'So it would seem.'

She tilted her chin in challenging defiance, her blue eyes cool. After what he'd done to her, did he really expect to make her feel ashamed of her lack of manners? Did he seriously expect her to apologise?

It would give her enormous satisfaction to ask him to leave.

But he'd disappeared into the library—as if he already owned the place—and she pulled in a deep breath, drew back her shoulders and followed.

She found Amy practically on her heels, the delicate china coffee cups rattling companionably on the tray she carried.

Claudia stepped aside at the doorway to allow the housekeeper passage, wincing as the older woman put the tray down on the long, polished table, a huge smile splitting her rosy face as she marvelled, 'Well, and isn't this a turn up for the books, young Adam? Who'd have thought—?'

'Thank you, Amy,' Claudia interrupted smoothly. Amy had had a soft spot for the young Adam Weston all those years ago, making sure he was lavishly supplied from the kitchens, that the old caravan he was living in was packed with creature comforts. He'd had the useful ability to charm just about anyone who could do him any good!

Pointedly, she began to pour coffee, both cups black and sugarless because that was the way she liked it and he could do what the heck he wanted with his. Amy suggested, 'Should I put a match to the fire? It's a bit nippy, don't you think?'

She was already bustling towards the wide stone hearth, but Adam's smile stopped her. His smile, Claudia remembered, could stop a runaway train. No problem. 'We're fine, Amy. Truly. Besides, after we've had coffee, Mrs Favel and I will be going to find a quiet pub for lunch, but thank you for the offer.'

This man had acquired authority, Claudia decided acidly as Amy melted away. Lashings of it. But nothing would induce her to have lunch with him. As soon as Amy had closed the door she said, 'I'm sorry to have wasted your time, but I've decided not to do business with your company after all.'

'Cutting your nose off to spite your face?' The slight smile he gave her as he picked up his coffee was a patronising insult. Claudia felt her entire body seizing up, every bone, every muscle going rigid with tension.

Over the past six years she'd really believed she had come to terms with what he had done, with his wickedly cruel betrayal. If anyone had told her that seeing him again would affect her like this—as if he still had the power to give her pain, to make her go weak and boneless with one look from those smoke-grey eyes—then she would have laughed until her ribs cracked.

He drained his cup, his eyes assessing her over the rim. 'I've had a shock, too, Claudia. You were the last person I expected to see this morning.' He put the cup back on its saucer with a tiny click and suggested, 'So why don't we both take a deep breath, put on our business hats, and start again?' He made a small gesture with one lean, strong-boned hand. 'Won't you, perhaps, sit down?'

She ignored the seamless way he was taking over, her brows frowning above her thickly lashed eyes as she picked up her cup and carried it over to one of the deeply recessed window embrasures—because her legs felt distinctly shaky, and for no other reason at all. Sitting down on the padded cushion, she tilted one interrogative brow.

'Who else would you expect to see? Widow Twanky? You can't have forgotten who owns Farthings Hall.'

'Six years ago Guy Sullivan, your father, owned the property. I hadn't given the place a thought until the impending sale was brought to my attention. The name Favel meant nothing to me. Your father...' For the first time he looked unsure of himself, as if he had only just realised that the change of ownership might mean Guy Sullivan was no longer living. 'Your father always treated me fairly,' he said quietly.

Sarcastic swine! He'd been long gone, on that rattletrap old motorbike of his, well before her father had returned that day, so he had no way of knowing what Guy Sullivan would have said and done had he been told—as Helen had threatened—what had been happening in his absence.

He'd got the treatment he deserved from her and from Helen. Had it given him pleasure to hammer home the fact that he hadn't given her a moment's thought in six long years?

But she put him out of his misery in one respect. 'Dad's visiting a friend for the day.' She saw the slight tension drain from his face and knew with a small shock of surprise that he was actually relieved.

'But you are the present owner?' He was leaning back against the table, half sitting, his arms folded across his chest, his eyes narrowed as if he was weighing up everything she said.

'Yes.' She didn't have to tell him any more.

'Sole owner?'

She dipped her head in acknowledgement and he

drawled, as if the prospect didn't much appeal, 'Then you and I do business. At this stage, there's no need for me to view the property; I remember as much as I need to right now.'

Claudia forced herself not to flinch at that callously casual reminder. He might have been able to wipe her from his memory banks with no trouble at all but during his time here he'd surveyed every inch of the property, so no, he wouldn't have forgotten what he'd seen, and decided to have.

They'd roamed every inch of the acreage together, the formal gardens, the paddocks, the headlands and the lovely unspoilt valley that led down to the cove, following the well-trodden path meandering beside the clear, sparkly waters of the stream, hand in hand, blissfully happy. Or so she'd thought.

And he'd obviously known enough about the interior of the house to go straight to Helen's bedroom the moment a suitable opportunity arose. He had never troubled himself to find out where her, Claudia's, room was. He'd made love to her in many places: the soft, moonlit grass of the headlands, the silky sand of the cove, even in the caravan on that claustrophobic bunk bed; but never here in the house.

Had he had too much respect for Helen, been too overawed by her golden, sizzling sexiness, to believe he had any hope of seducing her at all in the great outdoors or the mouldering old caravan? Had he decided his chances would be greater in the comfort of her own suite of rooms, between the luxury of satin sheets?

'So, since the restaurant here is closed at lunchtime

during the off season, I suggest we find a quiet pub and discuss generalities over lunch.'

Claudia blinked herself back to the here and now. He seemed able to operate as if there had never been anything between them in the past, or as if what had happened between them was not worth remembering, she thought resentfully, beginning to burn with a slow, deep anger. Perhaps the only way a person could live with the memory of their own despicable behaviour was to ignore it, as he seemed to be doing with great success.

Claudia rose and returned her cup and saucer to the tray. Her face was calm, icily controlled, hiding the raging inner turmoil. She was about to repeat forcefully her earlier statement that no way would she do business with him but, before she could get the words out, he stated coolly, 'You're married.'

That had to be obvious, of course, from her change of surname and, of course, he looked and sounded utterly detached. Why should he look anything other? His emotions had never been engaged where she was concerned, only his greed.

'So?' Her mouth was trembling. She thinned her lips to make it stop. 'Are you?'

'No. But that's hardly relevant. Your husband isn't a joint owner of the property?' The grey of his eyes was, if anything, even more austere, his mouth twisting in a parody of a smile. 'Don't look so defensive, Mrs Favel. My interest in you and your husband isn't personal. On a professional basis I need to know exactly who I have to deal with.'

He was astute, she had to give him that, Claudia

acknowledged shakily. He could tell she felt threatened—her body language must have given her away. And, truth to tell, she had been threatened ever since she'd walked into the kitchen gardens six years ago and feasted her eyes on the stunning perfection of him.

He had threatened her happiness, her innocence, her unquestioning belief in the intrinsic goodness of human nature. Threatened and destroyed. So she had every right to look defensive.

'I'm the sole owner.' She could see no reason to tell him of Tony's death, to tell him anything other than, 'However, it's entirely academic. Maybe you weren't listening, but I distinctly remember telling you I'd decided not to deal with your company.'

She swung round on the low heels of her court shoes, facing the empty hearth rather than see him watching her with those chilling, empty eyes.

'And I said you'd be cutting off your nose to spite your face,' he reminded her dryly. 'However, if you prefer to take your chances on the open market, and keep your fingers crossed that whoever fancies taking this place on has got the necessary financial backing to deliver the asking price, rather than consider the obvious advantages of dealing privately with a successful outfit like the Hallam Group, then that, of course, is your prerogative.'

He'd followed her. He was standing right behind her. She could smell the cool, lemony scent of his aftershave, the rugged undertone of dominant male. It flummoxed her, made her feel disorientated. She despised him totally yet could understand completely why her younger self had fallen for him, had gladly given all she had of herself, would have unhesitatingly given her life for him had it been required of her...

Claudia swallowed roughly, her movements jerky as she put distance between them. She really hated to admit it, but he was right. A private deal between her and the Hallam Group would save a lot of grief. A company as secure as his wouldn't haggle over a fair price. She needed the best deal she could get to pay off those massive debts.

A quick, private sale would be easier on her father, too. He wouldn't have to suffer the local speculation that would precede a public auction. Having to sell up at all would affect him badly—he could do without the added stress of having to explain why to anyone who felt inclined to ask.

The book she'd been reading recently was lying on a side table. She hadn't been enjoying it. She picked it up because it was something to do, and hopefully it would make him think she was perfectly composed, unaffected by having to share room space with him.

But her fingers were agitated, clumsy, as she tried to slot it into a vacant space on the packed book-shelves. It fell, spine up, to the floor, the snapshot of her and Rosie, taken earlier this year, the one she'd been using as a bookmark, landing on the soft, jewel-coloured Persian carpet.

He had picked the book up before she had time to think, handing it to her but keeping the snapshot. Claudia felt physically sick, her hand going up to cover her mouth. A dull flush mounted his jutting cheekbones, his eyes glittering hotly as he raised them to meet hers.

'You have a daughter?' he asked harshly, glancing down again at the two grinning images and swiftly back up at her, forcing her to nod the affirmative.

'Look—about lunch. I agree. We can discuss business in neutral surroundings. I might as well hear what you have to offer.' She would have said anything—anything at all—to change the subject, to take his mind off that photograph. She swept past him, plucking it from his fingers with a murmured, 'Thank you,' as she went. She felt his eyes boring into her back, right between her rigid shoulder blades, as she made for the door. 'I'll collect my handbag and let Amy know I'll be out. I won't keep you waiting more than a minute or two.'

Back in her bedroom, she pressed her fingertips to her throbbing temples. If the past six weeks had been a nightmare, then Adam Weston's appearance put the tin lid on it! After her meeting with the bank manager she had foolishly imagined that nothing very much worse could happen.

How wrong she had been!

Stifling a groan, she surveyed her image in the dressing-table mirror. She looked haggard, middle-aged, careworn. She shrugged, turning away, taking her bag from the top of the chest of drawers where she'd left it earlier and tucking the photograph safely inside.

So what did it matter if she looked like death warmed up? He wasn't interested in her, in the way she looked. He never had been. All he'd been interested in was her prospects.

Nor did she want him to be interested in her. Of course she didn't. She was no longer a silly teenager who thought the world a beautiful place and the people in it perfect angels. She knew better now. And she could hack it; she could face having lunch with that snake. For the sake of her father and her child, she could endure it and would, she determined grimly, stick out for the best price she could possibly get.

Business, it seemed, wasn't on his mind. And it had fled from hers as soon as they'd realised where they were.

The Unicorn. A mythical beast, which was fitting because it had been here that he had declared his mythical love all those years ago, she thought bitterly as she eyed the tiny, stone-built pub from the side window of Adam's Jaguar.

'Remember it?' he asked now, removing the key from the ignition, and she gave him a blank-eyed stare.

'Should I?' She exited the car.

Of course she remembered it. The tiny pub, tucked away in a narrow, wooded valley, well off the beaten track. She hadn't been back in all this time, but she could have given him an inventory. However, she wouldn't give him the satisfaction of knowing she'd ever thought about the place after that night.

They'd ridden here on his motorbike one glorious evening, scraping enough money up between them to buy a glass of cider each and an enormous, bursting-with-flavour Cornish pasty, which they'd shared.

After they'd eaten, they'd sat outside on one of the picnic benches, slowly drinking the cider, and he'd reached over the table and wiped a bead of moisture from her mouth with his thumb, rubbing softly, slowly, his eyes heavy, his voice low and warm, so warm. 'I love you, Claudia. I want you. Always. So now you know.' His eyes had lingered on her mouth and she had known he wanted to kiss her. 'You've got the rest of the summer to get used to the idea of having me around, loving you, wanting you.'

She hadn't needed the rest of the summer to get used to that. She'd gloried in the idea of him loving her and wanting her. She'd felt exactly the same and had been ecstatic about it.

He'd touched her before, of course, the slide of a hand over her hip, a kiss—nothing heavy—stroking her breasts very, very lightly, as if he wasn't sure of himself, or of her, making her hold her breath with the wonder of the sensations, of what was happening to her body. After his declaration of love she'd known there would be more; known that neither of them would be willing or capable of holding back.

Neither of them had spoken much about that. They'd ridden back to Farthings Hall, her arms clasped tightly around his body, and she'd known what it felt like to be in a trance. The moon had been up by then and after he'd parked the bike he'd drawn her away from the caravan when she would have gone inside to make coffee, as she always did after one of their evening excursions.

She hadn't asked where they were going. She hadn't had to. Somehow she'd known that the moonlit cove would be where she would give herself for the first time to the man she would love for all time.

Only she didn't love him for all time, of course, she reminded herself staunchly as she trod firmly over the cobbled car park ahead of him. Her love had died the moment she'd learned the truth from Helen. And she'd die herself before she allowed him to know that she remembered anything about this place or had anything but the very haziest of memories about that lost summer.

Small though it was, the Unicorn had a reputation for good, unpretentious, home-cooked food. At a table in a quiet window alcove, Adam handed her the menu. Claudia put it down, unopened. 'I'll have a green salad and coffee.' Her mouth compressed. It would be foolish and wasteful to order anything more when she had the feeling her stomach would reject whatever she tried to feed it.

A sable brow quirked with sardonic intent. 'Is that how you've lost so much weight? Living on a lettuce leaf washed down with black coffee?'

So he hadn't totally forgotten. He remembered enough about her to be able to compare the gaunt woman opposite with the eighteen-year-old who'd been blessed with all those lush curves. Hearing him as good as admit it gave her a spurt of savage pleasure. He'd tried to give the impression that he hadn't given the Hall, or her, a second's thought in all these years, and had just now proved himself wrong.

But then, he was an expert liar. He probably had a first-class degree in the twisted art!

'We're here on business,' she reminded him, unfolding the large linen napkin and shaking it out over her knees as their food arrived. 'I suggest we stick to that, rather than descend to the personal.'

'Descend?' He almost smiled. 'In the past, when talk reached a personal level, things tended to go up, not down.' He forked up some of the seafood pie he'd ordered but didn't eat it, she noticed as she ignored his unsubtle innuendo, applying herself to her salad. She managed to swallow some but gave up altogether when he leaned back in his chair and asked, 'Your daughter... What do you call her?'

'Rosie.' She hated having to tell him, but she could hardly refuse. She didn't want to discuss her beloved, infinitely precious child with him at all. Ever.

'Pretty.' His unsmiling eyes bored into hers. 'Rosie Favel. It rings a faint bell. Favel? Should I know your husband?' he persisted.

Claudia sighed. It was none of his business. She would have told him just that, but practicalities had to come before pride. She had the future welfare of her father and her child to consider. She needed to get the best deal she could out of this man and continued rudeness wouldn't do anything to help in that respect.

She stirred her sugarless black coffee slowly, gathering patience. 'Perhaps,' she granted, then took a heartening sip of the hot and excellent brew. He was not to be fobbed off with that, however. His intent, unblinking expression told her that much.

'You probably saw him around at odd times during the summer you worked here.' She refused to elevate the couple of months he was at Farthings Hall higher than that, give it more importance. 'Tony was my father's accountant. He came around fairly regularly.'

'That fair-haired guy who always seemed to be hanging around your stepmother.' His mouth curled derisively and his voice was bitter. Because Helen had shown the young and sexy part-time gardener off the premises, preferring the more experienced attentions of her so-called distant cousin?

Had he seen what she and her father had signally failed to recognise—the ongoing affair between those two? She felt her face go red. The idea was hurtful and somehow very degrading.

'He has to be twenty years your senior.' His eyes were cold, as if he despised everything about her.

Claudia corrected him hotly, 'Twelve, actually. Not that it mattered. He was kind.'

Whatever else Tony had been, or hadn't been, he had always shown her kindness. It was ironic, really, that she hadn't discovered how cruelly he'd treated her until after his death.

'How nice for you.' Adam showed his teeth. As an attempted smile it wouldn't rate one out of ten, and his subsequent, 'So when did you marry your well-healed, ageing Lothario?' made her grind her teeth.

'October. Exactly six years ago. Satisfied?' He hadn't picked up on her earlier use of the past tense and she frowned, wondering, just for a moment, why she didn't come right out with it and tell him Tony was dead. And knew the answer: because she couldn't afford to have him know too much about her situation. 'Maybe now we can change the subject and talk about why we are here at all.'

'Gladly.' He drained his coffee cup. 'How old is Rosie?'

Her blue eyes clouded with anger. Why the heck couldn't he leave it? 'What my daughter's age has to do with the sale of Farthings Hall escapes me.' She bunched up her napkin and dropped it on her largely untouched salad, gathered her handbag and swept to her feet. 'I can only imagine you have no intention whatsoever of making an offer, that you brought me here with the sole objective of causing me as much aggravation as possible because, six years ago, I had the temerity to dump you!'

Claudia stalked out, leaving him to settle the bill, and she was waiting impatiently by the Jaguar when he finally strolled out after what seemed to her to be an inordinate length of time.

'I liked the outraged dignity act.' He was actually smiling for the first time that day. Claudia looked quickly away. That smile of his had always been lethal and nothing had changed in that respect except he used it a lot less often. Round her, at least.

'I hate wasting time, Mr Weston.' She glanced at her wristwatch. They should be back at Farthings Hall in time for her to collect Rosie from the village primary school. She prayed that he wouldn't hang around. There wasn't going to be a deal. This morning had been a painful waste of time.

'So, Mrs Favel, do I.' He opened the passenger door. 'Though I wouldn't agree our time has been wasted—even though more questions have been raised than answered.' He ushered her into the passenger seat and closed the door. While he walked round to the driver's side she wondered what he was talking about and decided she definitely didn't want to know.

One thing she was sure of was the unlikelihood of him making any offer for her home on behalf of his company. That, she reasoned, would have been ruled out of the question the moment he'd realised who she was. He probably still felt bitter about the way he'd been ordered off the property six years ago when he'd been just the hired help.

He wouldn't be inclined to do her any favours. She breathed out raggedly, shifting in her seat as the powerful car tucked neatly into the side of the narrow lane on a particularly tight bend.

'Relax,' he said coolly. 'I'll have our surveyor go over your property. One day next week, perhaps. Our formal offer will depend on his report.'

Claudia did as she was told. She relaxed. Well, as much as she could, given the company she was keeping. He hadn't written off the possibility of a sale, so she could keep the harmful truth from her father for another few days—until she was forced to tell him everything by the imminent arrival of the surveyor. Every day he got a little stronger, so the longer she could keep the dreadful news from him, the better.

A few more minutes and they would be back at the Hall. After Adam dropped her off he'd drive away, she consoled herself, and she would never have to see him again because all further business could be handled through their solicitors. And she could begin again the process of forgetting how very much she had once loved him, and how very much she had hated him for the first few years, and—

'That is Rosie?'

The car had swept up the gravelled driveway and she hadn't noticed. His query brought her out of her bitter ruminations. Her daughter was careering down the flight of stone steps from the open main entrance door, dressed in cotton dungarees, her soft black hair flying around her face, Amy red-faced and puffing in hot pursuit.

Adam braked, the action controlled and smooth, and Claudia practically fell out of the door, reaching out and catching her squealing and giggling offspring and lifting her protectively into her arms.

'Mummeee! Amy said to watch for the car—I saw you come!' That wide, heart-stopping smile lit up the gorgeous little face, the wide, smoke-grey eyes. 'The roof of the school fell down,' she exaggerated wildly. 'The whole school nearly fell down!'

'Just the ceiling in the cloakroom, and only part of it at that,' Amy explained breathlessly. 'But Miss Possinger phoned at lunchtime to say could one of us collect her because all the children were being sent home early. They're getting the plasterers in to fix it this evening.'

Claudia unwound her daughter's arms from their stranglehold around her neck, her poor heart pounding. 'Run along in with Amy, darling. I won't be a moment.' She wouldn't have been that long even if, in her haste to stop her exuberant little girl hurtling off down the drive, she hadn't left her handbag behind in the car. 'Then I'll get changed and maybe we'll take a picnic down to the cove.'

She didn't want her daughter around Adam Weston for one split second longer than necessary and she cursed the fates that had made it necessary at all, and held her breath as, the promise of a picnic as bait, Rosie slid to the ground, took Amy's hand and trotted willingly back to the house.

Everything was OK. Claudia let out a relieved sigh of pent-up breath, then broke out in a cold sweat and felt the ground tilt beneath her feet as Adam said, his voice very cold, very precise, 'That child is mine.'

CHAPTER THREE

'WHAT did you say?' Claudia gasped through lips that suddenly felt stiff and parched.

'You heard.' The dry ice in his voice made it crackle with cold fury. Her stomach clenched in painful reaction and heat scorched through her body and then just as rapidly drained away, leaving every last one of her senses in total deep freeze.

'Her age would be right and her colouring's spot-on. She's a Weston. That child is not Tony Favel's.' His tone was dark, hard, as if what he said was irrefutable—and heaven help anyone who tried to argue the toss.

Claudia's skin prickled in warning. She would have run into the house, locked the doors and turned it into a fortress, but her legs would barely hold her upright, never mind leap into a sprint.

'Well? Not denying it?' His words were harsh and bleak, as raw as the winds which scoured the granite tops of the winter hills. Claudia's eyes were riveted to his in shock. Wide eyes and wild, looking for a way out of a nightmare and not finding one.

Exasperated by her stunned silence, he took her arm, his fingers lean and strong. Claudia shuddered convulsively as her frozen senses came to life. Having him touch her, actually touch her, was far worse than anything else that had happened today.

It was as if he'd pressed a magic button that had transported her to that untroubled past, plunging her deep into her those wild and heady sensations, all that long-forgotten needing, the wanting, and the loving...all those old sensations she had been so sure she had safely buried away like the dead and useless, unwanted things they were, buried away and forgotten, never, ever to be remembered again.

'You're mad!' she muttered through chattering teeth. She shook her head in hectic denial of his basic and frighteningly primitive effect on her, and her butterscotch hair slipped from its confining clasp and tumbled around her face. She tried to tug her arm free, but his fingers gripped all the tighter as he hauled her closer to his rock-solid body.

He ignored her feeble insult, single-minded determination glittering in the slate-grey depths of his eyes. 'I mean to know, Claudia. Even if I have to insist on DNA tests.' His mouth thinned. 'And I will insist, if I have to.'

She knew he would. The cloak of charm he'd worn so easily when she'd first met him had been well and truly discarded. He had no need of it, no need to charm a woman who was near bankrupt. She had nothing material for him to covet. Now all he needed or wanted from her was an answer and he'd stop at nothing to get it.

Claudia shivered in the Indian summer sun. He must have read the defeat in her eyes because he smiled grimly and tugged her just a fraction closer. Close enough to let her feel the way the raw tension coming from him scorched her skin. 'So?' he persisted. 'I want the truth. Is Rosie my daughter?'

Too choked to speak, she nodded, dipping her head so that the thick, slippery strands of her hair fell forward to hide her face. She heard the breath hiss out of his lungs and met the blazing impact of his eyes as his other hand cupped her chin, forcing her head up, his fingers hard against her jawline.

'You knew you were pregnant with my child and yet you married Favel,' he deduced, his voice bleakly judgmental. Claudia felt her heart bang sickeningly against her ribs. Never, in all of her life, had she been looked at with such a wealth of black scorn. And it was undeserved. That made it worse. He, for being the man he was, was to blame for what had happened.

'Yes, I married him!'

It was too much, all of it! To have done anything other than agree to Tony's suggestion that they marry would have been, at that time, unthinkable. 'What choice did I have?' she blazed at him, anger and pain deepening the glittering blue of her eyes. 'What damned choice?'

'You had choices,' he said coldly. 'You found yourself in need of a husband and a father for your child because, presumably, you couldn't cope on your own, or didn't want to have to. So you made your calculations and you chose. The well-heeled accountant would have seemed the better bet. Better than a casual manual worker without the price of a pasty in his pocket! The tiny fact that I was the natural father, had undeniable rights too, didn't come into your calculations.'

He stepped back, dropping his hands, breaking the physical contact that had quite obviously been utterly distasteful.

Sudden tears brimmed in her eyes as she glimpsed what looked like pain flare briefly and vividly in his eyes when he raised his stormy gaze and glanced towards the steps down which, only minutes before, his young daughter had exuberantly erupted.

But then the fleeting insight into the soul of the man had gone, so maybe she'd imagined it, imagined the regrets of a man who had missed out on five years of his child's life, because all she could see now was cruelty, the cruelty that had prompted him to make her revisit the Unicorn, the scene of his declaration of love. Had he set out deliberately to remind her of how gullible she'd been, how utterly foolish, how easy?

She shuddered, feeling ill. How like him to fix the blame on someone else. It was, she supposed, the mark of a true con artist. Charm the folks into thinking black was white then, if the truth ever did hit them between the eyes, tell them it was all their own fault for not seeing straight in the first place.

'Does Favel know the child isn't his?'

Claudia wrapped her arms around her body. Any moment now, Rosie would come bounding down the steps again, wondering what was keeping her, telling her to hurry, reminding her of that promised picnic.

There was no point now in trying to escape the truth. He would find it, no matter how hard she tried to hide it. So she had to get it out before her little daughter made another appearance.

'Tony died in a road accident less than two months

ago.' She made her voice unemotional because it was the only way she could handle this. 'And yes, he knew Rosie wasn't his. He adopted her.' That had been part of the bargain. 'No one else knows, not even my father.' That had been part of the bargain, too. The most important part. 'And I'd like to keep it that way.'

She wondered bleakly if there was any hope of that. In keeping all knowledge of his child from him she had done him a terrible injustice, she freely admitted that. He would look for all possible means to make her suffer.

He didn't answer. He gave her a long, totally unreadable look, swung on his heel and strode back to his car.

'Now tell me all about it.' Amy sat down at the long, scrubbed-top table and stirred her cocoa, eyeing Claudia's goblet of red wine with a tinge of disapproval.

It was her second glass and probably wouldn't be her last of the evening, Claudia thought half hysterically. Usually, this was one of the best times of her long, busy day. Satisfied diners departed, the part-time helpers finished and collected by their respective husbands; time to relax and have a natter, as Amy put it.

Ever since Adam had driven away she'd been avoiding spending any time alone with the housekeeper, dreading her questions, which she knew from long experience would be myriad.

'Whoever would have thought Adam Weston would turn up again like that? It will be too early for him to make a firm offer, we all know that, but just fancy—all those years ago when you and he were going around together he didn't have sixpence to call his own! I can remember how grateful he was to work around the place just to get somewhere to sleep and something to put in his stomach. And now he turns up offering to buy the place!'

Hardly that. He wouldn't lift a finger now to help them out of the deep, dark hole they were in. Claudia swallowed some wine. Nothing for it but to nod her agreement, though she knew she had kissed goodbye to any hopes of Adam recommending that the Hallam Group make an offer for Farthings Hall, now that she had confessed his relationship to her daughter.

He had driven away from her and everything to do with her as if he meant it. There would be no offer, no further contact.

Strangely, stupidly, what hurt most was his lack of interest in his child. Having wrested that confession out of her, he had turned his back on his little daughter, expressing no interest whatsoever in ever seeing her again.

But surely she had done the right thing in telling him the truth? He'd had his suspicions about Rosie's parentage and if she'd continued to deny the truth he would simply have put his head down and gone after it himself, wreaking heaven only knew what havoc.

So this way there would be no waves. He had the truth and he'd walked away from it, and no one would know any differently. Stupid to feel hurt because he'd turned his back on Rosie, indifferent to her well-being, her future, coldly excluding his child from his life.

Stupid, because she didn't want him back in her life, or in Rosie's...

'So you'll be breaking the news to your father now? You can't leave it any longer, not now you've started the ball rolling.' Amy had finished her cocoa and sat back, folding her arms across her roly-poly bosom. 'It's bound to upset him, but try not to let it worry you too much. He's a lot stronger now than he was. It's the business with the debts that will hit him the hardest.'

As if she didn't know that! She was dreading having to tell her father exactly why they were having to sell his family home.

She was going to have to explain to him that not only had his wife been having a torrid affair with his daughter's husband, but that they'd been syphoning off large amounts of income from the hotel and restaurant business, leaving huge unpaid bills behind, bills there was not a hope in hell of paying unless the property was sold. It would hurt and humiliate him and he'd already been hurt enough.

And there was absolutely no hope of carrying on here. A further hefty mortgage was out of the question, so the bank manager had told her.

Claudia took her empty glass to the sink and rinsed it. Much as she was tempted to anaesthetise herself with alcohol, she knew more wine would definitely not be a good idea. 'I'll break the news on Monday.' She collected Amy's mug. 'We'll make the best of the weekend and give him a couple more days of relative peace. Relax in the sun. The forecast's good again.'

The restaurant was closed on Sundays, out of season, and she'd always made a point of making it a real family day, a relaxing, do-as-you-please kind of day. No matter how on edge she was herself, she would make sure that this Sunday was no different. Monday would be soon enough to bring Guy Sullivan's world tottering around his ears.

'Right.' Amy heaved herself to her feet. 'Time for bed. I'll ask Edith on Sunday what she thinks about me going to live with her. When this place has gone, of course. I wouldn't think of going until then.' The housekeeper's face suddenly crumpled and Claudia's battered heart twisted inside her breast.

Amy spent every Sunday with her sister, Edith, in nearby St Mawes. They could tolerate each other in small doses, but that was as far as it went. Edith was too fond of harping on about her sister's unmarried state for Amy's liking, rubbing in the fact that she had a husband and children and her sister didn't. 'It won't need to be for long, mind,' Amy added, her voice wavering. 'Just till I can find another live-in position.'

'Oh, Amy!' Impulsively, Claudia hugged the older woman, offering what comfort she could, wondering how much more misery she could take.

Amy had been housekeeper here for as long as she could remember, always there for her—particularly after her mother had died. And all she, Claudia, could offer in return for those years of devotion was her deep affection.

Hardly a helpful commodity to someone who was staring a homeless, jobless future in the face.

* * *

'Why does Old Ron like so many pies?' Rosie, dancing at Claudia's side, wanted to know. Rosie hated pies of any description and this Sunday, as on every Sunday, they had delivered two to the flat above the stable block. Steak and kidney, and apple. Rosie would rather have sausages and ice cream.

'Because he knows what's good for him.' Claudia smiled down at the bundle of energy bouncing around her feet. Her colouring—that silky soft, near-black hair, those huge smoky grey eyes—was so like her father's she could hardly credit that those who had known and remembered the young Adam Weston hadn't cottoned on.

If only things had been different and Rosie could have been brought up by both parents, she thought, her throat tightening with unwelcome emotion. But it hadn't been possible.

At the time, Tony Favel's offer of marriage, as a way out of her difficulties, had seemed, if not an easy option, the only viable one.

How could she, on that October afternoon almost six years ago, have known how devious Tony was, how dark his character, what his true intent had been when he'd found her weeping helplessly, huddled up at the foot of the service stairs? In her mind she could still hear his voice as he'd said, 'Claudia? Whatever's wrong?'

If she'd been less distraught she might have wondered what her father's accountant was doing, creeping down the service stairs. Wondered, drawn certain conclusions, and maybe prevented what was bad, very bad, from getting very much worse.

'You—er—you mustn't upset yourself. Your father's well on the road to recovery. Out of Intensive Care and expected home next week.' He had touched her lightly on her shoulder, offering awkward comfort. 'He'll be fine—as long as he takes care.'

Claudia's sobs had intensified at that. She'd known she was embarrassing the poor man, but she couldn't help it. Her father's first and near-fatal heart attack had struck out of the blue a week ago and his cardiologist had expressly warned against upsets or anxieties or stressful situations for some time to come.

So how could she possibly tell him she was pregnant? Naturally, he would ask who the father was. How could she tell him that? Knowing her father's love for her, the determination of his character, he would move heaven and earth to locate the now absent Adam Weston.

How could she tell him that she wouldn't marry Adam Weston if her life depended on it? Pretend she'd had sex with him simply because she'd felt like it, that she hadn't loved him? How could she make herself cheap and tacky in her father's eyes?

And how could she tell him the truth: that she wouldn't tie herself to a man who had deliberately made her fall helplessly in love with him, proposed marriage to her, made passionate love to her—probably getting her pregnant quite deliberately to trap her—simply because her father owned an extremely valuable property? A man, moreover, who had sneaked upstairs while his back was turned and tried to seduce Helen, his wife!

'Look—' Tony cleared his throat. 'You visited him

this morning. Was he worse? Is that why you're so upset? I'll help if I can... Well, I'm sure you know that, Claudia, my dear.'

That was all it took to have her blurting it all out. He was her father's business accountant, practically a family friend, unfailingly courteous, kind, yet a disinterested onlooker, someone who wouldn't be too shocked, or disappointed in her, or upset.

'I'm pregnant! And I don't know how I'm going to break the news to Dad. He mustn't be upset—we all know that! I don't know what to do!'

'It's that odd-job chap's, isn't it?' Tony hazarded after a few moments of intense silence, his voice heavy. 'I couldn't help noticing the time you've spent together this summer.'

She nodded, too choked to speak, hating Adam, hating herself for letting him fool her. And Tony said quietly, 'Let's find somewhere to talk. Perhaps I'll be able to help you decide what's best to be done.'

He took charge and she was happy to let him. Of course, they couldn't talk on the stairs. The kitchens were deserted, the staff off duty until this evening. But Helen, who had earlier retired to her room with a migraine, which was why she hadn't been able to visit the hospital in Plymouth, could appear at any moment.

Secretly, Claudia had been glad to convey her stepmother's excuses, and love, and promises to visit tomorrow. It meant she'd been able to stop off and buy the pregnancy testing kit without the danger of Helen deciding to come into the chemist's with her.

'The chap walked out a couple of weeks or so ago,

didn't he?' Somehow, Tony had got her as far as the arbour in the rose garden without them being seen by any of the staff. 'Do you know how to contact him?'

Claudia sat hunched up on the seat, balling her sodden hankie in her palms. Helen had said it was best to let everyone think Adam Weston, in typical drifter fashion, had simply moved on. Nobody but them knew what had really happened. It was best, her stepmother had insisted. Less humiliating all round.

She shook her head wildly from side to side. 'I never want to see him again.' Then it all came out. How he'd made a fool of her, used her and betrayed her. How he'd then told Helen that he'd only ever been interested in her prospects.

How she'd told him with savage emotion just how much she hated him—but remembering through her distress that it was probably better not to tell Tony how the louse had tried it on with Helen, quite sure that her stepmother would hate it to be generally known. Helen had even warned her, Claudia, not to mention it to her father because she wanted to forget that such a loathsome thing had ever happened to her.

'Claudia—' Tony took her hand and patted it gently, his calm voice cutting through her emotional tirade. 'You're not in any state to think straight at the moment, I understand that, so just listen to what I've got to say and mull it over. Give it a day or two before you decide.'

She lifted red-rimmed eyes to him. If he was going to suggest an abortion then he would have to think again. No way would she terminate the life of her unborn child. Even if its father was a louse!

But her mouth dropped open and stayed that way when he said, in all apparent seriousness, 'I'll marry you. No one need ever know I'm not the father of your child. That would be kept private, between the two of us.' He smiled, his pale blue eyes compassionate. 'I've seen you blossom this summer and, to be truthful, I envied that young layabout. He could ask you on dates, spend time with you. I couldn't. You might have said, "On your bike, Grandpa!" and that would have made me feel terrible!'

She almost smiled. 'You're not that old.' And then the import of what he'd actually said hit her. 'You can't possibly mean that!' she gasped, her breath gone. 'That you'd marry me... Why on earth should you?'

She searched his face with bewildered eyes. She'd known Tony Favel for years but, she realised now, she had never really seen him. He was, she supposed, good-looking in a typically English way, even though his blond hair was beginning to thin and his waistline to thicken.

He had his own accountancy business and an apartment in a classy area of Plymouth; he drove an expensive car and she'd heard the two waitresses talking about him, giggling, saying he was sexy and he could play with their figures any time he wanted! He would be considered by many females to be quite a catch. So why would he want to tie himself down to someone who was expecting someone else's baby?

He smiled, his eyes twinkling. 'Because I want to? Or isn't that reason enough?' He answered her earlier question. He took her hands and held them gently.

'I've known you for years and to my certain knowledge there isn't a mean or spiteful bone in your body. Claudia, I've watched you grow from a gawky schoolgirl to a mightily desirable young woman. And yes, I was jealous of young what's-his-name, I freely admit it.'

Claudia flushed and looked away. Looked down at their linked hands and, almost as if he'd read her mind, he released her and said, his voice reasonable, 'A month ago I had my thirtieth birthday. I've sown all the wild oats I'll ever want to. I want to settle down. I want a family. I can't have children, Claudia—an illness in childhood saw to that. I would accept your child as my own—happily—and I'd be very proud if you would agree to be my wife. All I ask for the moment is that you think about it.'

And so she had, she thought now, watching Rosie dance ahead as Guy Sullivan waved from his seat on the terrace, where he'd settled with the morning papers after breakfast. Marriage to Tony Favel had seemed the wisest solution to a terrible problem.

She'd been as honest as she'd known how, telling him that she both liked and respected him and, perhaps, in time, could grow to love him. But she would never be in love with him. It had been his understanding that had finally tipped the balance, made her accept him, not only as her husband but also as a father-figure for her unborn child.

As for her father, well, he hadn't hidden his surprise at the suddenness of their announcement, as at the fact that she had immediately given up all thoughts of teacher training college. But he'd ac-

cepted it. And had given his heart completely on his
first sight of his red-faced, squawling granddaughter.

And Guy Sullivan's deep love for his little Rosie
was heart-warmingly evident as he allowed the black-
haired little imp to clamber onto his lap and demand,
with perfect childish logic, 'If you can't play tag any
more, Bompa, then you can tell stories. Stories can't
make you tired.'

'I'm sure you're right, poppet.' He tilted an en-
quiring brow at his daughter as she sat in the chair
facing his across the cast-iron table. 'Old Ron OK?'

'As ever.' Claudia leaned back in the warm autumn
sun and managed a relaxed smile. Today was going
to be as normal and comfortable as she could make
it, her own scalding anxieties over the future, her
dread of having to break the shattering news of the
loss of their home and livelihood not allowed to surface, not today. 'Enjoying a good old grumble.'

She didn't say more. She couldn't. The customary
half-hour spent with the old man, listening to him
grumble about everything from the lack of rainfall to
the shortcomings of his replacement, had added to the
burdens she was carrying, almost breaking her heart.
The new owners would not allow him to stay on in
his beloved little home, pay him for 'overseeing' the
work in the gardens, allowing him to feel useful.

So she wouldn't let herself think about him, or
dwell on the shock of seeing Adam again. Not today.

'Ready for coffee?' He'd been told to cut down on
his intake of caffeine and alcohol, to throw away his
cigars. He had refused point-blank, his theory being
that if he was about to pop his clogs then he'd do it

happy, not miserable. Secretly Claudia believed that
he refused to follow doctor's orders because since the
shock of Helen's death and the blow of her long-term
infidelity he saw no reason for living.

'I guess for once I might settle for orange juice,'
he told her, making her eyes widen with surprise. And
then his gaunt face split in a huge grin. 'You'll never
guess who phoned and invited himself to dinner while
you were visiting Old Ron!'

He looked happier than she'd seen him look in
months and she tipped her head on one side, smiling,
'Father Christmas, by the look of you!'

He grinned. 'Not quite! Nearly as good, though.
You'll remember him—there was a time when you
were a bit sweet on him as I recall. Adam Weston—a
nice lad, I always thought, far too bright to be bum-
ming around picking up odd jobs here and there. I
was sorry when he just drifted away the way he did.'
He unwound Rosie's strangling arms from around his
neck and smiled fondly as the little girl slipped down
from his lap and went to play with her ball, oblivious
of his daughter's suddenly ashen face, her frozen features.

'He's really come up in the world—he's head of
the Hallam Group, would you believe? Nice of him
to get in touch, don't you think?'

Claudia just stared, her stomach looping. This
couldn't be happening. It couldn't! But it was! 'Did
you say—say he was coming to dinner?' she managed, smothering the impulse to scream. 'When?'

'Tonight. You won't be busy with the restaurant.
He'll take pot luck. He said so.' He gave her a puzzled

look. 'You won't need to go to any trouble. I thought
it would do us good—fresh company, and all that. I'm
looking forward to finding out how he went from an
odd-jobber, scraping a living, to head of a company
like Hallam's.'

Claudia could have said, He stepped into dead
man's shoes, but didn't. 'I'll fetch the drinks.'

She got out of the chair, her legs shaky, and her
father said, his frown back, 'You don't mind, do
you?'

'No, of course not,' she made herself reply. But she
minded very much, so much so that she only made it
to the staff cloakroom in time to part with her breakfast.

She felt like death. Dazed blue eyes met her reflection in the mirror above the washbasin where she'd
sluiced her face in cold water. She looked like it, too.

She had to pull herself together. Fast.

She had no idea why Adam had invited himself to
dinner. To flaunt his affluence and power in the face
of their near-bankruptcy? To tell the man who had
once allowed him the use of that very basic old caravan, fed him and paid him pocket money in return for
labouring work about the place that he was now in
the position to buy him out a thousand times over,
but wouldn't because his daughter had borne his child
and kept it from him for over five years?

Would he be that cruel? That mean-spirited?

She had no way of knowing. All she did know was
that she had to be the first to see him this evening,
grab enough time alone with him to threaten to kill
him if he even thought of such a thing!

Pinching her cheeks to give them some colour, she stood tall, took a deep breath and went to fix the mid-morning drinks. She then spent the remainder of the day worrying and doing her damnedest not to let it show, so she was a nervous wreck when it was time to change out of her cotton jeans and old shirt, ready for dinner.

What to wear? Her mind in too much turmoil to make any sort of a decision, she pulled out the first thing she put a hand to in her wardrobe. A classic black silk crêpe, cut on the bias to skim the body, sleeveless with a discreet V neckline. Smart, classy.

She couldn't remember when she'd last worn it. Probably for a wedding anniversary dinner. The first? Just a few months after Rosie's birth? Must have been. By their second wedding anniversary Tony had ceased to bother about such things.

As if any of that mattered now, she told herself crossly, fumbling with the back zip. She'd heard her father go downstairs a short while ago, so she'd have to manage the wretched thing on her own. He would put a match to the fire in the morning room, which was where she'd decided they'd eat, he'd said earlier, mindful of their guest's comfort. Although the Indian summer days were unseasonably warm and sunny, the nights could be chilly.

Not that Claudia cared whether Adam Weston froze. All she cared about was getting to him before her father did. According to Guy, Adam would arrive at eight. Which gave her a good three-quarters of an hour.

Thankfully, Rosie had gone straight to sleep, tired

out after their visit to the cove, while Guy had rested that afternoon. She stopped, frozen in her struggle with the zip, her thoughts instinctively flying to her sleeping daughter. What if Adam had decided to fight for custody of his child?

He could, she agonised, make a terrifyingly solid case. Her keeping the child's existence a secret from him, passing the little girl off as another man's. The fact that, after the sale of Farthings Hall and the settlement of the huge outstanding mortgage, the horrendous debts, they would be forced to live in cramped, cheap accommodation while she found full-time work of some kind to keep the three of them, leaving the little girl in the care of a grandfather whose health was frail, to say the least!

The possibility terrified her. It made her heart thunder sickeningly, her mind whirl with agony. And the sound of a car drawing up at the front of the house, directly beneath the window of her small gable bedroom, paralysed her.

But only for a second.

She yanked at the zip and was at the window in almost the same frenzied movement, her worst fears confirmed as she saw Adam exit the Jaguar. Dressed in a light grey suit, casually yet expertly styled, he looked what he was—a lithely, powerfully potent male in his prime with a do-as-I-please arrogance about the set of those wide, rangy shoulders, an arrogance that had never been there when she'd known him, loved him...

Cursing inelegantly under her breath, she took two seconds to stuff her feet into her shoes and another two to scan her reflection and register, appalled, how dreadful she looked.

The dress that had once skimmed her lush curves now hung like a badly cut bin bag on her much thinner frame, making her look gaunt. No time for make-up or to fix her hair.

But it didn't matter. How could it? She didn't care if he thought her a fright. All that mattered was for her to get to Adam before her father did and plead with him, if necessary, to say nothing to upset the older man.

How like the new Adam to arrive early. He'd probably done it deliberately, to throw her off balance. After discovering that she'd kept the existence of their child from him, had given the role of Rosie's father to another man, he would do everything in his power to make life hard for her.

But her headlong flight down the wide staircase paid no dividends. Her father was ahead of her, already welcoming Adam Weston into his home. An Adam who was all smiles.

Claudia slowed down, struggling now for a dignity she feared she had irretrievably lost. She didn't trust this suddenly strangely affable man. How could she?

'My, it's good to see you!' Guy Sullivan looked ten years younger as he warmly shook the younger man's hand, plainly happy to enjoy the company of someone—or so he thought—who had nothing to do with the family tragedy, looking forward to an uncomplicated evening. 'You've toughened up, my boy, and, from what you told me, achieved so much. I look forward to hearing you tell me about it. Rags-to-riches stories are the ones I like best! Claudia, don't hover—come and say hello to an old friend!'

'We've already renewed our acquaintanceship,' Adam said warmly, his smile pure theatre, Claudia thought acidly, steeling herself now to hear him recount the details of their abortive business meeting, wondering hectically how she could limit the damage. Then she stared at him with naked distrust as he covered the few paces that separated them, his smoky eyes holding hers with a frightening intentness.

'Before we say anything else, Claudia and I have something to tell you, don't we, my love?'

Adam slid a possessive arm around her waist, his hand warm against her silk-clad flesh, making it tingle with unwanted awareness. That, and his closeness, the lean length of his body pressed intimately against hers, making her pulses skitter unbearably, plus that preposterously false endearment, took her brain and shook it to mush, making her incapable of speech, of movement.

All reason flew completely out of her head, leaving her brain a quivering mass of scrambled thought waves, when the man who was looking down at her so tenderly stated, 'I know it's early days after the loss of her first husband, but when we met again we realised that what we felt for each other, all those years ago, was still there, and important to us. It just happened. Neither one of us could deny it—we both believe it would be hypocritical to pretend otherwise. So we plan to marry just as soon as it can be arranged and we hope, sir, that you will understand, give us your blessing and be happy for us.'

CHAPTER FOUR

CLAUDIA felt her father's questioning eyes on her and flinched. The silence wrapped her like a shroud. She shivered with tension. What could she possibly do or say? Adam's bombshell had left her shell-shocked. She made herself look up, saw the unspoken query in her father's eyes, the slight frown, and made herself smile.

Apparently reassured, the older man's features relaxed as he said gruffly, 'Well, this calls for champagne!' Then he took charge, ushering them into the morning room where, as promised, he had a fire crackling cheerfully in the stone-hooded hearth.

Claudia's legs would barely hold her; she was actually glad of Adam's supporting arm around her waist.

Her father's eyes were suspiciously moist as he said, 'You're both old enough to know what you want and you've got my blessing, both of you. Of course you have, Adam.' His voice thickened. 'After what Claudia's been through—she'll have told you, naturally, and I'd prefer, and I know you'll understand why, to leave it at that—she deserves all the happiness she can get. I knew you two were sweet on each other when you worked here that summer. I'm only sorry you felt you had to leave so precipitously, Adam. I never did understand why.

'But—' his smile was suddenly wide, transforming his gaunt features '—'nough said. I'll dig that champagne out of the cellar and then we can really celebrate—look to the future and forget the wretched past.'

Despite the moistness in his eyes, Claudia knew her father was happy with the situation. Puzzled by the swiftness of it all, but happy. He had taken the younger Adam Weston at face value six years ago, and liked him, and was doing the same now, taking him at face value and admiring him for what he had apparently achieved. She was the one who would eventually have to tell him he had been mistaken before and was mistaken now.

A sob lodged in her throat, choking her. At long last her father looked as if he had come to terms with what had happened to them both, was beginning to put it behind him and was looking forward to the future. He was a man suddenly and unexpectedly at peace with himself. For now. It wouldn't last.

'How could you do that?' she cried, moments after Guy had left them alone. She had no idea what Adam was up to; her mind didn't function along Machiavellian lines. But, whatever it was, it wasn't good; it couldn't be, because the man who had once been her lover was now her enemy. The scars she had inflicted on him ran deep, apparently.

'Easily.' The smile had gone; the warmth had leached from his eyes, leaving them cold as the winter mists that drifted in from the sea.

He straddled the hearth, his hands deep in the pockets of his trousers, his lightweight jacket pulled away, revealing the sleek black silk of his softly tailored shirt. 'You saw how happy my announcement made him.' He gave a minimal shrug. 'You can always tell him it was all lies, of course. But I wouldn't advise doing that to a man with his medical history—and yes, my dear—' his upper lip curled '—I made enquiries. Three heart attacks in six years, the latest quite recently. I'm afraid I've boxed you into a corner and you can either stay there and go along with whatever I say, or tell him the truth—that I despise you—and get out of it. The choice is yours. But think hard before you decide. You had choices when you discovered you were expecting my child, and you made the wrong one.'

Her head was spinning. All the blood had rushed out of her brain. She sat down suddenly in one of the chintzy armchairs. 'But why? I don't understand what you're saying!' She put her fingertips to her now painfully throbbing temples. 'You can't have any intention of going through with it, so why tell him such a load of lies? Why on earth would you want to force me to marry you if you despise me so much?'

'I don't lie, Claudia.' His voice was harsh, as harsh as the level look from his slaty eyes, before he turned abruptly and pushed a log back in place onto its bed of glowing cinders.

Claudia glared bitterly at his broad back. He hadn't lied six years ago when he'd proposed marriage. But he'd lied when he'd said he loved her. She would never forgive him for that.

'I don't lie,' he reiterated. He turned back to her, his eyes holding hers briefly before slowly and comprehensively sweeping the cosy room that caught all of the morning sunlight but was now rich with the firelight gleaming against the dark oak panelling, glowing on the warm, faded shades of the soft furnishings.

It was as if he was mentally totting up the value of everything in the room, from the Victorian lacquer screen, the delicate Regency whatnot to the satinwood Pembroke table already laid for supper.

'But, for your father's peace of mind, I suggest you do. Lie your heart out, that is. You shouldn't find it difficult, given your track record. He'll be back soon,' he added with a complete lack of any kind of emotion. 'If you place any value on your father's and our daughter's well-being, not to mention your comfortable lifestyle—and yes,' he drawled, his voice cruel, 'I'm bright enough to guess that financial difficulties are forcing you to sell Farthings Hall—you will say nothing, just agree with everything I say.'

And that was the trouble, she agonised as her father, right on cue, came through with champagne on ice and three glasses: there was no time.

No time to puzzle it out, even if her whirling brain were capable of deductive thought. Which, right now, it most certainly wasn't. She couldn't take it in, any of it, much less make sense of what he was doing and plan a counter-move.

The two men were talking, laughing. Claudia didn't take any of it in; she was too busy thinking what a devious, two-faced swine Adam was. The way he could turn on the relaxed charm at will made her shudder. Why hadn't she been able to see through him all those years ago? Too young, too inexperienced, too much in love, the answer came bleakly. Far too much in love.

She frowned, oblivious of everything but her own black thoughts. She barely noticed the foaming glass of champagne her father had placed in her nerveless fingers until he gave her a straight, underbrow look, put an arm around her stiffly held shoulders and murmured understandingly, 'Relax, sweetheart! Does it matter if everyone mutters behind their hands about it being too soon for you to remarry after Tony's death? We three know the truth of it, and that's all that matters.'

So she smiled and drank her champagne as if she were dying of thirst and said in a thin little voice, 'Excuse me while I see to supper. I'm sure you're both hungry.'

There was nothing to see to. She'd poached the salmon steaks and made the salads this afternoon. She needed only to take them from the huge catering-size fridge. But she needed time to herself, some space, an opportunity to sort through her chaotic thoughts and try to find a reason for his monumentally shattering announcement of their forthcoming marriage.

He had already said he had guessed that financial difficulties were behind her sudden need to sell what had once been a highly profitable enterprise. The hotel—more like a country house where the privileged guests were treated like valued friends, where there wasn't a bar or a reception desk in sight—and the restaurant, a beautifully restored and tastefully appointed former barn, joined to the kitchens by a covered walkway, had, in the old days, been fully booked for months ahead.

He had only to use his eyes to see that everything looked a little bit tired now, sorely in need of refurbishment; and he only had to ask around to discover that the restaurant now offered a limited menu only and was only fully booked on Saturday nights and by a far less affluent clientele.

So he wasn't wanting to marry her for her prospects this time around. And he wasn't even pretending to be in love with her. Far from it. He looked at her as if he loathed her and had frankly admitted that he despised her.

She sagged weakly back against the tiled wall, tears seeping beneath her closed eyelids. The man was doing her head in!

'Sulking, Claudia? Or can't you face not being able to call all the shots, all of the time?'

Her stomach jolted, nausea burning the back of her throat. He was standing directly in front of her and she squeezed her eyelids together more tightly to shut him out.

'I came to see if you wanted any help. At least, that's the excuse I made to Guy. He's a contented man, and swallowed it.' He put his hands on her shoulders and shook her gently. 'Look at me.'

The touch of his hands on her body sent her senses haywire, heat raging through her; the pull was as strong as it had ever been. It frightened and disgusted her, this betrayal of her own body.

She opened her eyes because she didn't know what he would do if she kept them shut, releasing the tears to trickle over her cheeks. She scrubbed them angrily away, knocking his hands from her shoulders in the process, hating her weakness, hating to have him see her like this—haggard with all the worry and unremitting hard work of the last weeks, a dreary-looking, scrawny woman in a too big dress.

He stood back a pace, looking at her, and she lifted her chin and glared right back.

What did if matter if she looked dreadful? With any luck it would put him off the idea of marrying her—no matter what his twisted and devious reasons had been for making that ridiculous announcement in the first place.

'Is there anything about your marriage to Tony Favel I should know about?' he asked coldly. 'From a couple of remarks your father made I get the distinct feeling it wasn't exactly a bed of roses. If you're not still in shock and grieving for him then it doesn't change anything, but it makes what's happening a damn sight easier on my conscience.'

To hell with his conscience! As far as she knew, he didn't have one. 'My marriage to Tony has nothing whatever to do with you, so back off! He was twice the man you'll ever be!'

Which wasn't true. There was nothing to choose between them. They were both as bad as each other! But if he was looking to her to ease his so-called conscience, then he could go on looking until he was old and grey.

'Please move out of my way,' she snapped, pushing past him to wheel one of the trolleys close to the fridge. She was beginning to haul herself together at last. It was as if his mention of easing his conscience had made him ever so slightly vulnerable and had given her some kind of an advantage.

Pulling dishes from the fridge, she loaded them onto the trolley, relieving a little of her inner tension by banging them down with a satisfactory, if childish, series of crashes. 'And while you don't have to put on an act for my father's benefit you can tell me what's behind your lunatic suggestion of marriage.'

'To get my daughter in my life on a permanent basis—what else?' he told her, rocking back on his heels. 'I've thought long and hard on the best way to achieve that,' he admitted coldly. 'My gut instinct was to go for custody, but that wouldn't be the answer. To take her away from you and Guy would harm her, and I wouldn't put any child—let alone my own flesh and blood—through the trauma of being separated from a much loved parent. I've been there, and it's not a pleasant place.' He took a dish of *maître d'hôtel* butter from her shaking fingers and found space for it on the trolley.

'I don't like people who turn their backs on their children.' Grey eyes raked her ashen face. 'I won't be one of them and I won't be a part-time parent with limited and possibly grudging access. I intend to be there for my daughter. So, it follows, if you want to be part of the happy family scene, then you toe the line.

'If you prefer to take your chances and fight me through the courts, then go right ahead; be my guest. But,' he added coldly, 'if you choose that route, be sure you accept the possibility of losing. I can put up a good case and have the wherewithal to hire the best lawyers in the land to put it for me. Consider, too, what such a fight could do to our daughter—not to mention your father.'

Claudia grasped the bar of the trolley in white-knuckled desperation. She needed the support. He meant it, every hateful, chilling word. He wanted his child and he was going to make her suffer for keeping Rosie's existence from him. And there was nothing she could do, not without harming the two people she cared most about.

And how could she risk fighting him through the courts when there was always the chance he would win?

She looked at his face and found no comfort, nor any hope of it. He had stated his position, posted his intentions and knew his own strength. Smiling blankly, his eyes cold, he opened the door and made a slight after-you gesture. She trundled the wretched trolley through, wishing it were a tank so she could run him over and squash him out of existence, secretly shocked and dismayed by her own unsuspected capacity for violence.

But any mother would resort to violence if her child were threatened, she reasoned as he stepped in front of her and held open the door to the morning room. It was only natural. Yet she instinctively knew that Adam Weston didn't threaten Rosie. He had only just discovered that the adorable moppet was his daughter. And he wanted her.

It was she, Claudia, he threatened. And on many more levels than he knew about!

'I thought you'd got lost!' The twinkle in Guy's eyes showed he'd thought no such thing.

Adam smiled disarmingly, spreading his hands, his rangy shoulders lifting slightly, very elegantly. 'Our reunion was very recent; Claudia and I have a lot of catching up to do. You must forgive us.'

'That goes without saying!' Guy was happy, pouring out more champagne, having a ball. 'I can only marvel at Claudia's ability to say nothing about what has to be the best thing that's happened to her in years!'

'Yes, I'm sorry about that. But you see, Guy, in view of recent tragic events, we thought it best to say nothing until keeping quiet about our feelings became impossible. I'm sure you understand.'

'Completely!'

Claudia, unloading the contents of the trolley onto the table, resisted the almost overwhelming impulse to throw the lot at the wall. Adam Weston could say a thing and, by sheer intonation, make it sound like something completely different! He'd probably been born with the knack!

Controlling herself, swallowing a few inner screams, she invited the men to the table, invited them to serve themselves and gave up the pretence of eating the little she'd put on her plate when Adam laid down his fork, hooked an arm over the back of his chair and said, almost diffidently, for him, 'I've got a favour to ask and a proposition to put to you, Guy.'

'Fire away.'

'After the wedding I'd like to move in here, make it my family home, if you've no objections, of course.

At the moment, I'm in a somewhat sterile service flat near the City.'

'Done!' Guy couldn't disguise his relief. 'I'm delighted that Claudia's found happiness at last, but I must admit I'd been wondering how far you'd be taking her away. I'd find life pretty bleak without her and Rosie.'

'Then that's settled. That was the favour; now my proposition. How would you feel if we closed the place down as a hotel and turned the restaurant back into a barn, or maybe an indoor swimming pool? I'd like Claudia to be able to concentrate on being a wife and mother, enjoy life, rather than being at the beck and call of anyone with the price of a meal or a room.'

He couldn't have said anything more calculated to get the older man on his side. If there was one thing more important to Guy Sullivan than the once thriving family business, it was the welfare and happiness of what was left of his family, Claudia thought, seeing her father nod his head in total, unreserved agreement.

'There would need to be alterations, naturally. The kitchens, for instance. Ideal for servicing a busy restaurant and meeting the needs of hotel guests, but hardly homey. I'll be more than happy to foot the bill for any such alterations, plus any other work we find needs doing about the place.'

And so it went on. Proposals and agreements. Her father suggested that Amy be kept on as housekeeper.

Done.

That Old Ron be allowed to keep his home over the stable block.

Done.

Adam suggested, 'Why don't you leave the winding up of the business in my hands? You don't need the hassle and it would free Claudia up to plan for the wedding.'

'Gladly. I've hated seeing her run herself ragged trying to keep things going. Since—well, let's just say things have been difficult recently. And me getting ill didn't help.'

Claudia, drinking more wine than was sensible, decided that her father looked as if heaven had decamped to Farthings Hall and had elected to stay.

He had no idea that all this largesse was based on blackmail and hatred. She couldn't tell him.

Adam was right. He had put her in a corner and the only way out was unthinkable…

'Sweetheart—Adam's making a suggestion and you're miles away!' Her father's gentle chiding had her blinking blearily, squinting a little to focus on her tormentor. He was smiling, but then he did when her father was around. She could do without any more of his loaded 'suggestions', the way he was taking over her whole life and running it for his benefit.

He was probably going to voice the great idea that after the wedding she be taken to the attics and permanently boarded in—for her own good, of course!

But all he said was, 'I think it might be a good idea if you and I—with Rosie, of course—revisit old haunts tomorrow. If the weather holds we could take a picnic to the cove. Missing one day of school wouldn't hurt. Could you square it with her teacher? It would give Rosie and me a chance to get properly acquainted.'

The almost gruff note of pleading he hadn't been able to keep out of his voice was undeniably honest. His need to claim his daughter was probably the only honest thing about the wretched man.

She almost felt sorry for him, for the lost years. Then reminded herself that he'd brought it on himself by his own duplicity, and said dully, 'If the weather holds, then yes, I'll square it with her teacher.' She watched that small amount of tension leave his eyes because he obviously hadn't been certain she'd agree, and felt a sliver of remorse prick her heart, but put it down to slight inebriation.

She would have let her father see him out after being thanked profusely for the meal, but Guy said, 'Lock up when you come back in, sweetheart. I'll load the dishes and take them to the kitchen.'

So she had no other option but to see Adam to the door, not if her father was to continue to believe in heaven on earth.

But Adam was no more inclined to linger in the still night air than she was. All he said was, 'I'll be here at ten in the morning. And I suggest you draft a notice for the local papers stating that the restaurant is closed. If you've any bookings, chase them up and cancel. As for the wedding, I'll arrange that. Civil and quiet. Neither of us will want any fuss.'

She didn't watch him walk away. Closing and bolting the huge main door, she leaned back against it, tears stinging behind her closed eyelids. What had she ever done to deserve the series of catastrophes that had been coming her way with hateful regularity?

'Honey?' The query in her father's voice brought

her eyes open and she tried to smile to hide the glimmer of tears. It didn't work. 'Come here.' His arms enfolded her in love and caring and she wanted to blurt everything out. But she couldn't put her problems onto him. She had to be strong.

'I'm fine, Dad. Really. I drank too much and was too wound up to eat.' And wasn't that the truth? But for a totally different reason from the one he would fondly imagine!

'That's only natural,' her father soothed, patting her back. 'We've both been through the mill—with the accident and—and what we found out about the pair of them.'

And that was only the half of it. She'd hidden the financial nightmare from him. And if she married Adam it could stay hidden for ever. She shuddered.

'Let it go,' Guy murmured. 'Have a good cry—get rid of that stress. It's been worse for you—what with my illness, your having to run this place practically single-handed and me no more use than a dead weight. So let it go, then enjoy planning your wedding. How did you and Adam meet up again? When?' Being the considerate man he was, he was changing the subject, taking her mind off the stress that was in the past, reminding her of what he fervently believed was her happier future.

He couldn't know how wrong he was, and she'd been dreading his questions, had known they would come. And she didn't know how to answer him, so she stuck as nearly to the truth as she could.

'He was in the area and looked me up. We—we had lunch at the Unicorn.' She deliberately avoided saying when. He would never swallow 'the day before yesterday'! 'And everything snowballed.'

And how! She shuddered again and Guy, releasing her, said, 'I couldn't be more pleased for you both—if that's what you truly want.' She didn't answer the query in his voice; she couldn't. With one stroke she could tell him the truth and make them both penniless, homeless, with a custody battle on their hands. She couldn't do that to him.

Taking her silence as assent, he said more briskly, 'While you were organising supper he told me a bit about his position in the Hallam Group. I was very impressed. He's certainly come a long way. Tell you what, why don't I make you a hot chocolate and you can tell me more about him? He couldn't wait to tell me any more,' he chuckled. 'Too keen to help you in the kitchen!'

What she could tell him about Adam Weston and his shock insistence on marriage would make her father's grey hair fall out! She gave him a watery smile. 'Some other time, Dad. I'm out on my feet. And I don't want you getting over-tired, either. It's still early days.'

'Fine.' He gave her a goodnight peck on her cheek. 'Run along, then, and don't worry about me. Happiness is a great healer!'

His parting words didn't help her to sleep. He was happy for her and what he saw as her blissful future. So how could she tell it the way it really was? As hard as she tried, she could see no way out.

'She's adorable.' Adam's eyes barely moved from the tiny figure running ahead of them down the narrow path that wound through the wild, rocky valley, turning and running back to them like a bouncy puppy.

Clad in scarlet shorts and matching T-shirt, her soft black hair flying around her cute little face, Rosie was utterly adorable. Claudia's stomach clenched. She didn't want Adam to get too attached to his little daughter. She had prayed the weather would change, that the Indian summer would give way to the rain and gales that could lash the coast with brutal ferocity, so that this sort of getting-to-know-you scenario would be automatically ruled out of play.

But the day, if anything, was even softer and warmer and she had conceded defeat, phoned Rosie's teacher and made excuses for her absence.

Towards dawn she had come up with what she hoped was a way out of the corner he'd put her in, a way that didn't involve marriage, living with him. Living with Adam would test her sanity to its limits.

'Going to the cove with a picnic is her favourite outing at the moment; it's about the only thing that would make up for her missing school. She loves it. School, I mean. And I don't want you to think you can make a habit of keeping her away,' she said repressively.

She didn't look at him. When he'd appeared this morning wearing washed-out, hip-hugging blue jeans and a soft black T-shirt that clung to his upper body, she had gone into shock. She remembered, exactly and with blush-making explicit details, how it had felt to be in his arms; how she had taken his body into hers and almost died of rapture. So many times. So long ago.

She had craved him then with her body, heart and soul. She craved him still, but only with her body. There was the difference.

So she carefully didn't look at him. Why fuel something she was deeply ashamed of? Something that would become an agonising problem if she went along with his marriage plans. Which was why she was trying to find the right moment to drop her own bombshell and put her counter-proposition.

'I wouldn't dream of it,' he came back dryly. 'Today's the exception. I want to forge bonds, and there isn't much time before I become a permanent fixture in her life. Three short weeks,' he reminded her. 'When we're married I'd like to persuade her to call me Daddy. When she's older and has fully accepted my place in her life, I'll tell her the truth—that I'm her real father, that Favel was a substitute.'

And a poor one, Claudia had to acknowledge. Adam would involve himself with every aspect of his daughter's development; she had only to recall the way he'd involved the little girl in conversation earlier this morning, not talking down to her, explaining about the unexpected holiday and asking if she'd like to show him her favourite beach, listening to her ensuing chatter with smiling, soft-eyed absorption, drinking in every word.

Tony had never taken any interest in his adopted daughter. He'd never been unkind to her; Claudia would have given him short shrift if there had ever been even a hint of it. He'd showered her with expensive gifts at birthdays and Christmas, but he'd kept his distance. Her childish chatter had left him bored and indifferent and her very occasional tantrums had had him flying for cover.

'How were you so sure she was yours?' The words came welling out of her subconscious, completely unbidden. It only went to show how it had been preying on her mind, his seemingly instinctive knowledge, and the depth of her own shock had precluded any conscious prevarication.

She could feel his eyes on her. It set every inch of her skin on fire. She wished she hadn't asked and moved ahead of him on the path, her eyes fixed on Rosie's dancing figure.

But the leather soles of her sandals slithered on the sand-dusted stones and only his quick reflexes, the strong arm that snaked out around her waist, hooking her back against the solid wall of his body, saved her from an undignified tumble.

For endless seconds she stayed exactly where she was, pressed against the hardness of him, the clamouring warmth of him, while rapacious sensations racketed through her veins, every millimetre of her flesh; his hand on her tummy a brand.

'It didn't need the brain of Einstein.' His whispered words, so close to her ear, flayed her. 'I vividly recall that first time. I was unprepared, wanting you yet not expecting it to happen so soon. You were so eager for it, and I was swept away. Off guard. All the other times—there were so many I lost count—I made sure you were protected.'

He put her away from him, steadying her with firm

hands. 'Apart from that, there is the likeness. Not only the colouring but, feature for feature, Rosie's a dead ringer for my mother at that age. I could produce the photograph.'

He walked away, his stride casual, almost arrogant in its easiness as he caught up with his daughter.

Claudia shivered convulsively, rooted to the spot. His body heat had scorched her; his words, cruel and heaping all the blame upon her as usual, had burned themselves into her brain, reviving memories she simply didn't know how to cope with. Now she felt as if a cold wind had blown in from the Arctic, swirling round her with vicious intent. The skin of her arms prickled with goose-bumps.

It was a miracle that she made it down to the cove. But she did. Somehow. Adam and Rosie were sitting on the soft white sand, companionably investigating the picnic hamper he'd carried down. She'd packed it herself this morning, hurriedly, while Amy was hoovering upstairs. The housekeeper's reaction to Guy's news of the forthcoming marriage had been, in her own words, 'gobsmacked'!

Claudia knew she was in for some intensive questioning from that quarter. Amy knew just how recent their 'reunion' had been. Whether to tell her some wild fairy tale or tell her the truth was something Claudia wasn't ready to think about just yet. But if the marriage was called off, as she devoutly hoped would be the case after Adam had heard what she had to say, then that wouldn't arise.

'We're having our yoghurts and juice!' Rosie carolled cheerfully. 'You have some, too. Sit down.'

'Later, bossy-boots!' She forced a smile. At all costs she had to act as if nothing was wrong. Even though Rosie had never been close to her adoptive father and her 'Steppie', her small world had been rocked by their sudden deaths. She had developed the habit of asking if Daddy and Steppie were happy in heaven and Claudia, of course, had said yes, privately thinking they were more likely to be languishing in regions more nether. She didn't want her small daughter to get worried by any antagonistic vibes she might pick up between her mother and this stranger.

So she sat, well away from Adam, spreading her full cotton skirt around her legs, picking an apple out of the hamper and forcing herself to eat it, listening unwillingly to Adam's dark velvet voice as he talked to his daughter.

'I used to come here a long time ago. Thank you for showing me the way again. I'd forgotten how beautiful it is. I like the way the sea creams around the headlands, and how very big the sky is. And blue.'

The cove in a smiling mood, Claudia thought. But sometimes it could be wild, threatening, even in summer when black clouds could pour in and obliterate every trace of blue, gales whistling in, making the waves crash and roar.

It had happened to them once, taking them by surprise. They'd clung together in the driven, soaking rain, defying the storm, so sure of themselves, until, hunger calling, they'd struggled, laughing at the state they were in, back into the valley. Then, breathless, they'd collapsed into the lea of a bank of sheltered wild fuchsias where, seconds later, another type of hunger had taken them, shaking them more severely than the storm.

Claudia blinked the painful memory away, fighting the hurt in her heart, and heard Adam ask his daughter, 'So what do you like best about the cove?'

'Fishing.' Rosie jumped to her feet, a half-eaten chicken sandwich landing in Claudia's lap. 'You can come and help if you like,' she offered magnanimously, wriggling as her mother caught her and changed her miniature trainers for a pair of canvas slip-ons. Knowing that her child's notion of fishing was stamping in all the rock pools in turn, she always brought spare clothes along on this particular jaunt.

'I'd love to help you.' Adam was watching the proceedings, warmth in his eyes. 'You run along. Your mother and I will be with you in just a minute.'

Claudia knew that Adam would remember enough about the cove to know that Rosie could come to no harm. The rock pools she loved to splash in were smooth and shallow, with no sharp edges she could hurt herself on.

Nevertheless, her sense of outrage was strong. He thought he could dictate to her, make her stay here with him. She started to get to her feet to follow Rosie, but his next words outraged her further.

'You've changed.' His smoky eyes, lazy now, swept slowly over her body. Lingered on her breasts, smothered by the baggy cotton blouse she wore. 'Six years ago you were voluptuous. A highly sensual, sexy lady. What happened? Where did that delightful lushness go?'

Her outrage was so great she could barely speak.

He was cruel. Hateful! Her voice emerged thinly, sharpened by pain. 'You might despise me, but there's no need to be so damned personal. The way I look has nothing at all to do with you!'

'I disagree. I prefer you looking the way you do. Our marriage will be in name only; I'd like you to understand that. I'm a normal male with all the usual needs—as I'm sure you can remember. If you were…let's say, as you were…you might have proved too big a temptation, which could have made our relationship awkward. As it is…'

He let his words die away. But she knew exactly what he meant. She was no temptation at all. She couldn't believe how much that hurt. Yet it shouldn't. It should not!

'Do you enjoy being cruel?' Her words emerged on a savage hiss. 'Do you like hurting people?' Sprawled out on the sand, his soft black hair slightly ruffled by the gentle breeze, he didn't appear to have a cruel bone in his body.

'Not as a rule.' He began, unhurriedly, to repack the hamper. 'Perhaps you've conveniently forgotten how adept you've been at doling it out. Can't take your own medicine?'

'I don't know what you think you mean!' The only thing she'd hurt when she'd told him she'd lost interest in him six years ago had been his pride, plus, of course, his hopes for lining his pockets in the future. Unless he was talking about Rosie, which would mean that she was right, had been right all along, and he'd never been emotionally involved with her. Just used her eager body to get what he wanted—an easy lifestyle.

And she proved herself right when he closed the hamper with a snap, his eyes flinty. 'Don't you? You deprived me of the first five years of my child's life. You put another man in my place, allowed him to see her first smile, watch her take her first steps, hear her first words. If you think that doesn't hurt, then you've as much sensitivity as the sand you're sitting on!' He sprang to his feet. Over six feet of male pride, battling anguish. 'So don't bleat to me about hurt feelings, Claudia. Just ask yourself if I should care if I make you suffer now!'

CHAPTER FIVE

His words, and the controlled passion with which they'd been delivered, shook her soul. After his calculated, callous treatment of her six years ago, she wouldn't have believed him capable of such deep feelings.

Incapable of speech or movement, Claudia sat in the sand and watched him join his daughter, saw him take the little hand, hold it tightly as he joined her enthusiastic splashing. He looked relaxed, grinning from ear to ear. He looked like the man she had fallen in love with a long time ago. It made her heart ache.

What would it be like to discover you had a five-year-old daughter, right out of the blue?

Putting herself reluctantly into his place—yet somehow compelled to do so—she knew she would hate it, be deeply resentful of all the lost years, all the small landmarks in the child's development that could never be repeated. She would hate the person who had kept her child's existence from her.

Guilt swamped her. She could understand now why he looked at her as if he loathed the very sight of her. The hot tide of remorse swept relentlessly over her body, making her cringe. She didn't want to feel this way, to sympathise with him. She wanted to despise him for the man he was, keep reminding herself of his betrayal because that was the only way she could feel safe from her body's instinctive response to him.

Then, through a haze of sudden, unstoppable tears, she saw Adam lift Rosie in his arms, swinging the happily squealing little girl high in the air before carrying her back to where she still sat.

Almost sick with emotion, Claudia watched him delve into the old duffel bag she'd carried down, extracting a towel and the obligatory change of clothing as if fatherhood were long-standing and not a totally new and shattering development.

'Let's get you dry and comfy.' He seemed totally at ease, removing the sodden garments and gently towelling the squirming little body, helping her into a blue and white checked blouse and cotton dungarees. 'If Mummy agrees, would you both like to come for a drive this afternoon? We could find a McDonald's for tea.'

'Yeah!' Rosie's face was ecstatic as she plopped down in the sand and stuffed her dry feet back into her trainers. 'Can we, Mummy? Say yes!'

Claudia couldn't think of anything she'd like less. But she nodded; she had no option but to agree; refusing to go along with his plans would only make life more difficult for her than it already was.

Yet there was a small spark of hope. After what she had to say to him he would probably get in his powerful car and drive away at the speed of light.

Rosie gave a delighted peal of laughter as Adam rolled up the bottoms of his soaked jeans and grimaced at his sodden canvas shoes. He grinned right back at her and Claudia closed her eyes, shutting them out.

Adam and his new-found daughter were getting along famously and their likenesses—their colouring and that spectacular, heart-tugging grin in particular—were painful. Suddenly she craved to reach out and touch him, tell him she was sorry, beg him to forgive the unforgivable.

The need was so strong it horrified her.

It gave her the impetus to get to her feet, hoist the duffel bag over one shoulder, grab the hamper with her other hand and set off for the track back up through the valley. She didn't need his forgiveness. He had nothing to forgive.

She hadn't known she was pregnant when he'd hunted her down six years ago and told her he was leaving Farthings Hall. She'd only known, at that stage, that her heart was breaking. She hadn't bothered to wait to hear what kind of excuse he would make for his rapid departure. She'd known why he was leaving. Helen had thrown him off the property.

So she'd just shrugged and told him, 'Good. It makes it easier. I've started seeing someone else. Someone with a proper job and money in the bank.'

There hadn't been anyone else, of course, and his obvious lack of financial security, his lack of a settled job, hadn't mattered to her.

But it had been a way of getting her own back, hiding the raw hurt that had frozen her heart, made her voice come out as if rimed with frost, her face stiff, uninterested.

She'd stalked away then before she could disgrace

herself by bursting into tears, pain racking her, remembering how she'd seen him emerge from Helen's bedroom, so angry he hadn't even seen her—angry because, for all his charm and sex appeal, he hadn't been able to get to first base with the sizzling blonde. He had probably never suffered rejection before. Remembering, too, what Helen had said to her.

'Let me take the hamper.' Adam had caught up with her, cutting into her backward-looking thoughts. He was carrying Rosie, the little arms clasped tightly around his neck, her dark head resting in the angle of his shoulder. Practically asleep.

'I can manage. It's not heavy.' Resentment made her voice sharp. How dared he form such an immediate bond with her daughter? She was the one who had carried the child for nine long months, who had crawled bleary-eyed out of bed twice a night to feed her for goodness knew how long, who had walked the floor with her night after night while she was teething, who had cared for her, loved her, put her needs before anything else. And he had just waltzed in and Rosie was his adoring slave!

She huffed and stamped on. Remorse? Forget it! By being the slimeball he was, he had effectively deprived himself of his child. And she'd do well to remember it and stop torturing herself with unnecessary guilt. By the time she'd discovered she was expecting Rosie, he'd been gone for at least two weeks. She'd had no idea how to find him, even if she'd wanted to. Which she hadn't.

With hindsight, of course, she should never have married Tony. But six years ago, frightened by her father's illness, by the possible effect the news of her pregnancy might have on him, it had seemed the sensible thing to do. She'd been too young and inexperienced to handle the problem on her own.

'Do you really want to break a leg?' His voice, hateful with dry amusement, made her grit her teeth as she stumbled over a root of one of the stunted blackthorn bushes that crowded the path near the top of the track.

It gave her the opportunity to catch her breath, give him a withering look. Rosie, she noted with what she recognised as petulance and instinctively deplored, had fallen trustingly asleep, cradled in the arms of the man she hadn't known existed a short time ago, as if, on some deep subconscious level, she knew and accepted the bond of blood between them.

But at least it gave her the opportunity to give him the shock he so richly deserved. So far he had called all the shots; she needed him to know that she had some ammunition of her own, that she could hit him where it would hurt the most. In his pocket. Money had been his motivation before; nothing would have changed.

Then, while he was still reeling, she could put her counter-proposal to him—and hopefully come away with what she wanted.

'We need to talk, Adam.' She was composed now. Her coolness in view of the tangled and contradictory muddle of her recent thoughts surprised her. She watched one sable brow tilt ever so slightly upwards.

'Need we?' Boredom etched lines on either side of his mouth. 'I imagined it had all been said.'

Claudia snatched at her slipping composure. 'Then your imagination is sorely lacking. And, hazy as my recollection is, I don't recall your being this arrogant before.'

His eyes hardened. 'I have never been in this situation before. And don't push your luck. If you have only hazy memories of what happened between us—the seeming intensity of it all—then that suggests a degree of promiscuity that is mind-boggling. Add that to the way you gave me the push when sated, the reason you gave, and I have one more detail to hand the courts should you be foolish enough to risk going down that route.'

He strode past her to the head of the track and she stumbled after him. How could she hope to deal with someone this tricky? A man who could twist every single thing to his own advantage?

'There's a seat beneath the pines.' He was waiting for her at the kissing gate at the head of the track out of the valley. 'If you have something to say, you can say it there.'

She nodded, accepting. He had forgotten nothing about the property. The cedar bench placed beneath the stand of Monterey pines her grandfather had planted had been put there because it gave a panoramic view for guests to sit and admire in peace. He had made comprehensive mental notes of everything about the impressive property when he'd been helping Old Ron keep the grounds in order, no doubt working out how much everything was worth!

He sat, settling Rosie more comfortably on his lap, tenderly brushing a curling strand of midnight-dark hair away from her brow. 'Well?' His voice was low, not wanting to disturb the sleeping child, but he couldn't hide the bite of impatience. He was having to put up with the mother of his child because she was part of the package. But he didn't have to like it.

He was formidable. Before, when she'd loved him, she had never felt intimidated. They'd been equals, totally at ease with each other, almost able to read each other's thoughts. At one, or so she had stupidly believed, in every way possible.

Now those smoky eyes were quelling; the set of his sexy mouth, far from inviting her kisses, was inviting her to beware. She shifted on the bench, wondering if it would be easier to go along with him, let him have everything his own way.

Unconsciously, she shook her head at the weakness of that thought, lowering it, not wanting to see the naked dislike in his eyes. And he reiterated, 'Well? Second thoughts?'

Claudia pulled in a breath, lifted her head and hooked her hair behind her ears. She surely wasn't that weak! Over the years she'd taken a whole load of burdens on her slender shoulders and had prided herself on being able to cope. She wasn't going to let Adam Weston, of all people, turn her into a spineless wimp!

'Not at all.' She glared at him. She could make her eyes just as cold as his. At least, she hoped she could. 'I think you should know, before you make yourself legally responsible for my debts, just how enormous they are.' She named the sum the bank manager had given her; it still had the power to horrify her, make her blood run cold. It would surely give Adam Weston pause for some considerable thought; she knew, only too well, how mercenary he was. 'Add that to the alterations and refurbishments you so rashly promised and you're looking at a king's ransom.'

She watched him closely, waiting for the flinch. It didn't come. Not a flicker of an eyelash to alter his expression.

'So we add mismanagement, reckless extravagance and a complete lack of anything approaching business acumen to your sins.'

Her mouth dropped open, not because of his unjust castigation but because he wasn't already half a mile away, his feet flying, barely touching the ground.

'Well? Is that it? Or do you have anything else to confess before, as you put it, I make myself legally responsible?'

'Yes—' He was going to walk away, carry Rosie back to the house, no doubt to be met by her father who would be wearing that heart-breaking, happy-as-Larry look on his face. 'There's no need for you to take that debt on. What would you gain?' she gabbled, thankfully holding his interest again. 'Rosie, of course, but we don't need to go to the length of getting married! If the Hallam Group bought the property as a going concern, there would be enough left over—just—for me to buy something modest. And if—' She ran her tongue nervously over her lips. She could make concessions, swallow her pride. 'If you were to pay a reasonable amount of maintenance, I needn't get a full-time job. Just a part-time one to keep us going. And you could see Rosie whenever you wanted—I promise I wouldn't make difficulties.'

She could square it with her father. Nothing would have changed; the task of breaking the news about the debts would still be hers, but she'd been getting ready to do that, anyway. She would just need to tell him that she and Adam had had second thoughts about marrying.

But she would have to tell him that Adam was Rosie's real father. How else would she explain his frequent visits, the maintenance payments?

Was she being incredibly selfish in trying to wriggle out of marriage? Couldn't she keep the fatal attraction he had for her in check for the greater good of those she loved best?

She groaned. Adam smiled thinly, as if recognising her mental capitulation. 'Time to go. The marriage stands. Whatever your debts, it's a small price to pay for my daughter's well-being.' He stood up, holding the child as if he would never let her go. 'And remember this. I will expect you, at all times, to behave as if we are a contented couple. Ecstatic is too much to expect. But I demand an appearance of contentment. To all outward appearances, our marriage will work. Not for my sake, or yours. But for my daughter's.' He began to walk away, tossing over his shoulder, 'I want your father to know that Rosie's my child. Will you tell him, or shall I?'

In the event, neither of them had had to, Claudia thought as the Jaguar pulled smoothly away from the gravelled sweep in front of Farthings Hall three weeks later. She twisted round in her seat to catch a last glimpse of Guy and Rosie, waving and blowing kisses in the small cluster of guests who had attended the quiet wedding reception.

At the end of that day, the first full day Adam had spent with his daughter, after he'd finally left, Guy had said quietly, 'Adam's her father, isn't he?'

'He told you, then?' Claudia, clearing the supper things, had swallowed convulsively and her father had shaken his head decisively.

'No. He hasn't said anything; he didn't need to. I think I always knew. What I didn't know was whether Tony knew. Whether he found out and that was the cause of the erosion of your marriage.'

She'd pulled a chair away from the supper table and sat, doing her best to look relaxed. 'Tony knew, before he proposed to me. He wanted a family, he said, but he couldn't father a child. It seemed the best thing to do at the time. I had no idea how to contact Adam—there'd been a misunderstanding...'

She'd let her voice tail away. No way could she let him suspect that her coming marriage to Rosie's real father was nothing like it seemed.

He'd given her a level look. 'I've got enough confidence in the two of you to know you'll make your marriage work. There might be difficulties—it can't be easy for Adam to come to terms with the fact that Tony was around for the first five years of Rosie's life, and he wasn't. But you'll overcome them. I always felt you were made for each other—you were practically inseparable that summer. It was a joy to see.'

Coming at the end of a traumatic day when she'd finally accepted that there was no way she could wriggle out of Adam's plans for their future, Guy's knowledge of his granddaughter's true parentage, his acceptance of it, had come as a huge relief. It was one less thing to worry about. All she had to do now was prevent him finding out that Adam hated her...

Now the Hall slipped out of sight and they were deep in leafy lanes. Claudia turned back in her seat and sighed and Adam said, 'They'll be fine, both of them. Amy will see to that.'

Startled by the first hint of warmth or understanding in his voice, Claudia glanced at her husband of less than three hours. He had changed out of the formal dark grey suit he'd worn for the civil ceremony in Plymouth and now looked too gorgeous for his own good in a stone-coloured cashmere sweater which accentuated the olive tones of his skin, the soft darkness of his hair, and thigh-hugging black jeans which did nothing to disguise those narrow hips and endless legs.

She looked quickly away, hating the way her breath caught in her lungs whenever she looked at him, her voice edgy as she stated, 'I didn't want this. It's a farce,' her voice going thick and husky as she tacked on, 'I've never been separated from Rosie before, not even for a night. And I worry over Dad.'

Staring deliberately ahead, she avoided his sideways glance, biting her lip as he said smoothly, 'There's no need. Guy sailed through his last checkup and provided he takes things easily—and Amy will see that he does—he'll be fine. And as for Rosie—'

his voice softened as it always did when he discussed his daughter '—she and I had a long talk. She fully understands that honeymoons follow weddings. Besides, I promised to bring her a present back. She asked for a Thomas the Tank Engine train set. Isn't she into dolls?'

He sounded fondly amused and Claudia could have hit him. She wanted to be back home, with her family, not here with him, headed for a London honeymoon at the start of a marriage that was no marriage at all and which was already showing signs of being purgatory.

'We know the honeymoon's a farce,' he said, picking up her thoughts as he had often done in the past. 'But it's important that no one else does. It would look odd if we didn't want to snatch a few days alone together.

'So I suggest you stop acting like a petulant child and accept it for what it is—a week away at my London flat. I can spend the time sorting out the mess you made of your finances and you can go shopping. I've opened a current account and a credit account in your name and I've got the cards with me, ready for your signature. I suggest you use them,' he ended dryly.

Claudia felt her face go scarlet. She'd seen the look in his eyes when she'd arrived at the registry office wearing the pink suit she'd worn for her wedding to Tony.

Refusing to spend money she didn't have on a wedding she didn't want, she'd tried to alter it to fit and made a pig's ear of it. So she could understand that fleeting look of distaste, followed immediately by a radiant smile for the benefit of everyone else. He wouldn't want the woman he was supposedly in love with looking as if she'd been dressed by someone from a charity shop with failing eyesight!

Not that he, personally, cared what she looked like. Appearances were all he bothered about. Hadn't he already told her that he was relieved she looked a mess, nothing like the voluptuous young virgin he had so effortlessly seduced? She would be no temptation, none at all. Lust wouldn't complicate their paper marriage.

She hated the way that hurt! It shouldn't; it really shouldn't! But oh, it did.

So she wouldn't think about it. She said quickly, to take her mind off her body's reckless and feckless response to this man, 'Did you remember to give Dad the keys to Willow Cottage?'

'No, I threw them in the Tamar and told him to swim for them!' he answered with dry sarcasm. 'Of course I did! Will you quit worrying? And the larder's fully stocked, the electricity's turned on, and Amy's been ferrying clothes for the lot of them, not to mention Rosie's books and toys, down there for the past two days! Satisfied?'

Feeling a fool, Claudia fiddled with the car radio. Of course she knew that Willow Cottage—fully furnished and conveniently available for rental—was ready for her small family to move into. Hadn't she done most of the packing herself, shopped for the provisions?

Conveniently close to the village primary school,

they would be camping out there whilst alterations were done back at Farthings Hall. She and Adam would be joining the others there after their so-called honeymoon.

Adam had arranged everything. For the three weeks preceding their wedding, he'd booked into the village pub, saying he only needed a telephone, a fax machine and a laptop to keep his finger on the pulse of his business. And when he hadn't been spending time with Rosie—and, because it was unavoidable, her— he had been organising. The wedding, the small reception, the alterations to the kitchen and restaurant and heaven only knew what else.

Deciding he must run on rocket fuel because he showed no sign of strain or tiredness while she looked a complete wreck, she leaned back into the soft, comfortable leather upholstery and pretended to sleep.

And woke when he touched her arm.

They were in a brightly lit underground car park. 'Are we there already?' She felt groggy, disorientated.

He said, 'We'll send out for a meal and then you can turn in. You're obviously exhausted.'

He left her trying to wake up while he took their luggage from the boot. She must have slept for hours, she thought, struggling to drag herself out of her seat. She hoped her mouth hadn't dropped open, that she hadn't snored. Then soundly berated herself for caring and joined him as he led the way to the lift that whisked them up to the penthouse suite at the top of the tower block.

'You have a wonderful view.' She was standing at the huge windows that overlooked the city. It was dusk now, a myriad lights sparkling below them, right up to the horizon, the sky deep indigo running into palest azure.

'I've put your case in your room.' He didn't answer her comment. Her stomach clenched. 'Your room', not ours. That was a huge relief. Or was it?

Frowning, she turned to face the body of the spacious living room. Acres of soft dove-grey carpet, spartan black-lacquered low tables and floating bookshelves, a state-of-the-art sound system, dark leather two-seater sofas.

Very masculine, a little daunting. Like the owner. Who was sitting at the only period piece, an impressive antique desk.

'What would you prefer me to order? French, Italian, Chinese?'

No small talk. No, Would you like to freshen up? Have a drink? Phone Guy and tell him we've arrived safely, talk to Rosie if she's not in bed yet?

But she'd known marriage to this man would be like this. Difficult. Sterile. She longed to answer, Fish and chips and mushy peas, but didn't quite have the nerve. 'Whatever you're having.'

He lifted the receiver and punched numbers. Claudia walked out and found her bedroom. She wasn't going to wait around for him to take notice of her, make conversation.

Her case was at the foot of a low double divan, the burnt umber and cream striped duvet cover matching the curtains. An impersonal room with a small but immaculate *en suite*. Apart from the lack of a mini bar it could have been a hotel room anywhere in the world.

Tears welled in her eyes, and she blinked them furiously away. She was homesick already, missing the people who loved her, marooned here with a husband who despised her and didn't mind showing it. But that didn't mean she had to cry like a baby, did it?

She took a tissue from the box on the bedside table and blew her nose ferociously.

He had called all the shots ever since he'd discovered he had a child. He was running her life, but that didn't mean she had no pride. She dredged some up from where it seemed to have gone into hiding, briskly unpacked, and walked out into the main living room when she heard voices.

The delivery boy was just leaving. Adam transferred the huge pizza Margherita onto a china plate and tipped the green salad into a glass bowl then got busy with a knife.

'I thought you'd prefer something simple. Sit down,' he said, handing her a plate.

The portion he'd given her looked, to her appalled eyes, about the size of a football pitch, but she didn't comment. Why give him the opportunity to tell her it was past time she plumped herself up, got rid of her unattractive scrawniness?

Would he find her desirable again if she regained that lost weight, want her in his bed again? The thought came unbidden and she thrust it roughly aside. Her body might crave the magic of his but her heart did not and her mind shied away from the very

. idea. Sex without love was not for her and love had died a very long time ago.

Start as you mean to go on, she told herself, and told him, 'I'll phone Dad as soon as I've eaten. Ask if they've settled in. About a month, you said, before we can move back without falling over builders?' She cut into her pizza, winding the strands of melted mozzarella around her fork. She didn't get it as far as her mouth because she had the distinct feeling it would choke her. 'I suppose you'll be selling this flat now you've decided to make your home at Farthings Hall.'

'Stop trying to make small talk,' he said, his patience thin. 'If you're nervous, don't be. I'm not about to jump on you. You're quite safe. I could say I've been there, done that, and didn't much like the consequences.'

'You mean Rosie!' She could hardly get the words out, she was so appalled. He'd given every impression of doting on his child. Surely he couldn't mean—?

'No, of course not.' He sounded, suddenly, tired. 'How could I have the slightest regret about my beautiful daughter? There were other consequences to our affair, Claudia.'

There were silver shards in his eyes and they pierced her. She had no idea what he was talking about, and would rather he didn't tell her because she knew she wouldn't like it. 'You talk as if I gave you a dose of the clap!' she huffed, and went bright pink and wished to goodness she hadn't said that, but then he did seem to bring out the worst in her.

'There's no need to be crude,' he snapped right back, his mouth hardening, inciting her to retaliate.

'I appear to be learning from you!'

'*Touché!*' Something grimly amused lurked at the back of his eyes. 'So let's start again.' He poured red wine into two glasses. 'Small talk it is. Let's see— yes, you may phone Guy, by all means, and yes, I have offered the builders a fat bonus if they'll be finished and out a month from today, and no, I will not be selling this flat. I can run my business largely on the hoof, and from Farthings Hall, of course, but there will be certain occasions when I shall need the privacy of a place of my own.'

And she could guess what occasions those would be, couldn't she just? As she knew from experience he was one hugely sexy man, an enthusiastic lover. Theirs was to be a marriage in name only; he wouldn't remain celibate.

The upsurge of out-and-out jealousy was a searing, white-hot pain. She felt her face pale with the hurt of it and pushed away from the table, dialled the number of Willow Cottage, spoke to her father and tried to sound as if she wasn't crying inside, then went to bed and wept her heart out.

Although she disliked the man he had been and the man he was now, she still wanted him.

She ached with it, body and soul. She had tried to stop it; ever since he'd exploded back into her life she had recognised the danger and she'd tried to stop it. But she couldn't help it.

The thought of him making love with another woman, touching her the way he'd touched her, sharing all those rapturous and painfully remembered intimacies, drawing from another woman the wild and sensual responses he'd drawn from her, made her want to curl up and die.

She lay in the darkness and prayed she wouldn't fall in love with him all over again.

Somehow she could learn to cope with the wanting, the longing, the endless screaming inner ache. But she couldn't cope with that.

CHAPTER SIX

CLAUDIA left Adam making his breakfast coffee in the small and highly functional kitchen and went shopping. He could do what he liked with his day; she was going to spend his money!

Which was hardly an angelic thing to think. But she didn't care, she thought mutinously as she paid off the taxi driver in Oxford Street. He had made money available and told her to use it, so she would. He thought she looked a wreck and her mirror this morning had told her he was right.

Howling her head off into the small hours hadn't done a thing for her and the neat grey suit, normally worn around her country hotel when she wasn't wearing her chef's hat in the kitchen—teamed with the sturdy flat shoes she'd brought along for trudging round museums and galleries to kill time here in London—hardly made her look like anyone's idea of sex on legs!

She had pulled a disgusted face at her reflection and made up her mind right there and then. She could either mope around in her room all day, be a martyr, proudly refuse to touch a penny of his wretched money—of which he appeared to have come by oodles—or she could stuff her pride, take him at his word and go out and do her damnedest to enjoy herself.

Choosing the latter, she had poked her head into the kitchen, looked anywhere but at him and said, 'Good morning. I'm going out. Expect me when you see me.'

Which could be midnight or beyond. Depending. She might just take herself to a cinema this evening and follow it with a lavish late supper. He had made it quite clear that he had no desire whatsoever for her company, that he really didn't want her around. So she wouldn't be.

She couldn't remember when she'd last been out shopping for herself, and certainly not with a bottomless purse. And, despite beginning with a belligerent attitude, she soon found she was enjoying herself immensely, swooping on things she knew would suit her, flatter her newly slender frame. She floated away from the cosmetics department in Harrods on a cloud of Joy, reflecting that the sales ladies couldn't be more helpful when you pleaded complete ignorance and asked for help. She was dying to experiment with all her new make-up. Normally she was too busy to do more than rub moisturiser into her skin and run a lipstick round her mouth.

A snack lunch followed by a dedicated hunt for shoes and lingerie brought her to six o'clock and the realisation that the cinema was out. She wouldn't be able to see the screen over her exciting mountain of packages and carriers.

Determined to stay out as long as she possibly could without being arrested for loitering, she found a small Spanish restaurant. She ate her way through a sumptuous dish of asparagus and fried potatoes in a spicy sauce, followed by a wicked number of delicious meringues studded with toasted almonds, a few glasses of Rioja and coffee strong enough to lift her scalp.

She hadn't realised she'd been so hungry, couldn't remember whether she'd had three glasses of wine or four but wasn't going to worry about it, and felt decidedly floaty in the back of the taxi taking her home. Not home, though; home was not where Adam was. But she wouldn't think about that. She was looking forward to a fun girl's evening all by herself, trying on her gorgeous new purchases.

The lift to the penthouse suite made her head spin. But whether it was due to the wine or the achievement of spending his money—as he'd as good as ordered—and actually having a fabulous time once she'd got started, she didn't know.

He was in the sitting room, at one of the low tables, surrounded by papers when she wallowed through the door, clutching at slipping packages, getting tangled with dangling carriers. He gave her a dark, underbrow look and she gave him back a courteous 'Good evening', and clumped through to her bedroom, her sensible shoes slapping the floor.

But her heart was thumping heavily, the awful pain that always came when she saw him shafting through her with a vengeance now. But she was going to ignore it, wasn't she? *Wasn't she?*

She was. A shower helped, the warm water washing the stickiness of her busy day away. She wouldn't even contemplate trying on all those delicious new things while she was all hot and sweaty.

Unstoppering the bottle of one of her new, elegant fragrances, she patted it liberally over her pulse points, pausing as she caught sight of her naked body in one of the wall-to-ceiling mirrors.

She had lost a lot of weight recently but she wasn't as gaunt in the flesh as she appeared to be when wearing clothes that were far too big for her. Her shoulders and arms were a touch fragile-looking, her waist tiny and her tummy concave. But her breasts—though nothing like the lush globes that had driven Adam wild when he'd suckled them all that time ago—were pert and rounded, and her hips still held the remnants of that feminine flare that had, so he had told her, blown him away.

Giggling, she slipped into the seriously seductive new scarlet satin wrap she'd brought into the bathroom with her. She was, she admitted, just the tiniest bit intoxicated from the wine that had gone down so well with that Spanish meal. Otherwise she wouldn't be giving her body points out of ten. She hadn't given much, if any, thought to it since—

'Claudia?'

Adam was calling for her. She sailed out of the bathroom on a cloud of perfumed steam, reaching behind her for the sash of her robe to make herself decent. But she should have made sure of that before. She hadn't realised he was actually in her bedroom.

Her fingers fumbled with the sash. Dropped it. The slithery satin robe gaped and she couldn't move. Frozen by something greater than shock, she saw the dull flare of red stroke along the angular line of his cheekbones, saw his eyes darken, narrow, as they flicked over every curve and hollow of her exposed body.

She couldn't hear herself breathing. She didn't think she was. The air was suddenly thick, heavy, clogging her lungs. But she could feel—feel the tense expectancy of her body's instinctive response to him, the pooling of moist heat in her loins, the hardening of her breasts.

Her resistance to him was as non-existent as it had ever been and if he made a move towards her, even the slightest one imaginable, she would fly to his arms and beg him to take her to that wild and wonderful place they had inhabited so long ago.

But he said brutally, 'Cover yourself.'

So she did, the shock of his harsh words bringing her to her senses, watching him turn away while she fumbled to wrap the satin around her body, tying the sash so tightly she felt as if she was cutting herself in two. His shoulders were high and hard and rigid. His voice, as he walked to the door and finally turned to look at her again, was cold.

'I wanted to ask if you'd like to eat out tonight, or whether you'd prefer me to order in again.' A muscle flickered involuntarily at the side of his tough jaw, his mouth going tight.

'I've already eaten.' How sullen she sounded, she thought miserably. Frustration, she supposed, and her own despicable inability to control her body's desires where this man was concerned.

She had never thought of herself as being a lustful person before. When she and Adam had made love so rapturously six years ago she had been deeply in love with him. She hated to think she could desire a man without loving him. It made her feel cheap.

'Fine,' he clipped. 'Then you won't object if I go out. And, if you're interested, your father phoned around six. Rosie wanted to speak to you but you were out, so I filled the gap.'

So he wanted to make her feel guilty, did he? On top of everything else—like haggard, a spendthrift, a cheat and a liar.

Well, he'd failed. At least the shock of what had just happened had sobered her up completely. She glanced at her watch. A quarter to eight. Saturday tomorrow, no school, so Rosie might still be up.

She sailed into the sitting room and punched in the numbers with machine-gun rapidity and caught Rosie as she was on her way up to bed.

'I've had my bath and my hot milk and said my prayers with Grandpa, before I get into bed. I am being good. I am!' the little girl said when Amy passed her the receiver.

She sounded so pious that Claudia's maternal instincts went on red alert. This wasn't like her normal, bouncy, unsquashable daughter! She could just imagine those big grey eyes going huge and solemn and water-clear as they always did if she was upset or unsure about something. Imagine the droop of the rosebud mouth…

'How do you like the cottage?' she asked brightly, wondering if there was some problem there. Though she had racketed around like a hyperactive flying missile on the two occasions she had taken her with her when stocking the larder and deep freeze, opening every door and drawer, diving into cupboards, excited by the prospect of moving house, if only temporarily.

'It's all right,' Rosie answered after a significant pause and much heavy breathing. 'It would be nicer if you were here. When are you coming home?'

'Soon, darling. I miss you very much too.' She glanced across at Adam who was standing in the centre of the room, his hands stuffed into the pockets of his jeans, intent on what he could hear of the one-sided conversation, her eyes daring him to say one word as she added cheerfully, 'In fact, I miss you so much that I've decided to come home much sooner than I thought I would.'

And just you try to stop me! she fulminated when she finally put the receiver down. Aloud she said, 'Rosie's unhappy. She's missing me. I'm going home tomorrow. By train, if necessary.'

'Rosie's fine,' he said grimly. 'She's not too young to learn she can't have what she wants all the time. She's got Guy and Amy and, besides, what would they think if you travelled back alone tomorrow? That the marriage was falling apart before it had started.'

Claudia put her hands on her hips. She could not believe this! The way he'd been behaving ever since he'd discovered he had a daughter, she would have staked her life on his putting her welfare before any other consideration!

'You'd put appearances before Rosie's happiness? Good grief—she's only a child!' Bright colour stained her cheeks, heightening the intense blue of her eyes. Adam held her disgusted glare with cool grey disdain.

'I would put nothing before our daughter's well-being, as you very well know. You caught her at the wrong moment, on her way to bed, probably over-tired.'

Her glare flickered. There was probably something in that. When she'd spoken to Amy, before she'd handed her over to Rosie, Amy had told her of the schoolfriend's birthday party the little girl had attended that afternoon. There'd been a bouncy castle and lots of wild games and Rosie had come home grossly over-excited, and then got a fit of the grumps.

'And what about Guy's peace of mind?' Adam put in smoothly. 'If we cut our honeymoon short, or if you arrive home alone tomorrow, he's going to worry about the state of our marriage. Do you want that? An outward appearance of contentment was one of the conditions, remember?'

He knew she didn't want to cause her father any anxiety; that was the hold, or one of them, he had over her! She shook her head numbly. She had only agreed to this purgatorial marriage for the sake of her father's and her child's future well-being and happi-ness.

'Then that's settled.'

The blue glare was back in full force. 'I suppose you think you've cornered the market on "condi-tions"! I'm not a total doormat, Adam. You make conditions; you lay down the law. You get a child, and a mother for that child, and your freedom.' She was thinking of his freedom to use this flat for a string of extra-marital affairs and her temper was running out of control. Part of her deplored it, but she could do nothing to stop it. 'And what do I get? A husband who openly despises me—a tyrant—a husband who probably wouldn't blink an eye if I fell under a bus!'

'You get your debts paid,' he reminded her coldly. 'You get a decent roof over your head and a life of luxury—which is more than you deserve, given your predilection for overspending. And while we're on the subject of your debts, which, my dear, I have already discharged, there's something I'd like you to clear up for me.'

Predilection for overspending! Was he talking about the amount of shopping she'd done today? Well, he'd told her to, hadn't he? Was he the sort of man who said one thing and meant the opposite?

Of course he was. If the way he'd declared passionate, never-dying love for her, while eyeing up her prospects and trying to get between the sheets with her stepmother was anything to go on!

'I'm going to bed,' she said tightly. Whatever he wanted to 'clear up' could wait. She swung round, her head high, sweeping out, but he caught her arm in steely fingers and jerked her back.

'Sit down, Claudia. I want to talk to you.'

'And I don't want to talk to you!' she snapped back, trying to slap his obdurate fingers away. Which was a mistake because he only tightened his grip and hauled her closer. And that started the hurt up again, deep inside her.

He pulled in his breath; his teeth clamped together. He looked as if he wanted to shake her and was fighting a battle with himself. But when he finally spoke he sounded reasonable.

'Claudia, I know how much you resent me, what

you feel about me, but do you think we might try to act like rational, adult human beings instead of fighting a verbal World War Three? Politeness doesn't cost a thing and it oils the wheels.'

He had no idea how she felt about him! How she only had to see him to feel this wicked, wanton wanting start up inside her. It was sending her crazy with contempt for herself. But he was right about one thing. Politeness cost nothing.

She had matured out of recognition since Rosie's birth, had learned to cope with the bitter grief of Adam's betrayal, with the way her marriage had turned out, with the increasingly heavy burden of responsibility she'd found herself carrying for the hotel and restaurant. She had even managed to handle the trauma of the last two months with dignity and a gritty determination to try her utmost to limit the damage Tony and Helen had done to their lives.

Meeting him again, finding herself actually having to agree to this marriage, had turned her back into a hysterical, petulant child. One way or another, he had always had a catastrophic effect on her. It was time it stopped.

'What do you want to talk about?' She would show him she could be reasonable, too, a rational human being, just like he'd said.

'Let's sit down.'

Rationally, she could make no objection to that. Holding onto her composure as best she could, she allowed him to lead her to the leather sofa in front of the paper-strewn table.

Thankfully, he let go of her arm and she could

breathe more easily. She sat right at the far end, pulling the edges of the short satin robe firmly across her knees. He, she noted, sat much closer to the centre. As he leaned forward to sheaf some of the papers together, the soft fabric of his T-shirt stretched across the taut muscles of his back and she swallowed convulsively as something hard and hot tightened in her throat.

She clenched her hands savagely together in her lap to stop them taking independent life and reaching out to touch, to stroke. Then he straightened up, turned, his body angled towards her, and handed her some of the papers, one by one.

They were old bank statements, she realised sickly, making herself reach out, even though seeing them again was the very last thing she wanted, praying her robe wouldn't gape at the neck, or anywhere else, for that matter.

'Move closer. I won't bite.' The faint thread of amusement in his voice amazed and distracted her. If he was going to be only halfway nice to her, she would be lost. Her stupid heart would grab at any sign of softening in him, grabbing at the mistaken belief that things could once again be as they were.

Rational human being, she muttered to herself, like a mantra, inside her head. And edged, with great circumspection, close enough for them to look at the statements together.

He had ringed the statements in various places. The sizeable mortgages she and Tony had raised for the necessary refurbishments and the addition of a huge

Edwardian-style conservatory. Neither the refurbishments nor the conservatory had ever materialised.

Weeks later, the entire sum had been withdrawn. Adam had ringed that, too. And various other large sums had been withdrawn over the ensuing days, right up to their normal overdraft limit.

Claudia's hand shook. She felt ill, as dreadful as she'd felt when the bank manager had called her into his office.

'What happened to the money? What did you do with it?'

His voice sounded a long way away. She couldn't answer; she felt sick with shame. She shook her head speechlessly, but he persisted.

'I've repaid the bank and settled your debts. Don't you think I have a right to know?'

Of course he did. And why did he have to sound so reasonable? If he'd yelled at her, she could have responded in kind, told him to get lost.

She blinked the mist from her eyes, sounding strangled as she told him, 'It's—it's a long story.'

'We've got all night,' he countered, dry as dust.

'You were going out.' She seized on that. He hadn't yet eaten. He'd be hungry.

'I've changed my mind.'

She swallowed the hot constriction in her throat and squeezed her eyes shut to stop herself from crying. He was going to make her go over the whole thing and it made her feel desperate. She felt him move then heard the chink of glass on glass. 'Drink this. It might help.'

Brandy. She recognised the smell of it as he put

the glass in her hand, closing her fingers around it with slight but insistent pressure.

A huge slug. Another for himself. He sat again, angling himself into the corner of the sofa, long legs stretched out, smoky eyes intent. The same look he'd given her when he'd asked her to tell him about herself, everything, all those years ago, while never discussing his own background, where he had come from, what he intended to do with his life. It hadn't seemed to matter, not then. She supposed it didn't matter now—this need he seemed to have to dissect her, force her to bare her soul.

Brandy on top of the wine she'd had earlier would probably make her tipsy all over again. But she took a healthy sip anyway because that didn't seem to matter, either.

It helped, just a little. 'After I married Tony—after Dad's first heart attack, he—Dad, that is—put the property, the business, everything in my name. He thought it was the sensible thing to do.' She winced. It hadn't been sensible at all; in view of what had happened it had been the stupidest idea he'd ever had.

She sipped again, her teeth chattering against the glass.

'And?' Adam prompted. 'That must have been years ago. From what I've found out, going through the paperwork, the business appeared to go from strength to strength.'

'Oh, it did.' A tidal wave of bitterness made it easier and now the words came tumbling out. 'Helen and Tony had seen to that! And I helped, of course, sucker that I was! We all worked our socks off to begin with.

Profits were up; business was booming. I failed to see it was all being done on a shoestring. I was so busy getting through my working day, trying to rub along with Tony, care for Rosie and make sure Dad didn't overtax himself. And then he had another attack and I got even more blinkered to what was going on, if that was possible!'

She blamed herself for what had happened. If only she'd had her wits about her, they would never have got away with it. And she wouldn't be in this position now, beholden to a man who despised her.

'So what was going on?' Adam's arm was resting on the back of the sofa. If she leaned back he would be touching her, she thought frantically, feeling trapped, yet somehow relieved to be getting all of this out of her system, accepting the blame because it had to be hers.

'After our marriage—' she took a deep breath '—Tony decided to give up his accountancy business; it was only a one-man band, but he appeared to be doing well.'

'So I remember you telling me. ''Someone with a proper job and money in the bank'',' he drawled, and Claudia shot him a sharp-eyed look.

He had never been in love with her and only his prospects, through her, had been hurt, so why should he remember what she'd said in such detail? She didn't ask. It would be safer not to open that particular can of worms.

'He offered to take Dad's place in the business— look after the financial side of things. He had been Dad's accountant for some years. That was another idea I thought was bright at the time. It allowed Dad to sit back and freed me up to look after Rosie and the domestic side of the business and Helen did Tony's secretarial work, among other things.'

She didn't give him the opportunity to enquire what other things. She told him. 'They'd been lovers for years, and quite without scruples. Why should they care if they each married other partners? They could always insist on separate bedrooms and get together at every opportunity, and milk the business for all it was worth. Staff were fired, leaving double the work for those who were left so nothing was done properly. Nothing was replaced—bed-linen, china, that sort of thing. The property needed money spending on it, which was why we applied for that mortgage. He'd even laid the smokescreen of getting several sets of detailed estimates. We got it, the mortgage, and that was when they made their move.

'Everything was withdrawn, leaving masses of un-paid bills, not to mention the outstanding mortgage, which I had no means of repaying. God knows where they put the money—into some overseas account in a fictitious name, probably. They were leaving together when they were killed. We only found out about their long-standing affair when Dad was going through Helen's things after the funeral. And I knew nothing about the financial mess until the bank manager called me in.' She twisted her hands together in anguish. 'They took everything and left us damn near bankrupt and I was too stupid to see what was going on.'

Adam swore harshly under his breath and Claudia flinched. She guessed she deserved that, so she'd just have to take it. He already despised her, thought she was deeply unattractive, capable of ditching a man if a more financially secure one happened her way, so what did it matter if he added gross stupidity to the lengthy list of her other sins? She could take it because she knew she deserved it.

'Not too stupid. Too trusting.'

That did it. A few totally unexpected and undeserved words of comfort and she went to pieces. The glass shook in her hand, scattering droplets of brandy on her lovely new robe. Adam took the glass from her before she dropped it and her freed fingers shot up to cover her eyes. But that didn't stop the tears from falling, positively gushing, and he noticed; of course he did. How could he not?

'You mustn't blame yourself, Clo, you really mustn't.'

So soft was his vocal penetration of her frantic misery and the feeling of criminal failure that had haunted her ever since she'd learned what had happened. The softness and his probably unthinking use of the pet name he'd had for her once upon a time was a different type of torture.

'But I do!' she wailed thinly, scrubbing her eyes with her fingers as if that would stop the tears. 'I let them steal everything Dad ever worked for. I was too bound up in what I was doing to even think to ask to see the books and demand to know why he was letting bills mount up. I never asked why he was systematically getting rid of key personnel—always promising to replace them but never getting round to it. He was cutting corners, saving on wages, refusing to pay bills so that our joint business account would be as stuffed full as he could get it before they stole everything! It was my fault we lost everything!'

She bit her lip to stop herself from wailing. She sounded like a cat with its tail shut in a door. She could just imagine the look of distaste on his face!

What she would never have imagined in a million years was the gentle touch of his hand as he took her hands away from her face, the strength of conviction in his voice as he demanded, 'Look at me, Clo.'

She did, with supreme reluctance. She was still shaking with emotion and any minute now her teeth would start chattering again. And he looked so gorgeous, the smoky eyes intent yet compassionate, a compassion that was echoed in the softening of his sexy mouth. And if he'd thought she'd looked a wreck before, then after that crying jag she would be looking a million times worse. She hated him seeing her like this—a hysterical wreck!

It was unbearable! An enormous sob built up inside her. A prelude to yet another wailing session—she knew it was! And, as if he could see her struggle to contain it, he did the unthinkable and folded his arms around her.

Her heart stopped beating and then raced on, making her whole body shake with internal clamour. Did he know what he was doing? Did he really care? Impossible, surely. He patted her back with the sort of wary restraint she would expect to see in someone who was patting a strange dog for the first time, but at least he wasn't coldly telling her to pull herself together.

'It would appear to me that you had far too many burdens to carry. After all, you were still only in your teens when you had Rosie.'

With her head resting against his chest, she could hear the steady beat of his heart, feel the warmth of his strong body. It did crazy things to her, making her want to wriggle closer, wind her arms around his neck, pull his head down to kiss her.

But he would hate that, she reminded herself sadly, and to take her mind off what she wanted she said, a touch tartly, 'I grew up fast.'

'I guess you had to.' Was that grudging admiration in his voice? Oh, surely not. She was off her head even to imagine such a thing.

She had to remember, at all times—even at times like this when he had put his loathing of her momentarily to one side in order to offer comfort—that he neither respected nor admired her and that all he wanted of her was a paper wife who knew her place and stayed in it. And his daughter, of course.

'Clo, listen to me. You were overburdened; your husband took over the financial aspect of the business, which, apparently, he was well qualified to do. Why would you have tried to muscle in on his job when you had more than enough of your own work to do? Why shouldn't you have trusted him? Being a devious louse, he would have been pretty smart when it came to covering up, so there's no earthly reason why you should blame yourself. And you have nothing to worry about now.' He had been holding her, but stiffly. Now the tension left his body and he gathered her closer. 'Your home is safe and your father need never know how close he came to losing it.'

Claudia's head was swimming, her breathing shallow. Her breasts were beginning to peak and strain against his chest in silent invitation. What this man did to her was nothing short of actionable! And there seemed to be no way on earth she could fight it.

She slid her hands up over his body, resting them on his shoulders, and her voice was husky.

'I know. Adam—I appreciate what you've done. I guess I haven't seemed very grateful—but I am.' She inched her hands down, her fingers splayed, until they came to rest just above the place where her breasts were pressed against his body. She ached for him to touch them, to take the aroused tips into the hot moisture of his mouth and suckle her. The remembered sensations were sending her wild.

She wriggled her hips, moving closer, and his heart was beating faster now; she could feel it beneath her fingers. Was he remembering too? Remembering the way it had been for them, the sheer magical, ecstatic mystery of it all?

'You don't have to be grateful. I gained as well, remember?' His voice sounded thick, as if he too was breathing too shallowly, too fast. He lowered his head until it was a hair's breadth away from hers as his hands began to slide over her, from the nape of her neck to the flare of her hips and slowly back again, stroking her through the slinky, slithery satin. 'I've been too hard on you in that respect. I didn't know why the business had got in such a mess.' With every word he said his voice was growing more slurred, and it wasn't because of the brandy—he'd barely touched it. 'They gave you a hell of a rough ride between them—that louse of a husband and that bitch Helen.'

Hearing that woman's name on his lips should have brought her to her senses. But it didn't. Nothing could now. Her need for him was as uninhibited, as eager and hedonistic as it had been when she'd first catapulted into love.

She only had to move her head a fraction and their lips would be touching, and then everything would be as it had been before: the hunger of his mouth on hers; the sheer ecstasy of every exploratory caress; the desire that was never sated no matter how many times their eager bodies were joined in the wild music of love; the fact that it just got better every time. The temptation was too great, too much to handle. Her lips parted…

He put her away from him with hands that were suddenly hard and impersonal. He stood up awkwardly and went to the drinks tray, pouring himself another brandy, which he downed in one long swallow.

Claudia didn't know where she was. Everything had got turned on its head. She watched his back with huge, unblinking eyes, feeling the heat of desire drain away, leaving her cold.

She shivered. She had been so sure he had felt it, too. All the old magic. She had believed for a few moments that it had all come back. But how could it come back when it had never been there in the first place? Not for him.

She had made such a fool of herself and she was

still shivering when he eventually turned back to her, fresh brandy in his glass. And of course he hadn't been moved, or only by a slight feeling of remorse, because his voice was back to normal, even slightly more clipped than it usually was.

'I think you were right. If Rosie's missing you then we should go back. Tomorrow. I'll come up with something to make our early return seem reasonable. I'll dive out first thing while you pack and pick up a gift to take back for her, so if I'm not around when you get up you'll know where I am.' He lowered his eyes under the intense blue of her stare. For the first time in her life she saw him at what appeared to be a disadvantage.

Embarrassed? Embarrassed by the quivering expectancy he'd felt as he'd touched her? He'd only meant to be kind, to reassure her, and she'd practically sizzled with banked-down desires all ready to explode in his face. So he'd backed off. She could hardly blame him.

She felt ridiculous. She had humiliated herself. He said calmly, 'Why don't you go to bed? We've a long drive in the morning.'

She stood up, clutching at her robe, wishing she were wearing anything but this seductive thing. Should she apologise for clinging to him the way she had, put it down to being over-emotional because of what he'd made her tell him? She licked her lips and he said, harshly now, 'For goodness' sake, Claudia. Go to bed.'

CHAPTER SEVEN

'MUMMY! Daddy!' Rosie came flying down the path to greet them, arriving at the garden gate before Adam had turned off the ignition.

Claudia's heart jerked. Oh, how she had missed this small scrap of exuberance—and how naturally she had taken to calling Adam 'Daddy'! She had only been invited to, and only if she wanted to, at the small reception after their low-key wedding.

She was wearing a chunky pink sweater and a diminutive pair of red cords. She'd been playing in the garden, and the now chilly autumn air had brought a rosy glow to her cheeks, an extra sparkle to her huge grey eyes. She was doing her best to climb over the garden gate and Claudia scrambled out of the car and over the pavement to open the gate and scoop her tiny daughter up in her arms.

'Is anything wrong?' Guy, looking bewildered, asked from the doorstep, drawn out, no doubt, to investigate Rosie's delighted shrieks. 'I thought you were staying away for a week.'

'Nothing's wrong.' Adam joined Claudia on the path, smiling into his daughter's merry eyes. 'Hello, scrap.' He indicated the package he held under one arm and put the other round Claudia's shoulders. 'We've got something for you; we remembered our promise!' Then, smiling at Guy, he said, 'Unfortu-

132

nately, something cropped up. Something my PA believes only I can handle. But I'll make it up to you, Clo; you know I will.'

The warmly intimate look he turned on her took her breath away. But that, and the slow, heart-stopping smile, was for her father's benefit. As was the lie that came tripping so easily off his tongue. For his peace of mind Guy had to continue to believe that this was a marriage made in heaven, that his beloved only child had found real happiness at last.

Rosie slithered out of her arms, intent on getting her hands on the promised gift, and Adam said, grinning, 'Back in the house, scrap. You can open your present inside,' and followed the scampering feet, leaving Claudia to trudge behind.

The journey from London had been largely silent except when they'd stopped at one of the motorway service areas for lunch. Then they'd made small talk, but she'd still felt embarrassed over her behaviour of the evening before and he'd seemed lost in his own thoughts.

She still had no clear idea why he'd abruptly changed his mind about returning today. Perhaps he'd repented of his out-of-hand dismissal of her statement that Rosie was missing her mum.

In view of his kindness, the way he'd reassured her that the financial mess she'd been in had been none of her making, she could almost believe so. His heart was in the right place, sometimes. Certainly where his daughter was concerned. A smile curved her soft lips as she watched Rosie tug at her new daddy's hand, urging him over the doorstep to Willow Cottage.

Guy, walking at her side, said, 'Amy's down at the village shop, but I can rustle something up if you're hungry.'

'We stopped on the way, Dad.' She tucked her hand through his arm as they walked into the tiny hall together. There was no sign of Adam or Rosie but she could hear them through the closed sitting-room door, the little girl's excited babblings and Adam's deeper voice, warm with affection. 'But a cup of tea would be nice. I'll make it, though. How have you been?'

'Absolutely fine,' he assured her, giving the hand that rested on his arm a comforting pat. 'I haven't felt this relaxed in years. It's a relief not to have to consider the business. And I never thought I'd hear myself saying this, but after all those years of having other people—strangers most of 'em—in our home and paying for the privilege it will be nice to have it just to ourselves, enjoy Farthings Hall as a proper home. Which, of course, is all down to that husband of yours.'

Her heart plummeted. Did he know that they had almost lost everything? How could he know? If he did know, then he had weathered the shock far better than she could have expected.

But, 'He made sure the builders don't hang about! I drove up this morning and they're certainly shifting. I suppose they're glad of the overtime. Said they'd be working tomorrow, too. It would have felt a bit funny living there with the kitchens as they were, and a restaurant full of empty tables!'

So that was what he'd meant. Claudia gave a tiny sigh of relief. She would hate for her father ever to have to face the full truth of Helen's cruelty, face the final truth of his dead wife's complete lack of caring or concern, the way she'd been happy to leave him bankrupt, thrown out of his home with no place to go but down.

'It's a pity about having to cut short your honeymoon,' Guy said, apparently content to stay out in the hallway, chatting for hours. But, Claudia realised, he probably wanted her assurance that everything was fine, that the so-called honeymoon hadn't turned out to be such a disaster that they'd given up on it so quickly.

She gave it, forcing herself to smile. 'Yes, well, I guess that being married to the chief executive of a booming company does have its occasional downside! We'll probably take off next spring to make up for it—in the Easter holidays, maybe, so we can take Rosie along as well. And Adam and I have the rest of our lives together, don't forget—so it hardly matters if our honeymoon only lasted a couple of days!'

She sounded perky, but her heart ached. The rest of their lives together. Yet miles and miles apart when it came right down to it. She didn't know how she could endure it if this delinquent need for him, this turbulent wanting, didn't lie down, curl up and die. She had to keep reminding herself of what had happened in the past, how he had betrayed her, used her, telling herself she'd done the right thing in cutting him out of her life. If she didn't do that she would humiliate herself by falling in love with him all over again.

Thankfully, Guy appeared to be totally reassured.

He was beaming happily as he said, 'Will you just listen to that child?'

The excited chatter had given way to loud choo-choo noises. 'I'll make that tea,' Claudia said.

When she carried the tray through to the cosy sitting-room, the three of them were on the floor playing with the train set. Adam levered himself up reluctantly, accepting a cup. 'I'll have to go when I've had this. I'll miss you, Clo, but I'll be back just as soon as I can.'

She knew he didn't mean it, the missing her bit, nevertheless it did something to her heart and filled it with an emotion she wasn't up to examining too closely. But she had to go with him to his car; it would have looked odd if she hadn't.

Rosie wanted to go, too, but Guy held her back. 'It's raining, poppet. Stay with Gramps and play with your train set; show me how it works.'

It was, too. A fine, cold drizzle. The glorious Indian summer had gone and winter was round the corner. Winter in her heart, too, as he stood at the nearside of his car, jiggling his keys, silver ice in his eyes, frost in his voice.

'I don't know how long I'll be away. I'll phone you. I'll put some feelers out and see what I can do to trace that embezzled money. Go back inside before you get soaked.'

That was why he'd cut their smokescreen honeymoon short. Money. Not as a concession to her or Rosie's feelings.

Just money. He'd been prepared to shell out an enormous sum in order to get his daughter into his life on a permanent basis. But the prospect of getting it back had him forgetting his daughter and the need to keep up a front of a supposedly happy marriage and haring off into the distance like a pig after truffles.

Over the following days that thought kept coming back to her whenever she had an unoccupied moment. Amy said, 'You're pining for him, aren't you?' and Claudia didn't disabuse her. The woman who had been like a mother to her in many ways knew her too well. Claudia guessed the older woman was fully aware—as her father had been—that Adam was Rosie's real father.

Thankfully, she'd held her tongue on that particular subject. Claudia didn't think she could talk about it without breaking down and revealing her present misery. But she knew it couldn't be too long before Amy's curiosity got the better of her.

'Yes,' she said, gathering up her wits. 'But he said he wouldn't be away for much longer.'

He'd been gone nearly two weeks and every early evening when he made his duty phone call he said, 'Just tell them the problem's more involved than I thought,' and asked to speak to Rosie.

She had left her father reading in the sitting room in front of the fire and had come to the kitchen to get on with the ironing. She'd finished now, and folded up the board, and Amy, popping the pie she'd made for supper into the fridge, offered, 'How about a nice cup of tea? Your dad will be ready for one, if I know him!'

Claudia shook her head as the sudden need to get away from here swamped her. Every day of his absence brought increasing restlessness, an inner agitation that got worse with each passing hour.

'I thought I'd drive up to the Hall and check on the builders' progress.' She needed time alone. She'd check up on the work, of course, so that she could report back, but then she'd give the men a wide berth, find a quiet place and try to talk herself into some kind of acceptance of the way things were and were always going to be, an acceptance of Adam's bleak indifference.

'Would you pick Rosie up from school?' No hardship there, the village primary was so near. 'And give her her tea? I don't know exactly how long I'll be.'

'Of course I will. It's exciting, isn't it? It's going to be really lovely when we move back in. And don't you fret about that husband of yours—he won't spend a moment more than he has to away from you and Rosie!'

Claudia grabbed her padded coat from the utility room and fled.

It wasn't far, just a few miles, and after parking on the gravelled sweep she went to check on Old Ron. He insisted she take a cup of tea with him. She tried not to shudder as the powerful brew went down and couldn't help smiling when he assured her he was keeping an eye on them blighters, just to see they put they's back behind the job and didn't skip no corners!

What the workmen would think of that dour presence, hovering and watching every move they made, didn't bear thinking about. They had her sympathy!

The lightening of her mood was brief. She didn't bother inspecting progress in the former restaurant.

Redesigning the interior, excavating the pool, sorting out the heating and draining systems would take quite a while but the kitchen had been transformed.

The rows of professional hotplates, ovens and burners, the stainless-steel work surfaces and wooden chopping blocks had disappeared. Unglazed terracotta tiles rang sweetly beneath her feet; the shiny bright red Aga Amy had insisted on was already installed and there was a wealth of cupboards and fixed dressers sympathetically created from reclaimed pine.

The atmospheric country kitchen Amy had always dreamed of was coming to life. But what of her own dreams?

Claudia turned away from the workmen who had paused only long enough to give her a progress report; turned away quickly before any of them could see the sudden glitter of tears in her eyes.

She had no dreams. She couldn't afford to let herself have dreams.

The man she had loved had never existed. The man she had loved had been perfection. A fantasy, someone he'd created for her. The reality had been vastly different, as she'd learned from Helen.

Pausing on her way up the wide oak staircase, she felt her heart turn over in her chest. Could she really trust Helen's word?

Her stepmother had been a cheat, a thief who had plotted with her lover to take everything away from her cuckolded husband, leaving him with next to nothing. Had she told the truth, all those years ago, about what Adam had done and said?

For a moment she was filled with the brightness of

glorious hope and then it went, like a heavy door slamming in her face.

She walked on slowly, a white-knuckled hand gripping the carved bannister, her legs leaden. Even if she decided to discount completely what Helen had said, she'd had the evidence of her own eyes. She'd seen Adam walking out of her stepmother's room, slamming the door behind him, his face black with anger, his eyes too blind with rage even to see her.

She'd started to go after him as he'd stridden towards the main staircase, but had thought better of it. She'd never seen him angry before; didn't think she'd ever seen anyone quite that angry. So she'd gone straight into Helen's room and been appalled by what she'd heard.

Helen had had no reason to lie, not in that instance. She would have had nothing to gain. And of course Adam had been in a blind temper. He'd been sexually rejected and thrown out of his job in one breath! Only after her stepmother's death, such a relatively short time ago, had she learned what the woman was capable of—the lies, the deceit. It would be too easy now, with hindsight, to make herself believe she'd lied about what Adam had said and done. But she couldn't blind herself to the fact that Helen would have had nothing to gain by inventing such a story.

She reached the room that had been hers since childhood and switched on the light. For a moment she leaned back against the door, willing the emptiness to go away. An emptiness that seemed far greater after she'd allowed herself that moment of hope.

Then she crossed to the window-seat and watched the afternoon light fade from the sky.

It was completely dark when she heard the workmen leave. She'd told them she'd lock up so that wasn't a problem; she wouldn't find herself a prisoner, locked in, until they came back in the morning.

Even so, it was time she made a move. She rose, blinking, stretching the stiffness from her body. Far from finding an acceptance of her unenviable position as Adam's paper wife over the past hour or so, her mind had remained stubbornly blank.

She supposed her overwrought emotions had needed the respite. She had the rest of her life to come to terms with her situation, accept that Adam would never forgive her for keeping his child's existence from him, that he would always regard her, the mother of his child, as a necessary evil. She knew it shouldn't matter, that his betrayal of six years ago should make his opinion of her immaterial. But it did matter because it hurt like hell.

She walked to the door, but it opened before she got there.

He looked drawn, as if he hadn't slept for a week, as if he had something on his mind that had been draining the life force from him.

Raindrops spangled his silky dark hair, glistened on the shoulders of his soft leather jacket. Claudia's heart gave a sickening lurch then fluttered on in panic, making her breath catch in her throat. She ached to cradle his head against her breast, kiss the lines of weariness from his face. No matter what he'd done to her, the misery he'd created, she still loved him. That was the stark truth she'd been hiding from. And now she was going to have to cope with it.

'They told me you were here. That I might catch you before you started back.' He closed the door behind him, silver eyes intent on her frozen face. His mouth tightened. 'Nothing to say? Not even, How are you and did you have a good trip?'

She opened her mouth, but no words came. Yet her mind was shrieking. She was no longer a silly eighteen-year-old, putty in the hands of a handsome charmer, enthusiastically falling in love with a man who had a cash register where his heart should have been. She couldn't still be in love with him. She couldn't!

'I—I didn't expect you,' she managed to blurt out. 'Did you call in at the cottage?'

Stupid question! She deserved his dry, 'Naturally. How else would I have known where to find you? I arrived in time to have tea with Rosie and hear her read and let her beat me at Ludo twice.' A smile flickered briefly as if, finding himself in an unpleasant situation, he was recalling one he had enjoyed. 'I said I'd collect you and take you out for supper. Amy was of the opinion that you'd want to go back and change, but I told her you wouldn't bother; it wasn't important. We'd find a quiet pub somewhere for a snack.' He eyed her narrowly. 'They'd expect us to want to spend time together, on our own. It seemed to be the right impression to give.'

He was good at giving impressions. Claudia turned away, not wanting him to see the hurt on her face.

How easily he could make other people see him the way he wanted them to. Only she knew the real man behind the charming, considerate façade.

'I'm not hungry,' she stated woodenly.

'No. Neither am I.' He sighed. He had moved, was standing close behind her. The electrical storm that always shook her when he was near made her legs turn to water. She took herself back to the window seat and sank down gratefully, her breath coming in shallow, ragged gasps as she watched him take in the details of the tiny room that had always been hers, the soft colours of the pale blue and lemon sprigged wallpaper, the virginal white cover on the narrow bed, and willed him to go away and leave her in peace— or as much peace as she could ever hope to attain.

But he said, 'There's something I want to ask you.' He sat on the edge of the bed, facing her now, his eyes bleak. 'I'll understand if you refuse to answer because under the circumstances I probably have no right to know.' He inhaled harshly. 'Tell me about Tony.'

Her eyes went wide. It was the last thing she had expected. 'What about him? You already know he was a liar and a thief. What else is there you need to know?'

He gave her a level look. 'Your relationship. How was it? Was he good in bed? Did he satisfy you? Although I have only the vaguest of recollections of the man, I wouldn't think so. He was sneaking off to be with Helen at every opportunity and you, as I vividly recall, were exuberantly sexy...'

He let the implication hang on the air and Claudia

shot to her feet. She didn't have to stay and listen to this! She would have liked to slap his face but wouldn't demean herself. She would just walk out!

'Do you get your kicks out of being cruel?' she snapped through her teeth as she marched past him, but his hand snaked out, looping around her hips, pulling her down beside him on the bed. 'I don't have to tell you a thing!' she managed, just as soon as she got her breath back. 'You said so!'

'I think you just did. Answer it, I mean.'

He wasn't letting her go. If anything, his arm had tightened around her tense body. She was holding herself stiffly, too afraid to relax. This close to him, she didn't trust herself. Despite everything, her instinct was to turn to him, burrow into the warm, exciting maleness of him, forget everything but the sheer magic of him.

Madness. Dangerous madness!

The threat to her sanity grew worse when he said gruffly, 'I had to know. I needed to know. If you think I was being cruel, then you don't know the half of it. I always thought that the physical side of our relationship was very special, something that only happens once in a lifetime—and then only if you happen to get lucky. I hated to think of Favel—'

'Don't tell me you're jealous!' she injected scornfully, unable to bear the sudden rush of memories. Knowing that he remembered, too, made it so painfully poignant. But his memories would be different from hers. Hers were of long, perfumed summer nights filled with love. His would be memories of the same nights filled with great sex. All spiced up with his hopes of becoming the husband of the heir to a valuable property.

'Claudia—as I've said before, we don't have to turn every private encounter into a battle.' He released her. He sounded incredibly weary. She didn't move, even though she could have done now, sudden lethargy taking over. And he was right. Life would be even more untenable if every time they met they went for the jugular.

She had nothing to lose by telling him the truth. In a way it would be a relief to unburden herself. Then, perhaps, they could take the first tentative steps towards some kind of understanding, progress beyond this antagonism.

'Before I accepted his proposal I told him I didn't love him,' she said. 'He understood that. I liked him, then, even respected him. I was grateful to him for caring for me. I was a weak fool,' she admitted dully. 'Too scared—of lots of things, but mainly of worrying Dad—to stand on my own feet. He suggested we had separate rooms because he was a light sleeper and I was pregnant and needed my rest. Nothing changed after Rosie was born. He did make one attempt to consummate the marriage.'

Her face went a dull red as she recalled the acute embarrassment of that encounter. 'It was a total failure. He'd already told me he was unable to father a child and I took it for granted that he was impotent. And I'd been about as responsive as a block of wood.' She could confess that much, but couldn't explain that, after Adam, no other man could arouse a flicker of interest in her atrophied senses.

Her voice low, her fingers laced tightly together in her lap, she continued, 'It was a relief, really. Not to have to sleep with him. But he was always kind, very considerate. I guess it paid him to be, if his grand plan was to go ahead. I seem to be,' she said, her voice bitter now, 'a hopeless judge of character.'

He could make what he liked of that statement, but all he said was, 'Thank you for your honesty. You didn't have to tell me. I have no rights where you're concerned. My rights begin and end with my daughter.'

She sensed he was about to stand up, to suggest they leave, and she felt defeated. Stupid, she thought as she followed his lead and exited the door he held open for her, but she had thought—hoped—that there had been a shift in their relationship, that he might want to spend more time talking to her.

Stupid to imagine that he, too, would feel the need for them to draw closer, to put the enmity behind them.

Following the tail-lights of his Jaguar, she made herself concentrate on her driving. Let herself think of him, his extraordinary, dog-in-the-manger admission that he hadn't been able to bear the thought of her making love with her late husband, and she would find herself driving straight into a ditch.

They were back at the cottage in time to put Rosie to bed. At the little girl's insistence, it was Adam who read her a story. Claudia went down to the kitchen and made herself a pot of tea and worried about the sleeping arrangements.

Guy slept in the narrow single room above the

stairs, Amy and Rosie in one of the two double rooms. Thankfully, both had twin beds, but she still felt edgy about sharing a room with Adam. After what had happened at his London flat, she knew he wouldn't make advances. He had clearly demonstrated his total lack of interest, which should have been a relief because if he did she wouldn't be able to resist and then where would she be? Up the creek without a paddle, fathoms-deep in love with him all over again, and letting him know it!

She still felt edgy, edgy enough to excuse herself and go to bed early, leaving the others engrossed in a TV programme she couldn't name, even though she'd had her eyes glued to the set.

Out of the bathroom in record time, she pulled one of the worn old T-shirts she wore to bed over her head, scrambled between the sheets, and, before she could switch off the bedside lamp, Adam entered.

Pain darkened her eyes. Didn't he know that the only way she could get through the night with him in a bed only a few inches away from hers was for her to pretend to be asleep when he put in an appearance? But no, of course he didn't! As far as he was concerned she was a waste of space, someone he could ignore with no trouble at all.

'I came to see if you were OK. You've been very pale all evening.'

'I'm fine.' She jerked the covers up to her chin. 'Such concern! There's no need to fake it, though. There's no one else around to be impressed.'

He narrowed his eyes then shrugged. 'If that's the way you want it.' He turned to leave and a lump of remorse settled on her chest like a heavy load of rocks. He had shown compassion when she'd been upset before, so maybe she'd misjudged him and he had been concerned.

'Adam,' she said impulsively, 'can I ask you a question?'

He turned his head, grey eyes looking long and hard into the blue of hers. She saw the rigid line of his shoulders relax a little. He almost smiled. 'I guess I owe you one.'

'About Rosie.' She knew she risked bringing his wrath back down on her head. He would never forgive her for keeping the child's existence from him. But she had to know. She had tried to puzzle it out times without number and it had been running in and out of her head all evening, ever since he'd stated that the only rights he had were those concerning his daughter. 'It's different for me. I gave birth to her, I've loved her for all of her short life. But you didn't know she existed until a few weeks ago. Yet your need to have her permanently in your life was compelling enough for you to take on my debts and marry me, even though you despise me.'

'You find that strange?' He sounded more relaxed, too. Whatever it was that had drawn his features into a tight mask at her swipe at his show of concern had gone away. He turned back into the room, shadowy with only the light from the low-wattage bedside lamp.

'I wouldn't have expected you to turn your back on her,' she explained. 'I'd have understood if you'd wanted to see her now and then—but to saddle yourself—'

'With a mountain of debts that weren't of my making and a wife I despise,' he finished for her. He moved back into the room and sat on the edge of her bed. She moved her feet to accommodate him and he said, 'I did despise you. When I learned I had a child who was five years old I thought you were the pits. That was before I understood what had happened, why you'd acted the way you had. I don't condone it, but I can't condemn.'

Did that mean he no longer despised her? She wanted to ask, but didn't quite dare. In the dim light his eyes looked like smoky charcoal, his mouth softer. She wanted, oh, so badly, to kiss him.

She firmed her lips, as if that could stop her wayward thought patterns, and Adam said, 'Perhaps if I explain why I feel the way I do about Rosie, then you will understand, too, and stop looking on me as an arrogant tyrant. Will that be possible, do you think?'

'Try me!' If her reply was flippant, she couldn't help it. She could hardly say, I don't look at you that way, I look at you and love you! Suddenly, she felt released. She was no longer having to fight herself, fight her feelings. She loved him, always had and probably always would and, admitting it, could learn to handle it.

'We both come from one-parent families, but there the similarity ends. Tragically, you lost your mother when you were ten and that was a dreadful thing to happen to you, Clo.' The use of that pet name, when there was no one around to witness it, made her heart swell. But she hid her pleasure. He'd think her such a fool if he ever guessed how she still felt about him.

'But you had memories of happy family life, a father who loved you deeply—and dear Amy, of course. You knew why your mother had gone. My father deserted us when I was five and I didn't know why. After he went, my mother cried all the time, and pushed me away whenever I went near her. I thought it was my fault my father had left. I missed him dreadfully and kept asking when he was coming back, which only made things worse. She was bitter until the day she died.' His deep voice was soft with regrets.

Claudia's eyes stung with tears. 'Adam—I didn't know. How sad for you!'

She resolutely swallowed down the lump in her throat and he said, 'I would have been almost seven when Uncle Harold took over. He was my mother's brother, unmarried, owner of the successful Hallam Group. He later told me he'd never married because he'd got more sense than to tie himself to one woman, and to have to shell out half his fortune if said woman wanted a divorce. So, as you can perhaps imagine, he was a cold, hard, calculating man.

'My mother, he maintained, was making a mess out of bringing me up. We were to move in with him and he'd make a man out of me, fit to step into his shoes when the time came. The process involved sending me away to boarding-school. All I knew was that I didn't want to be made into a ''man'', or do anything my rather frightening uncle told me to do. I wanted my dad back.

'I can remember,' he said quickly, as if he sensed she was about to make more sympathetic noises and didn't want to have to hear them, 'the time when I told him all that—that I hated going away to school and wanted my dad back. He told me we'd never see him again. Neither did we. The last anyone heard he was in South America and that must have been a good twenty years ago. He then went on to tell me that my father had only married my mother for what he could get out of her.

'They came from a wealthy family, independent of the proceeds from the Hallam Group. My father had wanted life on easy street—flash cars, good suits, money to burn. When he finally realised that Harold—as trustee for Mother's share of the family fortune—wasn't going to play ball, he walked out.'

'That was a terrible thing to say to a small boy!' Claudia blurted, not able to stop herself. She wanted to weep, thinking about how lost, lonely and bewildered that small boy must have felt.

'Maybe,' he shrugged. 'In any case, I got over it. Settled down at school and made friends. And this is where I come to the point. Friends often invited me back for holidays and because of that I got to know what a close, loving family life was like. With two parents, both with different perspectives and life experiences—male and female—to give to their children. That's what I want for my child, for Rosie. Two parents who love her, who'll be there for her as long as she needs them. Stability, emotional security.'

'Oh, Adam!' Instinctively, she put her hand on his. She understood his motives now she knew of his background, the lack of love, the bitterness, the loss of a father who hadn't loved him enough to stay.

She had deprived him of the first five years of his daughter's life, made him—without his knowledge and against all his principles—an absent father. 'I'm so sorry!' Remorse was savage; it made tears fall unchecked. She felt his fingers tighten around hers.

'Don't,' he said. 'Don't cry, Clo.'

Which only made it worse. Sobs came and she couldn't stop them. Through the silent storm she heard him sigh, just before he moved closer and gathered her into his arms, holding her, rocking her until the sobs became shudders and died away.

It felt so wonderful to be held like this, as if she had finally come home after a long, lonely time spent in the bleak, dark wilderness of missing him. Missing his strength, his warmth, the feeling that he cared for her. But, most of all, missing his love.

He put her slightly away from him and she wanted to cry out, Don't leave me! Don't go! But he placed both hands on either side of her face, brushing the silky strands of toffee-coloured hair away from her damp cheeks, and gently kissed the last of the tears away.

The warmth of his lips branded her; she couldn't get enough of the sensation she had thought she would never experience again, and she was transported straight to heaven on a riot of breathtaking rapture and couldn't help herself when her hands pushed beneath the soft leather of his jacket.

She ran them lovingly over the fine cashmere of his sweater in ecstatic exploration and when he said, his voice sounding ragged round the edges, 'I don't think this is a good idea, Clo,' she unhesitatingly slipped her hands around his steely, tense body to his back and pulled him even closer.

The story of his childhood had touched her deeply and the remorse for what she'd done to him was hard to bear. Her emotions were all over the place and only constant was her love for him, her need. The past, what he'd done to her, no longer mattered.

She lifted her tear-stained face trustingly to his and she heard the rough intake of his breath just before he lowered his head and kissed her.

CHAPTER EIGHT

THAT kiss was like no other. Not even Claudia's explicit memories of the way it had been between them before—the explosion of sheer chemistry—lived up to the reality of this mutual, wildly passionate embrace.

She knew by the near-savage hunger of his mouth as it began to plunder hers more deeply that he was fully aware of the way her body was burning with the ravaging flames of desire, that she was desperately craving him, open to the fierce masculinity of him. He knew it and was responding to it as if he were a starving man who was being offered a banquet.

Her whole body shuddered beneath his hands as they began their fevered exploration, tremors of ecstasy, of wild sexual tension that reached deep into her heart and soul. This was her man, her love for all time, and nothing had changed. Not for her; how could it when she had been born to be his?

They had done each other deep injustices, but that was in the past. They could forget and forgive and go on to find a future together.

The sheer wonder of the thought made her want to weep again, with joy this time, but she didn't; she moaned his name aloud as he deftly removed her old T-shirt and bent his dark head to suckle her breasts.

Claudia squirmed beneath the sensual onslaught. It

was too much, yet not nearly enough; she thought she might die with the intensity of the ecstasy, the promise of more to come. And when he lowered his head, burning the soft skin of her tummy with hungry lips, she slid her hands on either side of his firm jaw and lifted his head, gazing at him with eyes limpid with love.

'Make love to me, Adam,' she murmured, her voice thick and throaty. 'Make it right.'

For a moment he went still, his eyes glittering deep into hers like hot silver knives. Her heartbeats turned hectic. Was he going to remind her that he'd said he had no intention of consummating the marriage and then walk away? Her world would fall apart if that happened!

And then his mouth curved in that wickedly sensual smile she remembered so well as she took her courage in both hands and tugged impatiently at his jacket.

Did that utterly sinful smile mean he was remembering all the eager enthusiasm for him she'd unashamedly displayed during that long, hot summer six years ago? She didn't know, and she didn't care. She was still as uninhibitedly eager for him, and only him.

Drenched in her own desire, she lay naked on the bed and watched him undress with smouldering eyes. His movements were smooth and economical, and he didn't take his eyes off hers for one second as he unbuttoned his shirt and dropped it on the floor, unzipped his jeans.

'Dear God in heaven!' he gasped raggedly when she wrapped her body around his as he slid onto the bed beside her. 'Clo!' Then he said no more, his mouth ravaging hers as her body instinctively opened to embrace his.

The dams had burst, and she surrendered willingly, easily, as if they had never been apart; surrendered to love and the driving rhythm of his body, her breathing as harsh and ragged as his. She had waited so long for this rapture, this slice of heaven that was theirs alone, waited so long for his fierce thrust of male possession, to have him fill her, body, heart and soul.

And when he finally rolled away from her he turned her in his arms and tucked her body into the curve of his, his face in her hair, his arm going around her as his hand rested intimately between her thighs.

Her head dizzy with the sheer magic of what had happened for them both, she heard his breathing almost immediately relax as he fell asleep, giving way to the weariness she'd sensed in him earlier. She gave a contented little sigh and clicked off the bedside lamp then wriggled closer, snuggling into him, careful not to disturb him.

She would not sleep. She wanted to savour every moment of this miraculous night. They were together again, in every way, and this was how it was meant to be.

When he woke they would talk. They needed to talk, to sort out the past and go on to their future. She would try to ensure that their new relationship went forward on a less tottery foundation than it had done up to now.

He most certainly didn't love her the way she loved him, but she could live with that if she had to. He wanted his daughter in his life and she understood his determination now. And he wanted her, the mother of his child, and as more than a wife in name only. He hadn't been able to hide his hunger for her.

Together, they could build a good future, give Rosie a happy, stable life with two loving parents, just the way he wanted it. And, if she was patient, he could grow to love her, too. Time and tenderness might make it happen.

Her sins would have to be confessed. She knew now that she could tell him without rancour exactly why she'd kept their child a secret from him. Surely he would understand that six years ago she had been too immature, too frightened by the threat that she might lose her father, to cope with his betrayal, to track him down, somehow, and tell him she was carrying his child because he had a right to know?

She'd taken the easy way out and had learned harsh lessons from her weakness. She couldn't condone what he had done but she could forgive. He was older, too, a fully mature adult, and he obviously had no need to look for ways—through charm and mind-blowing sex—to feather his nest.

Her brows drew together in a frown. He had never had to, had he?

She sucked in a long breath. Adam had known from a very early age that he was being groomed eventually to take over his uncle's company, plus the family wealth. Farthings Hall and her family business would have seemed very small beer by comparison!

There was no need to search her memory for what Helen had said; the words had been branded on her brain. He'd played up to her, proposed to her, because she was a considerable heiress admitting he'd messed around with her.

Now she came to think about it, really think about it, she knew Adam would never say anything like that; it was completely out of character. And he hadn't needed what Helen had said he saw as her future legacy—he had more than enough money and property of his own!

Helen had been doing what she'd been best at— lying and deceiving!

Yet during that summer he'd presented himself as a penniless drifter, content to take on the hard labour and odd jobs around the grounds to earn his keep—a pittance, and somewhere to hang his hat for a month or two.

He had never once hinted at the massive family wealth behind him. She wished he'd wake up so she could get it all clear in her head!

As if sensing her sudden restlessness he did just that, but the sensual slide of his hand up over her tummy to touch her breasts, the way he languorously turned her to him, chased every coherent thought out of her head. This time his loving was long and slow and afterwards she drifted off to sleep on a wave of exhausted contentment, and when she woke he wasn't there.

But, seconds later, Rosie was. 'Time to get up, Mummy! See—I dressed myself!'

So she had. Her sweater was inside out and her slippers were on the wrong feet. Claudia slid out of bed and into a robe and put her daughter right, gave

her a kiss and a cuddle and steered her to the door.
'Tell Daddy I'll be down in a few minutes.'

She showered quickly and dressed in a pair of
sleekly fitting amber-coloured cords and a cream
ribbed Italian sweater she plucked out of the booty
she'd brought back from London with her. She
brushed her hair until it shone like shot silk and left
it loose, and applied enough make-up to show she'd
bothered with her appearance.

She couldn't wait for this wonderful new day to
begin. The first day of the rest of her life with Adam!
Quite why Helen had lied she'd probably never know.
But lied she had. Adam had had no need of her future
inheritance!

And a glorious day it was, too! The sun shining
from a pale blue sky, hardly a breath of wind. There
would be a nip in the air but that didn't matter, not
if Rosie was warmly dressed. She usually planned
some kind of outing with the little girl on a Saturday.
Perhaps the three of them could drive to the coast,
have lunch somewhere, begin the process of bonding
as a loving family.

She would mention it to Adam over breakfast.

It was eight o'clock and the household was awake.
Guy, always an early riser, would have been to the
village stores for his preferred newspaper to read after
breakfast—which was already in the making, judging
by the aroma of bacon and coffee drifting up the stair-
well.

Adam would be waiting for her, listening to Rosie's
endless chatter, she thought happily as she practically
skipped down the stairs, wondering if he'd appreciate

the new-look Claudia in a sample of the perfectly fitting designer gear his generosity had enabled her to choose.

Her father and Amy were sitting over the remains of breakfast at the kitchen table and Rosie was wolfing down a bowl of cereal. No sign of Adam, no empty plate and only one unused place setting.

'Where's Adam?' Gone out for an early morning walk? She wished he'd waited; she could have gone with him, used the opportunity to ask the questions that had been pushed right out of her head late last night. As she remembered exactly why they'd been pushed out, her face went pink with pleasure. She reached out to pour herself coffee from the pot just as her father lowered his paper.

'He left at half past six, ten minutes after I came down. I expected you to be around to see him off. He'll be away some time. After all, he can't travel out to Florida on a daily basis.'

The implied criticism in her father's voice was nothing to the savage shock of knowing he'd left without saying a word to her about it. After last night she would have expected more, expected him to tell her of his planned trip, to take her in his arms and kiss her goodbye.

Her face went white and pinched and her father, obviously relenting, said gently, 'I know it must be a big disappointment—flitting hither and thither at a moment's notice, especially so soon after your marriage—but you've got enough common sense to take it in your stride. He couldn't pass up the opportunity for his company to buy into a huge leisure complex out there. That sort of thing won't happen on a regular basis.'

'And went without so much as a bite of breakfast,' Amy tutted. 'A long drive ahead of him and then goodness knows how many hours in the air, with nothing inside him!' She heaved herself out of her chair, fetched a plate out of the warming oven and put it down in front of Claudia. 'I kept yours hot for you.'

Grilled tomatoes and bacon. Claudia looked at it and felt sick, her stomach churning. Her father thought she was sulking, and her husband hadn't bothered to tell her he had a protracted business trip in the offing.

Or was it business? She drank her coffee, needing a caffeine fix, hating herself for having such a thought. What hope was there for them if she allowed such untrusting thoughts in her head? What hope when he couldn't be bothered to tell her of his movements, when he walked out without even bothering to leave her a note?

The next five weeks were a nightmare. Claudia was sure it rained every day, relentlessly, with gales sweeping in across the headlands, scouring the valleys and stripping the last of the leaves from the trees.

Having to stay indoors during out-of-school hours, Rosie grew grumpy as the days grew darker and wetter and wilder. They heard from Adam often, but there was nothing there to console Claudia in the stream of picture postcards, usually depicting Disney characters. Most of the available space was taken up with cheery messages for Rosie and his weekly phone calls were probably worse.

He'd talk to her first, and that was only for the look of it because his voice was always impersonal, clipped and cold as he briefly discussed work in progress, the new plans he'd had drawn up to higher specifications, the difficulty of finding contractors who would work to the high standard the Hallam Group demanded. All details she didn't want to know about, stuff she could relay to her interested father, nothing about how he felt, whether he was missing her, whether that magical night they had spent together had meant anything at all to him.

She wanted to ask him, to beg him to tell her why he was so distant, as if they were strangers, never lovers. But she couldn't, not while the others were in hearing distance.

And then he'd ask to speak to Rosie so she'd hand the receiver over and listen to their daughter's animated chatter and wonder, hating herself, how she could possibly be jealous of her own child. She didn't know what was happening to her.

The hardest part of all was keeping her misery to herself, making herself appear cheerful in front of the others, doing all the normal everyday things that made her want to scream and throw things at the wall. The only thing that had made her forget her inner brooding fears was when, three weeks after Adam's abrupt departure, the last of the workmen had moved out of Farthings Hall.

She'd thrown herself into the task of moving them all back as if her life had depended on it. She'd packed, ferried cases back and forth, scrubbed and polished Willow Cottage until it was as neat and shining as it had been on the day they'd taken up temporary residence.

And now, five long, painful weeks into his absence, they were home again, firmly ensconced. The builders and decorators had done a superlative job and Guy was delighted to be back in his own armchair, in his own home, with his own things around him. It was the only consolation Claudia had—seeing her father gaining so much strength, looking fitter every day. The past was behind him; he had no burdens now.

She smiled for her father across the hearth as he lowered his newspaper and wondered how long she could keep up the pretence of cheerful normality. Adam had been away for over a month and he'd made no mention of returning and, as if he'd picked up her thought waves, her father said, 'I hope Adam's home in time to go to Rosie's end-of-term school play. She's got the starring role, or so she tells me.'

Indeed she had; the little girl hadn't stopped talking about it for the last two or three days. She had made them all solemnly promise to be there to watch her and they'd cried in unison, 'Just try to stop us!' And had watched that heart-stopping smile brighten the impish little face.

So if Adam didn't show up in time she'd kill him! Because although the tiny girl hadn't had enough time to bond properly with her father Claudia knew she was proud of her brand-new daddy, looked forward to his regular postcards and weekly phone calls and was always asking when he'd come home.

He called that evening, just before Rosie's bedtime, and, aware that the little girl was hovering, her eyes big and shining, Claudia's first words were, 'Will you try to get home in time for Rosie's end-of-term play? She's got the starring role.'

Maybe she'd sounded too brusque, but her emotions were beginning to break through the tight lid she'd put on them and, her own feelings of abandonment apart, she was fiercely protective of her daughter's happiness. She was too tightly wound up to take in his response and had to ask him to repeat himself.

'I'm phoning from Heathrow. I'll be back in the small hours so don't wait up.' He sounded more remote than ever, if that was possible, but her heart skipped. Adam was coming home! They could sort out whatever it was that had caused this mental distance between them. After the long night's loving they'd shared, she was sure they could! Maybe he found it difficult to talk over the phone about anything that mattered. Maybe it was as simple as that!

'We'll talk tomorrow,' he said, as if reading her thoughts. 'And tell Rosie I wouldn't miss her play for a trillion pounds.'

'Tell her yourself.' There was a smile in her voice as she passed the receiver over and listened to the little girl's excited chatter about her part in the school play. She hugged herself, wrapping her arms around her body to contain her relief. Adam was coming home and, no matter what he'd said, she'd be waiting for him.

And she was, dressed in the most alluring of her new nightgowns—oyster satin with lots of lace—covered by the matching wrap. She bathed and perfumed herself after Guy and Amy had gone up to bed, both delighted that Adam was on his way home at last.

But nothing like as delighted as she was! And the fire was glowing in welcome, the lamplight soft, her blue eyes hazy with love and longing.

He closed the door behind him and leaned against it. He looked weary, hard lines bracketing his mouth. Wearing a dark grey business suit, he looked formidable. Claudia made herself ignore the blocks of ice that began crawling through her veins.

Of course he was tired, too tired to rake up a smile. Who wouldn't be exhausted after hours in the air and a long drive through the night? 'Welcome home,' she said, a strange catch in her voice, suddenly quite ridiculously shy.

'I told you how late I'd be. You shouldn't have waited up.'

Claudia smiled. 'Of course I should.' She stood up, saw his mouth tighten, a flinch of something that looked like pain flicker in his eyes before he looked quickly away, moved into the room and dropped his briefcase onto a table. He looked as if he'd lost weight, she thought with a protective pang, the urge to mother him surfacing for the first time, taking her by surprise.

He had always been the strong one but now he looked drained. His workload in the States must have been killing, she told herself. Maybe he'd worked extra-long hours to keep his time out there to the absolute minimum, anxious to return to his family.

The deduction gave her a rosy glow inside, thawing away the trickle of ice produced by his cold greeting. 'Sit by the fire and relax,' she said lightly. 'You need looking after. I know we've got lots to talk about, but that can wait until you've slept.' Apart from anything else, she had such wonderful news to tell him, but even that could wait. Right now he needed cherishing. 'I made sandwiches—roast beef and horseradish—your favourite! I'll fetch them. Would you like a hot drink, or would whisky go down better?'

'Forget the food. I don't want it.' He was already pouring whisky from the decanter. He tilted it in her direction, one dark brow raised, and Claudia shook her head, her mouth trembling. He was shutting her out. Something bad had happened since the night they'd made love.

'Since you chose to wait up, and the rest of the household is sensibly asleep, we may as well have that talk now. At least we won't be interrupted.'

His voice was flat, his words ominous. Claudia's bones turned to water. She stepped back shakily, feeling for the edge of the chair with the back of her legs, and sank down, watching him move to the fire, looking into the flames, his head bowed.

'Adam?' Somehow she found her voice, but it was a poor, thin thing. He turned and looked at her then, his eyes bleak, and in that moment she knew that whatever chance they might have had had gone.

'Right.' He dragged in a breath. He stood straight again, six feet something of hard male purpose. 'We might as well get it over and done with. It's quite simple. I made a mistake. Marrying you was the biggest mistake of my life and I apologise for it. It won't work. So I suggest we go for a two-year separation and then a divorce. We'll keep it amicable, for Guy and Rosie's sake. Naturally, I'll continue to support you all and I'll want to see my daughter regularly— her school play, for instance. Apart from that, we'll arrange access to suit you.'

A log fell in the hearth, sending a shower of sparks up the wide chimney. Claudia flinched, the small, everyday sound startling her. She couldn't get her head round what he was saying.

'You said you wanted your daughter to have two parents around—you even told me why.' She pushed the words out with difficulty. When he'd insisted on marriage that had been the overriding reason, so important to him that he'd taken on a wife he despised, shouldered the burden of her debts.

Yet now, when he'd heard her story and changed his mind about despising her, when he'd demonstrated just how much he still wanted her physically, he was calling it a day, walking out on them all. Savaging her heart all over again.

'It was a mistake,' he said again. 'You knew that before I did. You did everything you could to wriggle out of that commitment to begin with. I should have listened. Stubbornly, I did not.' He drained his glass, made a grimace of distaste—not at the whisky, she guessed, but at the situation he found himself in.

'Fortunately, no damage can have been done as far as Rosie's concerned. I've only been in her life for a very short time and not on anything like a permanent basis. I don't applaud it, but these days divorce is commonplace. Provided it's amicable and the child has regular access to the absent parent, then the damage can be limited. Especially in Rosie's case—she's never been used to having me around.'

Pain, bitterness, it was all there. Was he unable to forgive her for keeping his daughter's existence from him? Maybe if she explained just why she had it would help?

'Can't we discuss this?'

'There's nothing to discuss. The marriage won't work. I'm ending it.'

Just like that!

Her feelings didn't matter. Had they ever mattered to him? Did what he want always take precedence, even over his daughter? Didn't he care what havoc he left in his careless wake? Anger and outrage pulsed through her, making her shake with the intensity of it.

She stood up, her face white and tight with fury. 'Adam.' Her voice was low, a warning growl, warning of storms about to break. He turned away from her, pouring himself another inch of whisky.

'I'm not getting into a slanging match with you, Claudia. Just go to bed.'

The cold and expert dismissal drained the fight right out of her.

After a shocked pause she stumbled from the room, utterly diminished.

CHAPTER NINE

THE gale woke her before the alarm clock did. Claudia went through the early morning ritual of getting Rosie washed and dressed, ready for school, then put herself into old jeans and a thick woolly sweater. She did everything numbly, still in shock. She still couldn't believe that Adam had so coldly and finally ended their marriage. She could hardly take it in.

She didn't know where he'd slept; it certainly hadn't been with her in the sumptuous master suite she'd earmarked for their use. If she hadn't felt so numb she would probably have been crying her eyes out, she thought as she boiled Rosie's breakfast egg and made toast soldiers. At least she had something to be grateful for.

Amy and Guy were full of Adam's return, wanting to know what time he'd finally arrived, if he was going to stay put this time and do most of his work from home, as he'd said he would. For the first time in her life she wished the two of them, so very dear to her, a million miles away.

She fielded the questions as best she could, wondering how she would be able to break the news of the marriage breakdown, sounding regretful but adult about it, explaining that they'd both decided, amicably, that it would never work. She would probably break down completely, fall into a million miserable pieces. These two loving souls didn't deserve to have to share a burden of misery that was hers alone.

'I suppose he's still out for the count.' Guy smiled comfortably and Claudia mumbled something and helped Rosie into her school uniform coat, popping her beret on her soft dark hair and hooking her school bag over her tiny shoulders. It was almost as big as she was and at this point Claudia always grinned because who wouldn't? The little girl looked so cute.

But not this morning. Her face felt like a block of wood.

'Not out for the count but up and running,' Adam answered his father-in-law's comment from the doorway. Claudia's heart jolted painfully. The sight of him had pulled her back into the land of the living.

He looked as gorgeous as ever. Freshly showered, dressed in a slick waterproof over black sweater and jeans, there was no sign of the bleak weariness of the night before. Claudia could hardly credit that the scene between them had ever happened. Every time she saw him she loved him more and she mourned the loss of the numbness that had helped her through this morning because now she was stinging with pain all over again.

'I'll do the school run,' he offered, his silver eyes heartbreakingly soft as he smiled down at his diminutive offspring. But a muscle was jerking spasmodically at the side of his jaw so, try as he might to hide it, he was under strain, too.

Claudia said thickly, 'There's really no need.'

'Wait with her in the hall while I bring the car right up to the door; it's pouring with rain.' He spoke as if she hadn't said a thing. He lobbed a smile in the direction of the kitchen table. 'See you guys later.' Then he took hold of Rosie's hand and headed out.

When the Jaguar was parked he carried Rosie out and strapped her into the passenger seat. The little girl's face was bright with the excitement of having her daddy back and driving her to school, and Claudia could have wept her heart out.

He was back to where she was standing in the shelter of the doorway in seconds, raindrops glistening on the shoulders of his waterproof, spangling his hair. 'I suggest you break the news to Guy and Amy while I'm out.' There was nothing in his eyes to tell her what he was thinking, nothing but an endless blankness.

'Coward!' She spat the word out. His final words last night had stunned her but the numbness had gone now and all the anger and pain came blistering back.

He ignored the taunt, his tone as level and dry as a desert plain. 'It would be better if you quietly prepared the ground. I'll be back later to speak to them myself. I'll be leaving after that, but I'll keep in touch. I'll need to know the date and time of Rosie's play; I have no intention of missing that. We'll sort out a reasonable access agreement later.'

Claudia closed the door in his face and paced the floor, trying to get her rioting emotions under control. She wanted to hit him, oh, how she wanted to hit him!

Everything was for his own convenience. He decided something and it suddenly became immutable law! So he could sit twiddling his thumbs until his beard grew long and white because she sure as hell wasn't going to do a single thing he'd told her to!

Far from carrying out orders, she shot upstairs and made Rosie's bed and then her own, then stood staring out at the rain. The wind was blowing the trees into twisted shapes and Old Ron would be drinking his morning tea and muttering about the weather and Bill would probably be working in the glasshouses.

She didn't know why she'd been standing there, staring out, until the Jaguar purred to a halt on the drive. Adam was back. Unconsciously she'd been waiting for him. Her heart thumped painfully against her ribs. He would enter the house, expecting her to have 'prepared the ground', and find himself uttering platitudes to people who didn't know what he was talking about. Then he would have to explain, do his own dirty work!

But he turned away from the house, pulled up the collar of his waterproof and strode off, heading across the sodden lawns. There was only one place he would be going to from that direction and Claudia knew where that was.

She dragged a new, bright yellow padded jacket from the hanging cupboard, stuffed her feet into boots and headed after him. There was something she needed to tell him in private, and the cove in this weather was as private as it got.

If it was the last thing she did on this earth, she would make him listen, and he needn't think he could issue orders and then walk away, end their marriage, deprive his child of the permanent father he'd been so adamant that she needed.

How dared he do that to them without a single word of explanation? Saying it wouldn't work wasn't good enough. And why wouldn't it work? He hadn't told her. She would demand a proper explanation; he owed her that much!

The rain had eased considerably but the wind was a savage monster, rampaging up the narrow valley, making headway almost impossible.

As her feet finally hit sand she paused to snatch her breath back, her chest heaving as she dragged the sharp air into her tortured lungs.

Adam was standing near the edge of the crashing waves; she could hardly see him through the wildly tossing spray. The sound of the wind and water in turmoil was deafening.

He didn't see her or hear her until she touched his arm. His eyes narrowed against the onslaught of the gale, he looked down at her, his mouth tight.

Claudia opened her own mouth to let her anger and frustration pour out but shut it again because she knew he wouldn't hear a word she said above the noisy violence of the storm. She shouldn't have come, she thought, sinking back into the misery of despair. It had been a stupid idea. She should have waited for his eventual return and tackled him then.

As always, he seemed able to pluck her tumbling thoughts right out of her mind. He shrugged as if bowing to the inevitable then took her arm, helping her over the sand, farther up into the cove where the rocky outcrop of the sheltering cliffs gave some respite from the ceaseless buffeting of the wild wind.

'What do you want?' He released her immediately,

as if he couldn't bear to touch her, and pushed his wet dark hair back from his forehead with his fingers. She felt the fight, the painful anger drain from her.

A confrontational attitude would get her nowhere with this man. He would simply close down, shut her out. In any case, she no longer wanted to lash out at him, to try to punish him for his cold infliction of pain. She wanted to hold him, tell him how very much she loved him.

But wanting a thing didn't make it happen. She would have to find the courage to make such an admission, lay herself open to his scorn or disbelief or, perhaps worst of all, his indifference.

She raised troubled eyes to his. 'What brought you here, in this weather?' She had expected him to arrive back at the house, collect his few belongings, say his goodbyes and move out of her life.

'I wanted to say goodbye to my memories,' he answered tersely. 'Satisfied?'

Memories of the first time they'd made love? Of the time they'd laughed at the fury of that long-ago summer storm? Or the much more recent Indian summer picnic when he'd taken the first steps towards bonding with his daughter?

The latter, she guessed, not daring to ask.

She shivered, the chill of her flesh beneath her rain-sodden clothes making itself known. Adam said flatly, 'Get back to the house before you catch pneumonia.'

She wasn't going anywhere without him. She backed further into the shelter of the rocks and saw his eyes darken, as stormy as the elements that raged around them. It was, she knew, now or never. Her stomach clenched with tension and she had to force the words out.

'You've made up your mind to divorce me. I don't understand why, but I accept it because I've got no option. But I want you to know that I love you. I never stopped loving you.'

'Liar,' he came back dismissively. 'What sort of love rejects the father of an unborn child in favour of a man who is seen as a better provider?' His mouth was a hard, compressed line, the words snapped out through his teeth. 'I'm heading back; you can do as you damn well please!'

She caught him before he'd reached the open beach, dragging on his arm to hold him back. She would not take that accusation, not from anyone, not from him. 'Don't call me a liar! You did nothing but lie to me when we first met!'

He was staring straight ahead, not looking at her, not dignifying her accusation with a reply. But when she grated, 'You lived a lie. You pretended you were a penniless drifter and all the time you had a fortune behind you,' she watched the furious jerk of a muscle at the side of his hard jaw and knew her words had hit their target.

He turned and looked at her, bitterness in his eyes, his voice bleakly sarcastic. 'Now why would I do that, I wonder?' Then emotion powered its way through, making him sound tough, aggressive. 'I've been hounded by women on the make since I reached my late teens. Not for myself, but for the background wealth, because of who I was destined to become—the head of the Hallam Group. It was a hard lesson to have to learn, but believe me I learned it quickly and well. That summer I wanted time out to be myself. Since I was seven years old my uncle had mapped my life out for me; I'd just finished my degree course in architecture and land use studies and I wanted to bum around all summer, picking up the odd temporary job, taking time out before having to knuckle down to running the Group. And what happened?'

His mouth curled bitterly. 'I met you. I fell in love with you. I had never known such happiness. You loved me back, or so you said. Loved me for myself, not the Hallam wealth. You promised to marry me. I knew I'd have to tell you the truth about myself, but you got there first. Told me it was over, you were seeing someone else, someone with a proper job and money in the bank. You were worse than the others. You were carrying my child.' His eyes stabbed her. 'Now tell me you never stopped loving me!'

'But I didn't!' she cried. In view of what he'd just told her, the way she'd broken things off between them six years ago, she knew she had little hope of convincing him. 'I love you, penniless or not. I didn't know I was pregnant until you'd gone. I had no means of finding you. And to be honest—' she almost faltered there, but she had to be completely truthful because the need for honesty was all that was left between them now '—at that time I didn't want to.'

'So you married Favel.' His tone was an indictment. In his eyes she'd been tried, judged and convicted.

'I've already told you why.' The storm was dying

now but her voice barely carried. She injected more strength into it and told him firmly, 'The only thing I haven't told you is why I broke it off between us.'

'Now there's a thought,' he said dryly. 'Perhaps you didn't like the colour of my eyes or thought my feet a touch too big!'

'Don't!' Her eyes pleaded with him, huge blue pools in her small pale face. 'That day, I saw you storm out of Helen's bedroom—' She almost lost it there, so deeply ashamed of her younger, weaker self, but forced herself on, to lay her sins at his feet. 'She told me you'd tried to seduce her, knowing Guy was out of the way. That you'd said you'd been messing about with me because you wanted to marry money, but you wanted her.'

'And you believed her!' His eyes sharpened to pin-pricks of silver, total disgust written on his hard, unforgiving features.

'At the time, yes. She was everything I wasn't— slender, perfectly groomed, beautiful,' she confessed miserably. 'I saw no reason for her to lie about a thing like that. I didn't know what she was capable of then. We'd always got on well; I never dreamed she'd lie like that; why should I? But I've thought about it since—since we met up again and I knew what Helen and Tony had been like. Liars, both of them. Cheats. I don't believe a word of what she told me now.'

He stared at her. 'How big of you! Just for the record, she'd been giving me the come-on ever since Guy gave me that temporary job—in between disappearing for hours on end with the man you decided you wanted to marry. It sickened me! And on the day you're talking about—which was probably the worst day I've lived through—she asked me to go to her room to fix a curtain pole that was coming adrift.'

His mouth twisted sardonically. 'And wouldn't you know it, she was waiting, wearing next to nothing, offering a little of what she called "adult fun", something she was sure I wasn't getting from her teenage stepdaughter. She'd noticed the amount of time we were spending together and couldn't see what I saw in what she called "that naive lump"—unless it was her future inheritance.

'I saw red, called her a few unrepeatable names and, as you so aptly put it, stormed out, leaving her telling me to get off the property. Fast. I'd already suspected something was going on between her and Favel and I couldn't stand the thought of a decent, honourable man like your father being tied to such a creature. Of course I was angry! And your so-called love for me wasn't strong enough to let you come to me and ask for my side of the story.' The harsh lines of his mouth castigated her. 'You didn't trust me. You believed what that woman said. You sure as hell didn't give me a hearing.'

'I'm sorry.' It wasn't enough to repair the damage, but what else could she say? She bowed her head. She deserved everything he said to her. 'I don't have much defence, if any. But remember I was just out of school, naive as they come. I didn't have a cynical bone in my body; I believed Helen was in love with my father; I had no reason to think she'd lie. I just didn't think people acted like that. I was young, desperately hurt, but I had some pride. I wasn't going to snivel and grovel in front of you and I wanted to hurt you back. I didn't know, then, that the last thing you needed to do was marry for money. And anyway—' there was a rough edge to her voice now; some of the blame had to be his '—you spent quite a time, when we first met, asking me about the property, what it felt like to know that I'd inherit the lot.'

'So I did.' His eyes were unforgiving, unmoved by her feeble defence. 'We were in similar positions. I wanted to know if you felt—as I was inclined to feel in those days—that duty to family expectations and the management of a large inheritance wasn't all a bed of roses.'

He lost all interest, his eyes scanning the clouds as they scudded overhead. The rain had all but stopped and the wind was dropping. He said, finality stamped on his features, 'Your pride was stronger than your love. You didn't trust me. That's the bottom line. I don't think there's any more that can be usefully said, do you? Coming?'

She followed him across the wet sand, her heart as leaden as her legs. She had tried and had failed; there was no way she could get through to him.

He helped her over the rougher patches on the path up through the valley but there was no verbal contact. He'd shut off from her, effectively cutting her out of his life. She was yesterday's woman with a vengeance.

She felt too awful to do anything but accept it now and when they met Bill, barrowing a load of logs to the fuel store, she just stared at him blankly as if she didn't know who he was.

'You two been for a swim!' He eyed their sodden clothing with a grimace. 'Clearing up now, though. Oh, Amy couldn't find you, Mrs Weston. She said, if I saw you, to tell you as Mr Sullivan's driven her to the shops.' He grinned up at Adam. 'Something about a welcome-home dinner!'

He trundled his load away and Adam hustled her in through the door to the kitchen quarters. She wished he'd go now, just leave. Leave her to come to terms with a future without him. When he was around she just couldn't think straight. Perhaps she had never been able to. She certainly hadn't been thinking straight when Helen had told those lies.

She shivered in reaction to the warmth of the kitchen and Adam said roughly. 'Look, if it's any consolation, I was guilty, too.' He had shucked off his waterproof and was pulling off her soaked jacket. She couldn't think why he was bothering, not when he couldn't wait to get away.

'Thinking about it, it was hurt pride that kept me from refusing to accept what you'd said. I just went. And never came back. Before that day I'd believed I knew you, everything about you—you were always so open and giving. I should have known you weren't capable of being so mercenary.

'Pride sent me away and kept me away. I can understand now why you acted the way you did. And I accept an equal part of the blame. But pride didn't stop me loving you, wanting you, remembering. I looked at other women and only saw you. When I twisted your arm to make you marry me I was punishing myself. When I heard that the Hall was on the market I was compelled to come back. I thought you and your father and that bitch Helen were long gone. I thought I could find out what had happened to you. So I guess we're about quits.'

He was frowning at the wet patches on her sweater where the rain had soaked through her coat, at the way her sodden jeans clung uncomfortably to her legs. Claudia's mouth dropped open as she tried to make sense of what he'd just said. She stared at him, frowning, as he said briskly, 'You need to get those wet things off and have a hot bath.'

Common sense. But if she did that he'd be gone by the time she'd finished. Wouldn't he? She shook her head and gasped as the room swam round. 'I want—'

'A hot bath,' he stated firmly. 'You're on the point of collapse.'

He carried her up the stairs that led directly from the kitchen and she let him, winding her arms around his neck, clinging on weakly. Could he possibly have meant that he'd loved her for all this time, as she had loved him, deep in her heart?

Had she done or said something since their marriage to convince him that it wouldn't work?

He pushed at the door to one of the suites with his foot. So this was where he'd slept last night. His open suitcase was on the floor, the suit he'd arrived in flung all anyhow over the back of one of the chairs.

Marching through to the *en suite* bathroom, he propped her like a doll against the washbasin and bent to run hot water into the bath.

She said to his back, 'What happened to make you

think our marriage wouldn't work, that not even Rosie was worth staying on for?'

He swung round, straightening. He said thickly, 'You know what happened. We made love. When I proposed marriage with a non-consummation pact, I believed I could hack it, for Rosie's sake. I knew that if I ever gave in to the temptation to touch you I'd be putting myself through the emotional mill again. You'd had me on the rack before; I wasn't going to put myself there again—but I wanted our child to have two parents. Why do you think I cut our so-called honeymoon short? Because I wanted to make it a real one. I held you in my arms and wanted you like hell.

'So I dumped you back at the cottage and took off. I put my lawyers to work on tracking down the em-bezzled money—they traced it to a Swiss account and I heard yesterday that they've managed to release it through a court order. It's yours, by the way—your independence. Then, for the rest of that first time away, all I did was try to get my head straight. I didn't dare make our marriage a real one. I came back and look what happened—I took you to bed. It was the worst thing I could have done under the circumstances as I saw them then. I was laying myself open to the Lord alone knew how much hurt at the hands of the woman who'd kept my child from me, who had vowed she loved me in one breath then swanned off to marry a man with better prospects. So I removed myself from temptation and decided to call it a day. I couldn't handle it.'

He began to strip off her wet clothes and she saw how his hands shook. Her heart took wings.

'My brain's gone silly,' she whispered. 'Are you telling me you still want me as much as ever?' And dared she say it? 'That you still love me?'

He had stripped off the last wisp of underwear, and his eyes were smoky. 'I'll tell you if you promise that what you said while I was covering myself with drama down on the beach was true.'

'That I love you, that I never stopped?' She looked up at him with love-drenched eyes, her lashes wet with unshed tears. 'I swear it on our daughter's life!'

'That's got to be good enough for me!' His voice was gruff as he scooped her up and put her in the warm water. 'I love you, probably more than you'll ever know, and I don't intend to lose you to a chill, or worse.' He smiled at her through the haze of steam, that wonderful, bone-melting smile that never failed to make her lose her head.

But his eyes were moist with emotion as he touched her wet hair. 'Let's make this day the beginning of our marriage, keep this anniversary as our special secret.'

The radiance of her smile lit up the room. She held up her arms to him. 'I'm not the only one in danger of catching a chill. Why don't you join me? The water's lovely.'

Adam needed no second invitation. And when he slipped in behind her he stretched his legs along the length of hers, his hands taking the place of the scented water that lapped her breasts.

Claudia wriggled back ecstatically into his body, a

whole future of loving this man stretching enticingly before her. She turned her head to kiss the side of his jaw and whispered, 'I've got something to tell you.'

'I don't want to know.' His deep voice was tender, threaded with amusement. 'Talking's the last thing on my mind.'

'So I gather!' The extent of his arousal was impossible to ignore. Ignoring it was the last thing on *her* mind. But she said, 'Yes, you do. Want to know, that is.' Her words ended on a gasp as he began to nuzzle her neck. 'I'll set you a riddle.'

He groaned. His mouth moved along the damp skin of her shoulder, his hands stroking her breasts. His groan was more visceral; his brain was reluctant to engage in guessing games.

'What happens when two people get carried away on a tide of unstoppable passion?' she asked huskily. Her whole body was on fire now, burning beneath his caresses.

She'd turned her head to him and he leaned forward to take her lips, teasing them, his tongue playing with hers. 'This?' he asked throatily.

'No, no, no! Pay attention!' She tried to sound like a schoolmarm and failed. A giggle built up inside her. 'They don't stop to think of precautions. They just get carried away. At least, I don't know about anyone else, but that's what seems to happen to us.'

He went very still. She leaned back against him, no longer afraid of his reaction. Not even when he exited the bath in a shower of water, scooped her out and wrapped her in a huge, fluffy towel.

He carried her to the bed and laid her down, sitting

close to her, his eyes holding hers intently. 'Another baby?'

She nodded. His silver eyes were suspiciously bright. Tears or bath water? She levered herself up and tasted the moisture with her tongue. It was salt.

'Clo, my dearest love. You waited up for me last night to tell me.' He sounded in no doubt about the truth of that. 'And all I could do was give you a verbal thrashing.'

'Don't!' She reached out and drew him down onto the bed beside her. This was a happy time. The happiest. 'No more looking back,' she whispered against his mouth. 'Only forward.'

'Only forward,' he agreed, and sweetly deepened the kiss.

The welcome-home dinner was a huge success. Claudia felt as if she was wrapped in warmth and roses, never far from her husband's side, their eyes meeting, silently speaking to each other of deeply passionate love and tender devotion.

Rosie had been allowed to stay up. Claudia had put her in her very best dress, then picked out a pair of honey-gold, silky-soft trousers, matching jacket and cream-coloured camisole for herself.

She felt beautiful for the first time in her life, and by the way Adam looked at her she knew she wasn't kidding herself.

Amy had excelled herself and when they'd finished the first course Claudia insisted, 'Stay right where you are; you've done enough, Amy. I'll clear the dishes and bring in the pud.'

'It's only one of my trifles.' The housekeeper made it sound like nothing to get excited over, but her face was pink with pride at the compliments her beef Wellington and tender vegetables had earned her.

Guy insisted on helping her and while she was stacking the used dishes in the dishwasher he said, 'So, finally, everything's all right between you two.'

Claudia's face went pink. Could he tell that she and Adam had spent most of the afternoon in bed together? Her back still firmly turned, she asked, her attempt at lightness ruined by a husky delivery, 'What are you trying to say?'

'I tried not to let it show, but you two had me worried for a while.' His voice was amused but laced with deep affection. 'Seeing you together, six years ago, I knew you were meant for each other. Then Adam disappeared and you married Tony. I knew Rosie was Adam's child—the likeness was remarkable—and when he reappeared and dropped his marriage bombshell I guessed it was for the sake of the child and prayed you'd eventually get it together again.'

She straightened then, facing him. She should have remembered how perceptive her father was where her interests were concerned. About to reassure him, he did the job himself, his eyes twinkling at her. 'My prayers were answered. That air of invincible togetherness is back again. Come here.'

She went into his open arms and returned his hug. She couldn't speak for a long, emotional moment. She was surrounded by love and warmth and so much happiness. Her heart swelled to contain her huge joy and she managed throatily, 'Better carry the trifle through before Rosie expires from thwarted expectation!'

Together, she and Adam finally put their sleepy daughter to bed then walked down the great staircase, hand in hand.

'Shall we tell them the news about the new baby tonight, Clo? Or would you rather wait until it's confirmed, until you're quite sure?'

'Oh, I'm sure.' She grinned up at him. 'Would I have told you if I hadn't been?' She tugged at his hand. 'Let's tell them. Amy will have the coffee ready by now, and if I know Dad he'll unearth a bottle of champagne from somewhere!'

She was right on both counts, correct in assuming they'd be as delighted as she and Adam were. Adam touched his foaming glass to the modest inch in hers—a concession to her condition—and said, his eyes smiling into hers, 'From now on I'm the complete family man. What I can't handle from home will be delegated. I'm going to be changing nappies and wiping bibs well into the distant future!'

His secret meaning, just for the two of them, made her melt with happiness. This was her man, her love, and their future was only just beginning.

Susan Fox grew up on an acreage near Des Moines, Iowa. She has raised two sons, Jeffrey and Patrick, and currently lives with her feline friends in a house that she laughingly refers to as the Landfill and Book Repository. She's a movie fan and a bookaholic, with a variety of reading interests, who loves writing complex characters in emotionally intense situations. Susan hopes readers enjoy her stories and are uplifted by their happy endings.

Watch out for Susan Fox's latest emotionally uplifting story:
THE MARRIAGE COMMAND
On sale now, in Tender Romance™!

AN ARRANGED
MARRIAGE
by
Susan Fox

CHAPTER ONE

BLUE SUMNER rarely had anything given to him. The death of his mother when he was four years old had cut him off from the simple, exquisitely tender kind of giving that comes from the gentle heart and hands of a good mother. He'd learned quick not to expect anything to magically come his way, not love and certainly not anything more than what it took to keep body and soul together. As the son of a cowboy drifter who had spent more time drunk and out of work than sober and employed, Blue had grown up at the mercy of strangers who either pitied or scorned him.

The drive to amount to something, to work himself to death if need be so he could make a good life and have a home, had got hold of him before he was out of grade school. By the time he'd turned fourteen, he'd been so obsessed to make something of himself that he'd quit school, lied about his age and gone to work full-time on the biggest ranch in the county. Later, he studied for his GED in his spare time, then passed the test for his high school diploma about the time his old classmates were halfway through their freshman year of college.

As a boy who had faced daily ridicule for the poor quality of his clothes and his social ignorance, the loss of high school had been insignificant. His childhood

5

had already been lost, crushed out by the hardscrabble life of a drunk's son. He'd had to find success at something else, anything that would elevate his bad feelings about himself and give him a reason to leave liquor alone and stay on the right side of the law.

From the time he'd got his first job on that big ranch, he'd worked twelve-hour days, seven days a week. Days off were rare, vacations unheard of, but he'd persisted, saving every dollar he could get his hands on, until he'd at last put together enough money to take out a loan on a place of his own.

Eight years ago, he'd become the proud mortgage holder of a modest ranch. He'd sweated and bled over that piece of ground, living in the small run-down house that still had a room with a dirt floor, while he caught work for wages on some of the larger outfits.

The land itself had been rugged enough to nearly kill him. He'd raised animals that were dangerous on their good days, delivered their offspring, doctored their ailments, treated them like prize pups—and sold them for every nickel he could get. He'd lived lonely and hard, doing without a lot of things others took for granted, chasing the mirage of home and respectability...

Until the day he discovered that every inch of the dirt he'd slaved over just happened to be sitting on top of the richest new oil strike in a four-county area.

It was amazing what a sudden eight-figure net worth did for a man. Amazing and enlightening. Things he could only wish for in the past could now be his in the time it took to toss down a piece of plastic or write out a check. From the moment the news of his good luck had circulated, he'd been accorded a deference that had taken him aback the first few times.

He got invited to all kinds of high-toned get-togethers, about a million salesmen left messages on his new answering machine and every mother with an unmarried daughter made sure he'd been introduced and asked to supper. People who'd always kept a wary distance from him now went out of their way to speak to him or do business with him.

And though he could now buy anything he wanted and could do whatever he pleased, it shocked him a little to suddenly discover that the things he wanted most—a home, a family and respectability—had more to do with the quality of the woman he chose to marry than the sweat, blood and sacrifice that had brought him this far.

Because Blue Sumner had rarely had anything given to him, he knew right off that the kind of woman he was looking for could only be his for a price. A quality woman wouldn't willingly marry a man who'd come from what he'd come from; she'd never be interested in a man who'd grown up rough-mannered and hard. And because she wouldn't, Blue didn't intend to give her a choice.

Allison Lancaster drove her car to the mansion on the Sumner ranch, but stopped a distance down the driveway. Several vans and trucks, which she assumed belonged to various building contractors and their workers, took up much of the driveway space nearest the house. Leery of blocking the driveway, she angled her car to the side of the gravel and switched off the engine. She reached to the seat beside her for her handbag, then paused to stare at the huge house.

She'd heard Blue Sumner was building one of the finest homes around, and though it was still weeks from completion, she could see that it was just as impressive as the gossips had said.

The huge two-and-a-half story house was built in a Victorian style with a deep, roof-shaded veranda around the entire main floor. The house fairly shouted wealth and good taste, but Allison couldn't reconcile the sight of the house with her image of the rugged, elemental man who'd ordered it built.

For what had to be the hundredth time that morning, she mentally reviewed the handful of times her path had crossed Blue Sumner's. She'd never been able to quite forget the tall, hard-looking man who nodded respectfully to her each time they met on the street. She'd never understood the reason for the wild flutter in her middle the time his fiery blue eyes had blazed down at her from beneath his hat brim as he'd handed her a donation for a school fund-raiser.

And the time she'd been stranded on a country road by a flat tire. Why she could still remember the smell of sweat and leather and hot gravel, and could still recall the odd little sensations she'd felt as she'd watched him change the tire, defied explanation. But something about the way the ruggedly handsome rancher's big, work-callused hands had handled the task had riveted her.

Allison was suddenly aware that she was trembling. The shocking message her uncle Charles had given her that morning had upset her. And since the message had been from Blue Sumner, this foolish review of disturbing memories didn't help.

She tightened her grip on her handbag and opened the door to get out of the car. The sounds of hammers and electric hand tools filled the country air. The newly built ranch buildings and corrals she could see a distance away seemed just as active, with horses, cattle and ranch hands scattered around. At least she wouldn't be alone with the man.

She tried to settle her nerves as she walked with determined poise toward the huge front doors of the mansion, then groaned with frustration when she realized that a fine sheen of perspiration had broken out across her pale brow. As she walked, she took out a tissue and discreetly blotted her face, appalled that her hands were shaking by the time she slipped the tissue back into the handbag.

Remembering what Blue looked like, recalling her feminine reaction to his macho intensity had undermined her somehow. And now that she was on the verge of speaking to him face-to-face, the memory of his outrageous message struck fear in her heart. Surely he hadn't been serious.

Blue watched Allison's arrival from one of the unfinished guest rooms on the second floor of his new house. The woman was the very soul of femininity. From the shiny crown of her shoulder-length blond hair to the toes of her high heels, Allison Lancaster was petite, refined and as elegant as royalty.

The white linen dress she was wearing with the matching handbag and shoes probably cost more than the profit he'd made in any year of his life prior to striking oil. He couldn't imagine what her gold earrings, necklace or watch cost. All he knew was that now he could buy her hundreds of necklaces and watches and matching outfits, and never feel the slightest loss.

The prideful thought sent a breath of unease through him. Allison Lancaster was quality. She was used to the best. He could buy her the best—hell, he could snap his fingers and lay anything she wanted at her feet.

Anything except a gentleman husband.

The reminder chafed his pride and dimmed some of the pleasure he felt at the sight of her. But he'd learned that a man didn't have to be a gentleman to get what he wanted in this life. Not if he had money. And not if he was ruthless.

Blue turned away from the window and stalked from the room.

Allison hesitated just outside the open double doors at the front of the huge house, loathe to walk into the place unannounced. Though her uncle had told her that Blue had invited her to meet him there, good manners and caution prevented her from behaving with too much familiarity.

A short, wiry man appeared in the doorway. "You must be Miz Lancaster," he declared, then motioned her toward the door. "Mr. Sumner's waitin' for you inside."

Allison managed a stiff smile and started forward, her nerves jumping with tension and suspense. Once inside the huge entry hall, the man shouted a loud, "Noon break, boys, let's clear out," that startled her.

In a surprisingly brief time, workers came from every direction and swiftly exited the house. "Mr. Sumner'll be along directly, miss," the man told her before he, too, ducked out the front door.

Allison looked toward the windows and saw that the workers were all moving in the direction of the ranch buildings she'd seen earlier. The idea that they might be going all the way to the new cookhouse for lunch increased her nervousness. Suddenly the big house seemed quite isolated from the rest of the ranch headquarters. Uneasy with the notion of being alone with Blue, Allison glanced nervously toward the open doors.

The deep, rough drawl that echoed in the large, empty rooms gave her no time to make a graceful exit.

"I'm obliged to you for comin' out."

Allison jumped at the sound of the man's voice and couldn't help that she whirled to face him.

Blue Sumner's hard gaze seemed to swallow her whole as he came toward her. She suddenly had the impression that he saw everything about her, including the light shiver that raised tiny goose bumps on her arms.

At well over six foot, Blue was a big man—lean, powerfully built, with overlong black hair that dragged on his collar and a harsh, weather-tanned face that proclaimed him a man equal to the elements. The deep blue of his eyes beneath his hat brim met hers with blunt force, the hard sparkle in their depths no-nonsense and faintly dangerous. With his black Stetson, chambray shirt, worn Levi's and boots, all it would take was a six-gun strapped to his lean hips to make him look like an old-time gunslinger/outlaw.

Another shiver, this one deep down, sent a virtual earthquake of awareness through her as he came to a halt less than an arm's length away. Blue Sumner was more blatantly male than any man she'd ever come in contact with, and suddenly everything female in her reacted with a shocking mixture of attraction and feminine fear.

She was still staring, a bit dazed, when one corner of his hard mouth turned up in a curve that was unamused. Just that quickly, she realized how rudely she was behaving and forced a faint smile while she made an effort to recover.

"I was…surprised at the invitation to meet you here, Mr. Sumner," she began with painful formality.

He stared at her with a piercing, see-it-all intensity that made her want to squirm. "The invitation surprised you," he stated, his voice low and a bit rough. "What about the marriage proposal?"

"The proposal…troubled me," she admitted unsteadily. "I thought we might clear things up if I came out to have a word with you."

She really did mean to go about this as kindly as possible. Uncle Charles believed that having Blue Sumner's money in his bank was crucial to the bank's survival, so she didn't dare offend the man. And, no matter how tough and hard and macho he seemed, she had no wish to insult his pride or hurt his feelings. She could not, however, marry a stranger or a man she didn't love, no matter how rich he was.

When Blue continued to stare at her, his gaze moving over her face as if he were examining her every feature in minute detail, Allison felt her breath go thin. But when that gaze lowered to make a leisurely chin to toe tour that lingered almost indecently on every curve, her heart nearly stopped.

In the next second, hot color flooded her face. That was the same second Blue's assessing gaze lifted to meet hers.

"Then you don't want to marry me." The statement was delivered in a surprisingly quiet voice. A quiet voice quite at odds with the tension she sensed about him suddenly.

Instinct warned her to be careful. She didn't know the man and didn't know anyone who did. Blue Sumner had not only never been a part of her aunt and uncle's social circle, but he didn't seem to have socialized with anyone in town. She'd heard gossip about him, his newfound wealth and what he was doing with his money, but she knew nothing personal about the man, aside from the fact that he was now the most sought-after bachelor in the area.

Allison made herself give a faint smile. "I don't know you, Mr. Sumner."

The tension in him seemed to ease at her soft reply. His gravelly, "There's a remedy for that," and his step toward her made her stiffen, though she managed to stand her ground.

Blue's eyes narrowed fractionally on her face as if he'd sensed how close she was to bolting. He reached for her bent elbow so smoothly and suddenly that she didn't have time to evade his touch.

The feel of his callus-rough fingers closing so firmly on her arm sent a shower of wild tingles over her skin. Reflexively Allison pulled back, but Blue's gentle grip kept her close. The smallest tug brought her that next step nearer, and Allison couldn't help that her free hand came up and landed on his shirt-front.

The blue cotton was hot to the touch, heated by the warm flesh of the man who wore it. Beneath her fingers, Blue's heart thudded at a steady pace while hers raced out of control. And now that she was staring up into his rugged, handsome face, she felt her knees weaken and begin to tremble.

Blue didn't miss a flicker of Allison's changeable facial expressions. Surprise, wariness, attraction, fear—not exactly the acceptance and desire he wanted to see when she looked at him. But that little hand pressed against his chest directly over his heart felt like the business end of a branding iron. Though she didn't mean it at all, somehow she was setting a mark on him.

"I'd like to show you the house," he said gruffly, easing back so her hand would fall away. He didn't release his gentle hold on her elbow, however, until they started out of the entry hall to begin their tour.

Allison was relieved when Blue's firm grip went slack and she was able to casually move her arm away. Normally, courtesy would have made her submit to this tour of his home. But courtesy had nothing to do with giving herself this time to recover her wits.

She could still feel the warm imprint of his fingers on her skin, was still trembling with the excitement his touch had set off. Finding her hand pressed to his chest—a gesture that seemed quite intimate—had shaken her. Even the occasional meeting of their gazes as they walked through the huge home sent little bolts of sexual awareness through her.

Desperate to distract herself, Allison looked around, making herself focus on each room and ask appropriate questions. She didn't have to force herself to admire the big house. The main floor boasted the large entry hall with an open staircase to the second floor, a living room, dining room, den, small parlor, family room, a vast kitchen and a double suite of rooms for a live-in cook and housekeeper.

The second floor featured a master suite with an old-fashioned nursery connected and a walk-in closet easily half as large as the master bedroom. There were six other bedrooms and another small suite of rooms near the back stairs for a butler.

Allison couldn't help her curiosity. "A butler?"

Blue's gaze met hers, then ricocheted away. "Was invited to a house party in Dallas where they had a butler. I admired the order of the house he kept."

They ended in the spacious kitchen downstairs. "The decorator's planned out for curt—er, *window treatments* and carpets," Blue told her as he leaned back against a counter, his arms crossed over his chest, "but you can meet with her tomorrow to see if you approve."

He ignored her startled look and went on. "You can pick the furniture, just so our bed or anything I have to use isn't fussy or womanish. Or white, since I'm still a rancher and always will be."

Allison stared in mild shock as he casually laid out his plan for her to meet with his decorator and furnish his home. She'd been hoping that sometime during the tour he'd come to his senses and realize what folly it was for either of them to take his marriage proposal seriously.

Instead, submitting to the tour seemed to have signaled to him some measure of her consent. Allison shook her head. "Mr. Sumner—please understand. As flattering as your proposal is, I can't possibly marry you."

The hard gaze he leveled on her made her uneasy. "Not good enough, huh?"

It took her a moment to recover from the blunt question. And a moment more to register the flash of emotion behind the words.

"Good enough has nothing to do with my refusal,

Mr. Sumner. We don't *know* each other," she emphasized with gentle candor.

"And if we knew each other?"

The question unsettled her and Allison fought to suppress her sudden, secret reaction to the idea as she tried to give him a calm answer.

"We could know each other well and still not have the kind of love a marriage requires. I can't marry a man I'm not in love with. And I don't think you'd truly be happy marrying a woman you aren't in love with, either."

"Love..." The cynical gleam in his gaze chided her. "Love's nothing more than a rush of lust and hormones that fools mistake for sentiment. Soon as the lust is satisfied, the hormones settle. That's when those same fools think they've fallen out of *love*." His faint emphasis mocked the word.

Allison was taken aback. "You don't believe in love?"

The level look he gave her somehow made her sad. "Love's right up there with Santa and the Easter Bunny, Miz Lancaster. Kid myths, but myths all the same," he said, then went on somberly. "I wasn't born to wealth and I'm not college educated, but I'm steady, reliable and hardworking. I'll be a faithful, sober husband, a good father to my kids and a good provider to a faithful wife."

Allison glanced away, caught off guard by the intensity of his declaration, but struck by the absolute sincerity of it. Love was a myth to him, yet the things he wanted couldn't be achieved without it.

Thoughts of her aunt Petula's loveless marriage to Charles filled her mind. Uncle Charles had never been faithful to Aunt Pet and had never provided anything for Pet that hadn't originally come from her large inheritance. Because Charles had never loved her aunt, he'd never been interested in having children with her. Because he'd never loved her, their home was anything but warm and loving.

Allison's memories of her own parents, killed when she was only nine, were of two people completely in love who doted on each other and on the child their love had created. Allison hungered for that kind of love, that kind of marriage.

The alternative, represented by Charles and Petula's coldly formal relationship, was unacceptable. No matter how wonderful Blue's pledge sounded now, how long would it take for the loveless union he wanted to go wrong?

Allison made herself look directly at Blue as she spoke. "Those are honorable goals, Mr. Sumner. I think you must be quite a good man to have them." She hesitated, clenching her handbag in front of her to keep her hands from fluttering as wildly as her insides were fluttering. "But I can't marry a man who doesn't value love."

Blue didn't blink, didn't seem to even take a breath before he drawled, "Then your answer is no."

Allison somehow maintained eye contact with the burning probe of his gaze. "My answer is no."

Blue glanced down briefly, his eyes hidden by the brim of the Stetson he'd worn during their tour of the house. At just the moment Allison felt a strange tug of sympathy, the black hat brim lifted to reveal the determination in his gaze.

His low, ''Then I'll have to find a way to change your mind,'' came out in a raspy drawl that sent a flood of heat through her. The way he was looking at her now—as if he were about to grab her up and carry her off to a cave somewhere—made his declaration as much a threat as a promise.

A confusing mix of dismay and excitement sent color into her cheeks and a flush over her skin. Allison couldn't speak, couldn't move. The peculiar attraction she'd felt toward Blue in the past suddenly escalated to something breathlessly sensual and compelling. The notion that he meant to change her mind about marrying him was dizzying.

But the fact that he might somehow be successful terrified her. Surely she could never be seduced into marrying a stranger who didn't believe in love. But as she stood there frozen, unable to look away from Blue Sumner's ruggedly handsome face, she realized she might be in danger of doing just that.

Somehow, she regained her composure. Her stiff, ''Good afternoon, Mr. Sumner,'' and her abrupt turn and stilted exit from the huge kitchen did nothing to break the sensual pull between them. Though she was aware that Blue's booted stride echoed hers down the long hall to the entry and the front door, she managed to maintain a dignified pace.

She didn't breathe normally until she was safely out the door and was halfway down the graveled driveway to where she'd left her car.

CHAPTER TWO

ALLISON'S nerves were still jittery by the time she returned to town. To her surprise, Uncle Charles had come home early from the bank, and he was waiting in the formal living room with Aunt Petula when she came in.

"Hello, dear," Aunt Pet called as Allison walked into the tastefully appointed room. Petula was sitting on one of the three white sofas that were grouped around the low crystal coffee table. Charles stood near the liquor cabinet, his face expectant. A bottle of champagne rested in a silver bucket of shaped ice on a sofa table.

Allison's soft, "Hello all," was cautious as she stopped at the sofa and rested a hand on its back. She saw at a glance that Aunt Pet's expression was tense. Charles was almost never home in the middle of a banking day. The bucket of champagne and the warm look Charles was giving her combined to send a tiny arrow of alarm through her.

Charles didn't hesitate. "We trust you and Mr. Sumner have set the date."

Allison stared a moment as a feeling of unreality slipped over her. Charles was clearly pleased and excited. A swift glance at Aunt Pet caught Pet's nervous smile. All at once she realized that both of them must have expected her to accept Blue Sumner's astonishing marriage proposal.

Though Charles had already made it clear, in spite of her objections, that he was strongly in favor of her accepting Blue's proposal, until that moment she hadn't realized how eager he was for a marriage—and how certain he was that she'd accept. Which was amazing because she and Blue Sumner were complete strangers with almost nothing in common!

She answered hesitantly, "Well…no, Uncle."

"But you went out and spoke to him, saw the house," Charles prompted cheerily. "I'm certain he'll allow you to decorate it as you like. Most men are inept at that sort of thing," he went on, oblivious to Allison's growing look of alarm. "Sumner might have a lot of rough edges, but he's filthy rich now, and I doubt there's anything material he would deny you, as long as you're willing to make him a proper wife."

Allison quickly said, "I've rejected Mr. Sumner's proposal, Uncle."

Charles hesitated in the process of opening the champagne bottle to glance over at her, his wide smile faltering. "What was that?"

The silence stretched. Suddenly she was hesitant to repeat the words. Her mouth went dry. "I've rejected Mr. Sumner's proposal. I was as diplomatic as possible," she assured him when she saw the pleasantness drain from his face. "I'm certain he sees, as do I, that it would be better for him to wait and marry someone he's in love with."

Charles eased the bottle back down into the ice. His face flushed and his mouth flattened to a harsh line. He glared over at Petula, who was staring down at her clasped hands.

"I thought I made it clear to both of you—" his angry glance included Allison "—how important this marriage is. I'd hoped to avoid reminding either of you of the reason Chaney Bank is on the verge of insolvency, but I can see now that I should have been more direct."

A sick feeling swept Allison. The bank was struggling and Charles blamed her. Her college friend, John Blake, had worked at the bank until three weeks ago. Because he'd been so bright and capable, Charles had rapidly advanced him. Later, when an internal audit showed a huge amount of money missing from the accounts, Charles had suspected John right away.

He claimed that her reluctance to believe John capable of embezzlement had made him look elsewhere for a culprit, which resulted in the loss of an even greater sum. Days later, John Blake abruptly quit his job and left town. It was shortly after that when Charles realized not only the extent of the embezzlement, but that her friend was undoubtedly the thief.

"I never would have hired John Blake were it not for my affection for you, Allison, and my regard for your wishes," he said, his cultured voice arrogantly smooth, though he was clearly very angry. "Now, I think you should feel obligated to honor mine."

Allison felt as if a subtle trap were closing on her. She rallied to evade it. "Have you notified the authorities?'' She still couldn't believe that John was a thief, and Charles's certainty in the matter—as well as his method of dealing with the theft—continued to distress her.

''I explained why I wanted to handle the situation discreetly,'' he snapped. ''I can't help that the private investigators I've hired haven't been able to turn up anything.''

''Surely the accounts were federally insured against the loss,'' she reasoned. ''Besides, federal authorities have more resources—''

''That may be,'' he said, cutting in irritably, his voice rising, ''but the bank can hardly afford to have it become common knowledge that one of our own employees embezzled enough money to leave the bank insolvent.''

Charles's face was mottled and he was glaring almost hatefully at her. Allison was shocked.

''Blue Sumner can give this bank the kind of business it needs to stay on its feet,'' he declared. ''You, my dear, are the woman he has chosen to marry. Once he's a member of the family, I'm certain he'll be more open to not only transferring his accounts to us, but he'll naturally turn to me to be his financial advisor.''

Allison saw a small chance to avoid her part in Charles's plan and dared to ask, ''Has he guaranteed that he will transfer his accounts and have you advise him?'' On one hand, it would be foolish for Charles to marry her off to a rich stranger in order to attract his business, with no guarantee that he'd do so. On another, marrying her off to Blue Sumner to get his

business and have access to his money was tanta-
mount to selling her.

Charles pointed at her as if he were scolding a
naughty child. "You do your part and accept his proposal. Leave the business end of it to me."

Allison felt dizzy. Charles's scheme to save the
bank was unbelievable. Unbelievable and medieval
and ridiculous.

Charles's harsh, "You talk to her, Petula," tightened the knot of dread in her middle. "Maybe you
can make her see what an ingrate she's become. I'm
going back to the bank."

Neither Allison nor Petula spoke as Charles stalked
through the house and slammed out the front door.
Allison released a shaky breath and looked over at her
Aunt Petula.

Petula Lancaster Wallace was still a beautiful
woman. Though well into her fifties, her hair was still
blond, her fair skin still taut and the only wrinkles she
had of note were faint ones at the corners of her eyes
and around her lovely mouth.

But Aunt Petula seemed to have aged a good ten
years during Charles's brief tirade.

Allison stepped forward and came around the edge
of the sofa to sit down opposite Petula, the crystal
table between them. The silence in the wake of
Charles's temper was ominous. Petula's delicate fingers were shaking and she wouldn't meet Allison's
gaze.

Allison felt her heart swelling. Petula had taken her
in after her parents had been killed. No one else in

their far-flung family had seemed to want her, but Aunt Pet had.

Petula's motivation to take her in had far surpassed her sense of duty to raise her younger brother's only child. Petula had genuinely loved her and wanted her, and somehow she'd managed to soften the pain of the incredible loss Allison had suffered and brighten the life of a grief-stricken child.

Not surprisingly, Allison dearly loved her aunt, and Petula's happiness and well-being were even more important to her than her own.

And because it was suddenly all coming home to Allison that the bank was much worse off than she'd thought and that Aunt Pet seemed even more upset in her own way than Charles had been, Allison couldn't help feeling a little desperate. Finally she spoke.

"Is the bank truly so bad off that I might need to..." Her voice drifted off. Somehow she'd not been able to say the words "marry Mr. Sumner." "Forgive me, Auntie, but I'm...stunned." Her soft words seemed to increase Pet's distress.

Petula's blue gaze lifted to hers and welled tragically. Before she could speak, Allison quickly stood and rounded the table to sit with her aunt and take her small, beringed fingers in hers.

"Aunt Pet?"

Petula squeezed her eyes shut and a tear slipped down her pale cheek. Her choked, "I'm afraid the bank is quite bad off," was the prelude to more tears.

Stricken by her aunt's distress, Allison hugged Petula and felt tears sting her own eyes. Aunt Pet rarely cried. She was always pleasant and mild-mannered, and considered strong emotional displays a breach of etiquette.

Pet returned her hug almost fiercely. When she managed to get control of herself, she leaned back to lift a trembling hand to Allison's cheek.

"Oh, my sweet girl, the last thing I want is for you to marry some Neanderthal, whose only claim to respectability is that he's savvy enough to use his new fortune to buy it." Her fragile features stiffened and her pale cheeks flushed with fresh spirit. "I don't care if the bank closes and Charles loses everything. There *must* be some other solution than to condemn you to a loveless marriage to a cowboy."

Secretly Allison was heartsick. In spite of Pet's declaration, she was suddenly terrified that marriage to Blue Sumner would turn out to be the only solution to the bank's problems. Even worse, she was afraid that marrying Blue Sumner would turn out to be no solution at all.

Two days later, Allison found herself back at the Sumner Ranch in the late afternoon. Her aunt was now bedridden with nerves. Dr. Evans had been out to see her, but other than assuring them that Pet would be all right and that she'd probably be up and around soon, there'd been no substantial change in her condition.

The situation at the bank was little better. Charles hadn't missed an opportunity to pressure her, and her own secret feelings of guilt about John Blake had

worn her down. Finally she agreed to go to the
Sumner Ranch to speak again with Blue.

Charles had assured her that he'd already phoned
Blue and had, he claimed, smoothed things over.
Allison couldn't imagine that it had been that simple.
If Blue had any pride at all, giving a woman a second
opportunity to turn down his marriage proposal would
be anathema to him.

Allison's own pride was choking her. It was bad
enough that she was virtually being sold. It was even
worse to have to humble herself and drive out to the
ranch to grovel before a man who might delight in
turning the tables and rejecting her.

Two days ago, she would have rejoiced at the notion that Blue would lose interest in marrying her. But
after two days of Aunt Pet's depression and distress,
Allison realized she was willing to do anything to help
her aunt recover.

For all Pet's talk of wanting to spare her an arranged marriage, Allison was beginning to believe it
was impossible to save the bank any other way. Pet
had been born to wealth and had lived an upper-class
lifestyle. Allison knew well the terror of the rich when
it came to thoughts of losing their fortune.

And Pet's fear of public scandal was almost path-
ological. If the bank failed, Charles would naturally
be considered responsible. His judgment would be
suspect because of his failure to notify the proper authorities in a timely manner, and therefore his financial reputation would be sullied. Allison had no idea
how it would all impact their personal finances, but

the chance that it might prove disastrous was enough
to make her take this desperate step.

Aunt Pet had loved her and given her a good home
with all the financial advantages a child could possibly have. Allison would never be able to repay her
Aunt's generosity but, as Charles had so brutally
pointed out, marrying Blue was her one grand opportunity to do so.

And so she walked up the sidewalk to the veranda
that surrounded the new mansion. Today was Sunday,
so there were no workers around. Though she was
naturally apprehensive about being alone with Blue,
in many ways it was a blessing. No one would be
around to witness the scene if he'd changed his mind
about giving her another chance.

And, if she was truly going to marry him, she'd be
alone with him often. She might as well begin to adjust to him now, however much the notion panicked
her.

The large double doors were closed, their oval
etched glass panels providing a framed view of the
huge empty entry hall beyond. Allison walked up to
the door, then caught sight of the doorbell on the right
and put out a hand to press the button. She listened
nervously to the chimes as they sounded a series of
deep-pitched tones.

Blue had watched Allison approach the house from
the shelf-lined front room of the mansion, which
would eventually be the den. He'd glimpsed the apprehension on her lovely face when she'd stepped out

of her car. He'd seen the resolute squaring of her narrow shoulders as she'd started up the walk, then the
determined concealment of her feelings when she'd
blanked her expression.

His pride hadn't suffered at all when she'd refused
to marry him the other day, but it was taking a beating
now. Charles Wallace's spineless groveling on the
phone had turned his stomach, but the sense he had
that Wallace had bullied Ms. Allison into changing
her mind shamed him a little.

Though Blue had never wanted her to have any real
choice about marrying him, the actual follow-through
of his plan to get her made him feel as if he'd abused
her somehow. Demeaned wasn't a word in his normal
vocabulary, but he felt like maybe he'd managed to
demean them both. Particularly since she'd seemed to
set a lot of store by love, an emotion that by habit
and necessity, he'd learned to ignore.

But he hadn't worked his way up from the poverty
and homelessness of his childhood by being soft or
by veering from the goals he'd set for himself.
Marrying Allison Lancaster was just the next goal on
his list. If he thought of her in those terms, what he
had to do to get her troubled him less.

He turned away as she put out a hand to ring the
doorbell. He strode from the den into the entry hall
and then to the front door. The big chimes were echoing away when he opened it.

Allison's soft, ''May I come in?'' was a bit breathless. Blue wasn't wearing his black Stetson, but he
seemed a giant somehow. His handsome face was

stern, though she detected a faint wariness in the blue of his eyes.

He didn't answer verbally, but opened the big door to allow her to enter. She took four or five steps across the marble floor before she came to an uncertain halt and turned toward him.

He'd closed the door and stood staring over at her. Nothing in his expression gave her a clue to his thoughts until he said, ''I put an old desk and a couple of chairs in the front room there—the den.'' The gesture he made signaled her to precede him. Allison walked toward the open door and stepped through. Blue entered behind her and pushed the door not quite shut.

''The furniture is old and ugly, but it'll do until the house is done and I can get to Dallas to buy something better.''

His offhand remark about the old desk and the paint-spattered chairs seemed a sensible one to make, but something in his voice suggested he was somehow ashamed of it. A swift glance at his hard expression made her think she'd imagined the impression.

He reached for the folded white sheet that rested on a corner of the desk. He picked up the sheet and gave it a flick that unfolded it before he draped it over the better of the two mismatched chairs. He automatically repositioned the other chair opposite hers to straddle it and sit down before he realized she hadn't moved.

As if he were a schoolboy who realized he'd forgotten his manners, Blue abruptly stood up and waved a hand toward the sheeted chair. "Go ahead and sit down, Miz Allison. The sheet's new. Your dress will be fine."

Allison moved toward the chair and sat down stiffly, though her face was hot. She hadn't hesitated because she was afraid of getting her dress dirty. "I don't worry about my clothing as much as you might imagine, Mr. Sumner. I was waiting for you to invite me to sit."

Blue slowly eased back down and rested his muscular forearms across the chair back. He gave her a level look and said in a rough voice, "I reckon I don't need to tell you that I'm full of bad manners. Might be a while before I'm ready for polite society."

Allison stared at him, caught off guard by his directness. She felt herself soften toward him and found herself saying, "Good manners are really nothing more than making the other person feel comfortable."

"Then my manners must be especially bad," he said, his voice going lower and more raspy, "because you don't look too comfortable."

Allison glanced down at her clasped hands, a bit amazed to feel that her palms were damp. "It's the situation that makes me uncomfortable, Mr. Sum—"

"Blue."

The curt correction made her lift her eyes and look at him.

"The way you say Mr. Sumner makes me feel like I'm half a state away from you."

Allison's laced fingers flexed and her hands were gripping each other almost painfully. Wanting to ignore his remark about the distance she almost wished they had, she changed the subject. "I've come to ask you a few questions. Rather delicate ones."

Blue looked at her somberly. "Good. I don't want to worry about a question bein' delicate or not. We've got things to talk about and I'd rather you say what you mean."

Allison nodded, then got to the point. "My uncle seems to believe he's trading a niece for a multimillion-dollar bank account. He believes that once you're in the family, you'll allow him to advise you on financial matters."

Blue watched her calmly. "What I decide to do about your uncle and his bank is separate from you."

Allison tried to read his unsmiling expression. He'd worded his reply oddly and she wasn't certain how to take it. His face gave nothing away that would clarify his remark. Allison continued.

"Arranged marriages are usually about money. I feel as if—" she managed to get a breath "—as if I'm being bought."

"I need a wife," he said with that same unruffled calm. "I'm particular about the woman I want."

"But there are lots of women in Texas, Mr.—Blue. There must be hundreds of women around, even for a man who's particular about the woman he wants."

His unsmiling expression cracked a bit and one corner of his mouth quirked downward. "I reckon by now just about every available female in Texas has thrown herself into my path. Money seems to make 'em bold."

"So you think they only want you for your money? How are they different from…me?"

"Because you're the one I want." The low drawl wrapped around her. She sensed the intensity behind the burning look he was giving her and felt her heart flutter as his masculinity overwhelmed her.

In that moment she glimpsed his utter determination to marry her, by whatever means. He wasn't touching her, he didn't even try, but she felt his possession as surely as if he'd swept her into his arms.

Some bit of self-preservation—and selfishness—prompted her to tell him, "This isn't the marriage I'd hoped to have."

"It's the one I want."

The simple statement should have made her angry. After all, it was a blunt reminder of their inequality—of the fact that they weren't equals, that he had all the money and all the choices. And that she had none.

But Allison sensed another meaning behind the words. A man from Blue's background, who didn't believe in love, might not want to get a wife any other way. And, she realized, a man with social limitations might not know how.

The perception kept her from taking offense.

"Do you have a date in mind for the wedding?"

The date he named was only a bit more than a month away. Allison couldn't help the panic she felt.

"Th-then you prefer we see a justice of the peace?"

Blue shook his head. "I want it big, in your church, with your preacher, and grand enough that it makes the big city papers. If your uncle can't spring for everything, send the bills to me."

Allison couldn't conceal her reluctance to have the huge, very public wedding he wanted. "A wedding like that could cost a lot of money."

"How much?" His bluntness continued to take her aback.

"Why, a wedding such as the one you describe could cost upwards of twenty thousand dollars."

"I'm good for it."

She glanced away, not able to withstand the directness of his gaze. Or the embarrassment she felt at his offer to pay for an expensive wedding. She determined then that if it took every penny of her trust fund, she'd pay for her own wedding.

"That won't be necessary, Mr. S—"

"Blue." The soft drawl carried a faint demand that brought her gaze back to his. "A wife oughtta call her husband by his first name."

"Then you really want to go through with this." It was a statement she made so she couldn't possibly mistake things—or keep a reserve of hope.

That seemed to be the signal for him to stand. He straightened to his full height and swung his chair out of the way. With his blue gaze fixed purposely on hers, he stepped nearer and reached for her hand to pull her to her feet.

Flustered and excited by the strong, yet gentle grip of his callused fingers around hers, she couldn't break contact with the fiery gleam in his gaze.

"Just so there's no mistake about what I want. And

to help you remember there's no point in calling me Mr. Sumner..."

He caught her against him, lifting her slightly off the floor as his lips descended to hers. The kiss was only marginally gentle. Shock jolted her, and the involuntary gasp of air she took gave him the sudden access he needed to deepen the kiss. The blatant carnality of his mouth stole her breath and made her head spin.

The feel of his hard body was a new shock, and though she wasn't vastly experienced with men, even she knew he was aroused. His heat enveloped her while the forceful, yet expert invasion of her mouth turned her insides to a hot pulsing mass.

When he finally broke off the kiss, she was incapable of standing. She was only dazedly aware that she was clinging to him, and that even when his arms loosened around her, she was plastered against him.

"I reckon sex won't be something we have to put off till we know each other better," he remarked, his voice a husky rasp.

His words penetrated the sensual haze that fogged her brain, and she made a weak effort to shake her head. My God, she hardly knew the man!

As if he'd sensed her objection, his lips touched hers again. This time, his kiss was so tender, so wickedly persuasive, that she was incapable of thought. Years of well-bred reserve fell away, and she slid the manicured fingers of one hand into his thick dark hair and made a fist to hang on.

She'd been kissed before. She'd found kissing

pleasant enough, but nothing in her experience could have prepared her for either of Blue's kisses—the carnal devouring one, or this achingly sensual one that seemed to reach deep inside her and caress her very essence.

An emotion spiraled gently in her chest, swelling her heart. Before she could quite identify it, his lips eased away.

Her lashes fluttered up and she dizzily met the raging fire in his eyes.

"Say my name."

The demand was almost harsh, but Allison didn't feel threatened. Her soft, "Blue," was breathless with the sensuality that gripped her. She realized with some surprise that she'd moved her hand and that she was touching his lean cheek, stroking it.

Her even softer, "Blue," repeated the name that she suddenly realized would forever be attached to the strange new emotion she felt.

When Blue reached up to gently capture her fingers and pull them away from his cheek, she felt oddly disappointed. He slowly released her and eased her away from him.

The loss of his body heat seemed to calm the turbulent sensuality between them. But only slightly. Even when they were no longer touching, something a lot like raw electricity danced and snapped between them.

"I reckon you'll want to get yourself back to town and start makin' plans," he said gruffly. "I'll call on you tomorrow afternoon to see how you're comin' along.''

Allison was still too in thrall to speak. She felt an unexpected nick of pain when she sensed Blue withdraw emotionally. Suddenly aloof, he escorted her to the door, then outside and down the walk to her car. He opened the door for her, then shut it solidly once she was behind the wheel.

She drove all the way to the highway before she realized she was shaking violently.

CHAPTER THREE

THE month before the wedding passed in a frantic blur. Aunt Pet regained her good health and they both waded into wedding preparations like a pair of maniacs.

To her surprise, Allison rarely saw Blue, though she spoke to him daily on the phone to keep him apprised of wedding preparations. He sent his decorator to her aunt's house and even Aunt Pet was pleased by the plans he and the decorator had worked out, subject to Allison's approval.

At Aunt Pet's insistence, she and Allison spent an afternoon looking through the ranch mansion to give them both a better idea of the furnishings that would have to be bought. Though Aunt Pet was reserved and cautious with Blue and he was aloof with both of them, Aunt Pet came away from the ranch deeply impressed by the house he'd built.

Pet was sparing in her personal remarks to Allison about her future husband, but she did allow that Blue Sumner was ruggedly handsome and had a macho presence that could be considered exciting.

No one mentioned that this was an arranged marriage between two strangers, and sometimes Allison got so caught up in preparations that she almost forgot. Until she spoke to Blue on the phone or saw him face-to-face. He grew more remote by the day. It was as if the kisses they'd shared that Sunday afternoon had never happened. He seemed even more a stranger to her, and at times, she had to struggle to keep her downcast spirits about the marriage to herself.

While she and Pet were busy with the wedding details, Blue's house was finished and he set about ordering the furniture Allison had chosen. He also hired a butler, a cook and a housekeeper.

By the night of the rehearsal dinner, they remained little more than acquaintances. By mutual agreement, they'd limited their wedding party to a maid of honor and a best man, who turned out to be one of the wealthiest ranchers in the area.

Blue had once worked as a foreman for Ty Cameron, but their friendship seemed to have withstood Blue's distance and years away from the Cameron Ranch.

Charles was impressed by the connection between the two and, to Allison's horror, had immediately begun to speculate about attracting Ty to some of the mortgage investments he had in mind for Blue. His frequent comments about saving the bank continued to trouble her, as did his ongoing refusal to report the embezzlement.

Blue drove her directly home after the dinner, but they were more stilted than ever with each other. Their conversation was so sparse and infrequent that it was as if they hadn't spoken to each other at all.

On the night before her wedding, Allison laid in

her bed a long time, staring up into the darkness, certain she was about to make the mistake of her life.

The ceremony at Chaney Community Church was the largest ever held in Chaney, and the most perfect.

Allison had been to a lot of weddings. Something seemed to go wrong in every one of them, from a wedding cake that leaned off center, to a flower girl who dropped her basket of rose petals and burst into howls of dismay.

Nothing, however minor, went wrong at their wedding. On the other hand, everything was as wrong as it could possibly be.

Two strangers repeated vows to love, honor and cherish. Two strangers were pronounced man and wife. Two strangers turned fully toward each other, hesitated for the lifting of the veil, then pressed cool, stiff lips together at the preacher's enthusiastic, "You may now kiss your bride, Mr. Sumner."

Those same two strangers, perfectly poised and elegant in their wedding finery, smiled and walked down the aisle arm in arm. Later, they posed for wedding photos that the photographer swore were worthy of a high fashion layout.

Afterward, two strangers got into the limousine that took them to the Sumner Ranch for the reception. They officially received their guests, fed each other the traditional bite of wedding cake, then toured the gift room where a mountain of wedding presents had been displayed.

By the time Allison could slip up to the master

suite, where Aunt Pet would assist her with her gown, her nerves were shattered. The traveling suit she'd planned to wear to Dallas was laid out neatly on the huge bed, but suddenly, she was reluctant to face the idea of a honeymoon.

She'd not allowed herself to dwell on thoughts of what would come after the ceremony, but the sight of that pale pink suit on the bed triggered every worry and misgiving—every fear—that she'd repressed about their wedding night and all the other nights that would follow.

The memory of those two kisses a month of Sundays ago, flooded her mind. A flash of heat burst up from deep inside, and she suddenly felt dizzy.

I reckon sex won't be something we have to put off till we know each other better, Blue had said.

Allison couldn't recall that she'd actually voiced an objection, and she couldn't help the panic she felt.

Surely Blue wouldn't expect her to consummate their marriage right away. If he'd truly expected to, surely he would have taken time to actually court her these last weeks, or at the very least, he'd have given them time alone to get to know each other.

Allison pressed a shaky hand to her middle, then forced herself to give a little laugh. The stress of putting together the huge wedding on such short notice was beginning to tell on her. She was keyed up and exhausted and this worry about intimacy with Blue was likely nothing more than bridal nerves.

Determined to calm herself she crossed to the huge dresser mirror to start removing the hairpins that anchored her headpiece. She was facing a bit away from the mirror to reach an elusive pin when the bedroom door opened, then closed.

She called out a relieved, "There you are, Aunt Pet. I can't seem to locate all the pins—"

She turned her head to peer into the mirror's reflection of the room, expecting to see her aunt. Instead Blue stood just inside the door.

Slowly his eyes traced every bead and design detail of her gown, lingering hotly on every curve along the way. As almost an afterthought, his gaze at last came up to hers, and he stared intently at her flushed face.

The blatant lust in his gaze seemed to blaze higher. Allison was barely breathing.

"I was…expecting Aunt Pet," she said.

Blue's steady look never wavered. "She won't be coming up now."

Allison shook her head. "I need her help," she said as he started toward her. A fluttering cluster of nerves surged to her throat, choking her soft voice to a ragged whisper. "With the buttons."

Blue was so handsome in the severe black tuxedo that she couldn't make herself look away. The starched white of his shirt emphasized his tanned, weathered skin tones, which contrasted strikingly with the fiery blue of his eyes. The cut of the tuxedo faithfully followed his broad-shouldered, lean-hipped build, and Allison couldn't tell if she was excited or terrified by the sight of his breath-stealing physique.

Now that he could look at her as much as he liked, Blue couldn't keep his eyes off his bride. She was decked out like a fairy princess, all white lace and pearly beads and satin. The stiff white veil she still wore haloed her head and shoulders all the way to the floor, hinting at angel wings.

But it was her beautiful face that set it all off. Framed by curls and wispy gold ringlets, her face was flushed. Her eyes were nearly as vividly blue as his own, but wider, more innocent, kinder—though right now it would have been hard to miss the worry in them. Or the feminine interest. In the end, though, it was her lips that drew him: lush and sweet looking and almost cherry red.

The memory of how soft and crushable they'd felt, even though their wedding kiss had been bloodless and cool, burst in him like a craving. It took everything he had to keep from rushing her, to keep from grabbing her and devouring her as if she were a choice sweet.

Instead he moved slowly toward her, then stopped when his booted toes touched the belled hem of her dress.

His low "I'll help you with the dress" made the color in her cheeks go higher. He didn't realize until he felt the stiff netting between his fingers that he'd reached out to catch a pinch of her veil.

Allison could barely move, though her brain was struggling to save her. She couldn't possibly let Blue help her remove her dress. She wasn't ready for that kind—for any kind—of intimacy. "A-Aunt Pet wanted—"

"Aunt Pet's takin' care of other things," he

drawled as he lightly rolled the delicate netting between his thumb and fingers.

Allison tried again. "I need—"

"I'm your family now, Miz Allis," he said in a low voice that carried an edge of command. "From here on out, you're to look to me for the things she's always done for you."

She was so shocked by the order that it took her a moment to recover. Blue took advantage of that moment as he released the bit of veil, then reached for the headpiece that was still pinned to her hair.

The feel of his fingers gently searching for hairpins sent a warm flood of pleasure from her head to her toes, scattering her objection to his edict. Gently, one by one, he found every pin, tossing each to the polished top of the dresser. He removed the headpiece and set it aside on the dresser, leaving the sheer veil to cascade off the front of the dark wood like a white waterfall.

He stepped around her and she bit her lip to repress the flurry of shivers that began when he started on the tiny pearl buttons at the back of her gown. One after another, lower and lower he went, steadily releasing the buttons, his warm fingers grazing her bare back as he went. Allison had never imagined that anything so simple could be so arousing, but with every tug of fabric, every gentle brush of his strong, hard fingers, a spark ignited in her. Considering the number of buttons—perhaps fifty or more—by the time he reached the very end, Allison felt a conflagration building.

Just when she thought this was the end, that Blue

would leave her to undress in private, he placed his hands on her bare back. The heat of his callused palms scorched her and left her incapable of moving. She caught her breath when they pushed aside her open dress back, then slipped gently beneath the fabric.

The next thing she knew, he'd slid the gown off her shoulders. The neckline fell softly to her waist, exposing the bodice of her slip and the bra she wore beneath. Alarmed at being exposed—he could see her reflection in the dresser mirror—Allison clutched the front of the gown and tried to cover herself.

Blue's fingers caught the beaded fabric and prevented her from doing so. She felt a soft gust of breath on her bare skin, followed by the shocking feel of his mouth on the back of her neck.

He released the fabric and let his palms trail down to her waist and slip beneath the gown. He pulled her back against him while his lips moved almost hungrily along her neck and to her ear, where he kissed and bit and nibbled until her knees gave way.

For the next several minutes, the only sounds in the room were the sounds of ragged breathing and of satin, beads and lace brushing against fine black cloth. The wedding dress ended up in a poofed circle at their feet. Sometime during those moments, he turned her toward him, and his mouth found hers for a long, hot kiss. Later, his mouth moved off hers, found her throat, then went on an erotic tour that ended torturously short of the nipple his questing fingers had uncovered.

As if he'd meant all along to arouse her to nearly

the point of pain—and leave unfulfilled the ache to feel his lips on her breast—Blue eased her slowly away from him.

Allison could barely stand. She was too weak to keep her grip on his sleeves. The erotic haze that had burned away all her reason and all her inhibitions began to slowly lift. Her ability to stand on her own came back in the same proportions and she opened her eyes to look up at Blue.

It soothed her ego to see that his face was a mask of the same arousal she felt. But an iron control that she was too inexperienced to have developed was also there. She could see it in his eyes. She could see it, but she wasn't certain how she felt about it. Her reaction was equal parts relief and frustrated anger.

How dare he toy with her, bring her to such heights, then switch himself off—switch *her* off—and leave her with a wild hunger she'd never suspected could exist?

Yet, how grateful she was that he'd stopped! The confusing whirl of frustration and relief and ebbing desire kept her silent, kept her standing long after he turned from her and left the room.

The long limo ride to Dallas was quiet. Blue had withdrawn from her, though they sat together in the center of the wide back seat. They didn't speak, and the silence weighed on Allison.

Thoughts of Aunt Pet dominated her attention. Even after Blue had left the room, Petula hadn't come upstairs to help her. Instead the new housekeeper,

Mrs. Burns had come in to help her wrap her dress and veil in tissue for a trip to the dry cleaners for preservation.

She'd had only a brief moment in the front hall to hug her teary aunt, kiss her cheek and tell Charles goodbye before Blue had whisked her outside for the traditional toss of her bridal bouquet. Then he'd rushed her to the car too quickly for her to see who had caught it.

Perhaps it was just as well that neither of them spoke now. Allison wasn't certain she could keep her resentment to herself, and because this was their wedding day, she didn't want to mar it with an argument.

She also didn't want to react too quickly. She knew how stressful the past month had been for her. Surely it had been at least as stressful for Blue, considering he'd had to cope with getting the house finished and furnished well enough to hold the reception there.

His refusal to allow Pet to help her with her dress and his later rush to get away from the pressure of the large crowd of guests, might have been done out of worry that she'd linger too long. A man who had lived a solitary life in the country might naturally have a limit to the length of time he was willing to endure in a crowd.

In the end, it was her desire to understand Blue better that made her keep her resentment to herself. His actions today might simply have been an uncharacteristic response to a nerve-racking month and an overwhelming day. Most grooms put up with the pomp of a big wedding, but few of them seemed to truly enjoy being formally decked out and placed at the center of attention.

Blue was probably the same way, though to his credit, he'd taken everything patiently until the last.

The Dallas hotel Blue had selected was one of the finest in town. Allison felt a trickle of relief when she discovered he'd reserved a regular suite instead of a honeymoon suite. Surely that was a signal that he had no amorous intentions for their wedding night.

Nevertheless, Allison's tension kept her silent. She noted Blue handled himself well with the hotel staff and that he tipped appropriately. The fact that he politely thanked anyone who assisted them made her feel mildly ashamed to realize she hadn't expected it from him.

On the other hand, Charles was rarely courteous to anyone he considered inferior to him. Both she and Aunt Pet had been frequently embarrassed by his superior attitude and had always felt compelled to compensate for it.

Blue Sumner, despite his unprivileged background—or perhaps because of it—behaved with careful respect toward the staff, and that warmed her.

That warmth ebbed once the bellboy thanked Blue for his tip and exited the spacious suite. Allison stood stiffly, her worry about their wedding night surging uncomfortably. She tried not to glance toward the enormous bed she could see through the suite's open sitting room door. The fact that there was only one bed elevated her nervousness to panic.

Blue glanced her way, his gaze searching her face.

"Is there a restaurant you want to go to for supper, or do you want room service?"

The question set her a bit more at ease. She automatically rejected the idea of room service. The opportunity to escape the hotel suite was too good to pass up.

"A restaurant would be fine. I understand the ones in this hotel are quite nice."

Several feet of carpeting separated them. The distance suddenly seemed to span miles. Blue stood watching her, his gaze probing hers. Allison stared back, looking for anything that would give her a clue to his thoughts, his expectations.

"You look worried, Miz Allis." The candid statement caught her off guard.

Allison suddenly couldn't maintain eye contact with him and her gaze veered away. "Yes, well, I don't know how to avoid being worried." The admission was a big one for her to make, but she instantly felt better. She released a shaky breath. "We don't know each other at all—"

"And there's only one bed."

Allison's gaze streaked back to his, a bit shocked that he'd put it so bluntly. Suddenly the memory she'd worked so hard to suppress—of Blue helping her with her wedding dress—sent a bolt of heat through her. She felt some of that heat creep into her cheeks.

"I—" she hesitated, her discomfort rising "—I was wondering what you expected."

"All you have to do is ask," he told her, his voice

going rougher, though his tone had softened. "I'm not the kind to force sex on any woman, wife or not."

Allison started to relax, until he added, "That won't keep me from trying to get it other ways."

"But we barely know each other," she protested, clasping her hands in front of her as if to hold herself together.

"We know enough."

Allison was so appalled that at first it didn't register that he'd started toward her. "*I* don't know enough, Mr....Blue...I can't have sex with a man I'm not in love with."

Blue stopped in front of her. The sheer size of the man overwhelmed her and she couldn't help feeling vulnerable as she stared up helplessly at him. His hand lifted and he touched her cheek with the callused pad of his index finger.

The light contact sent a shiver of excitement through her. Years of ladylike behavior and reserve rushed up to counter the reaction, and she went so tense that she felt as if she might shatter.

"You might be surprised."

The next thing she knew, Blue had slipped his other hand around her waist and his faint smile vanished. She couldn't seem to move as she watched him lean toward her. By now, the touch of his lips on hers felt familiar, and her eyes fell shut. The slow pressure of his mouth was unhurried, but relentless. She felt her lips part beneath the probe of his tongue. In seconds, she was clutching the lapels of his jacket, awash in a flash flood of desire that made her tremble and grow weak.

Blue's lips slowly released hers, and with an effort, she opened her eyes to see the reason.

"All I have to do is touch you," he said, his low voice harsh with frustrated desire, "and you forget about whether you know me or not."

The stunningly accurate observation shamed her. Allison stiffened and pushed away. She turned and walked toward the sofa table where she'd set her handbag. She picked it up and started toward the suite's bathroom. "I'll be ready to go downstairs as soon as I freshen up."

She'd put everything she had into keeping her voice steady and making a dignified exit. Once she reached the bath, she closed the door, locked herself in and leaned against the wall, certain her new husband was too single-minded about sex to give a thought to her wishes or sensibilities.

CHAPTER FOUR

SUPPER, in the finest restaurant in the hotel, started well enough, though Allison had little appetite. She'd ordered wine with her meal, and ended up drinking two glasses. She tried to cover her nervousness by drawing Blue into conversation.

The usual dating ploys—getting a man to talk about himself, his business or his hobbies—failed abysmally with Blue. Any other man of her acquaintance enjoyed talking about himself. Clearly Blue did not.

Partway through the meal, he surprised her by switching the attention to her.

"I heard your aunt took you in after your folks passed on."

The statement caught her off guard, but then, she was beginning to expect directness from Blue. His refusal to allow Aunt Pet to help her with her dress, or to allow her a longer goodbye—and her resentment about it—made her answer carefully.

"I love Aunt Pet very much. I can't imagine being closer to my own mother than I am to her, so I'm sure you can understand how upset I would be if anything disturbed that closeness."

The faint flicker in his eyes told her he'd registered her calm remark. "What about your uncle?" Blue was leaning back in his chair. Though he appeared to be relaxed, his gaze was suddenly sharp.

Allison hesitated, searching for the right words. She was not as blunt as Blue. Any future financial dealings he planned with her uncle and his bank might well depend on how she answered him now. Aunt Pet was desperately worried about the bank. Allison didn't want to say anything that would ruin things for Charles and hurt Pet. However, she couldn't be dishonest.

"Charles and I have a civil relationship," she said tactfully. "I believe Aunt Pet might have been happier had she married someone else, but she is faithful to Charles and seems content to remain with him. Whatever affects him, naturally affects her." Allison saw that her message had gotten through. Blue's lips tightened as if he disliked the reminder about her aunt.

His reaction was disturbing. For weeks she'd worried about her uncle's high hopes and grandiose expectations. Even though she'd reminded Charles several times that nothing of what he'd planned for Blue's money was written in stone, she'd believed Blue would uphold his end of the unorthodox marriage arrangement. She would never have felt compelled to marry him otherwise.

But now that she'd done her part and gone through with the ceremony, the mere hint that Blue would somehow renege frightened her. Charles, though in the wrong about not notifying the authorities, would be in grave trouble. Trouble for him—scandal for him—meant trouble and scandal for Pet.

Her worry was strong enough to consider raising the subject with Blue. Which was just another reminder that if this had begun as a normal marriage, they'd have had more pleasant things to discuss on their wedding night.

She picked her napkin off her lap and blotted her lips while she scrambled to think of some way to gain Blue's assurance that all would be well. She set the napkin beside her plate and looked over at him.

"You and I haven't spoken on the subject of the bank and Charles's investment plans for you." Though she'd managed to get it all out in a casual tone of voice, the instant hardening of Blue's jaw and the faint flare in his eyes was unsettling.

"I already told you that what I decide to do about your uncle and his bank is separate from you."

His reply made her uneasy. For Petula's sake, she knew she needed to be persistent. "I understand this marriage came about because of an agreement between you and Charles."

Blue studied her a moment, his gaze piercing hers. "This marriage came about because I wanted a certain kind of woman." He picked up his mixed drink and took a slow sip, watching her face as he did. He lowered the stout tumbler to the tabletop. "The fact that you're related to Charles Wallace didn't matter, since there's no blood between you."

Allison's light brows drew together and she gave her head a shake. "I'm afraid I missed something. Charles is my uncle by marriage, but I don't see how it could matter, even if he was my blood relative."

"If you were blood kin to him, we might not be here."

Allison didn't understand the reason for the dark emotion behind his rough drawl. "Are you trying to tell me there are hard feelings between you and Charles?"

Blue studied her a long moment.

Intuition made her queasy. She went on with care. "As I said, what affects Charles affects Aunt Pet. And, you seem quite…angry," she dared to say, keeping her voice as reasonable as possible. "If there's some problem between you and Charles…"

Blue looked down into his drink and gave the stout tumbler a swirl that stirred the contents. "Maybe it's time for you to know."

Though he was a hard man and she felt vulnerable around him, until that moment—until he glanced over at her and she saw the temper in his eyes—she hadn't been truly afraid of him. Something was very wrong.

"What should I know?" she asked softly.

The silence stretched. Around them, other diners were eating and talking, and waiters were bustling among the tables. They were in a public place, but they seemed enveloped in an invisible force field that served to heighten the tension between them and provide a cocoon of privacy.

"Five years ago, I was dirt under Charles Wallace's feet," he said grimly. "Always was. He didn't mind if I had an account with his bank, but he wouldn't lend me a dime to improve my herd or buy more land.

When I got hit by bad cattle prices two years ago, he refused to loan me enough to keep covered.

"Turned out he wanted to buy my place. When nothin' worked to buy me out or run me off, he refused to grant an extension on my mortgage and started to foreclose. No other banker in the area wanted to lend me money, either. They'd covered other ranchers who'd got into the same fix with cattle prices, but even though my credit history was superior to most of theirs, I was turned down at every bank I tried."

Allison sat frozen as she listened to Blue chronicle his business history with Charles. Blue raised his drink and took a long swallow before he set the glass down and pinned her with a harsh look. "Think you want to hear the rest?"

She stared, stunned, but was now compelled to hear everything. She gave a slight nod and Blue went on.

"Charles wantin' my land bad enough to foreclose to get it, made me suspicious. But when I figured out he'd been talkin' to those other bankers, I knew something big was up. He might be an underhanded S.O.B., but he can smell money halfway across Texas."

His hard mouth twisted as he continued to watch her face. "So I got a loan with Ty Cameron's banker down in San Antone to buy my ranch outta hock, and Ty hooked me up with some friends of his in the oil business. That's when I found out for sure why Wallace was so hot to get my land."

He broke eye contact with her to signal their waiter

for the check. Allison sat stiffly as shame and shock churned inside. The waiter came over, oblivious to the tension between them. Blue scrawled his name across the bottom of the check, then got out his wallet to toss a generous tip onto the table next to the check.

He scraped back his chair and stood. Allison automatically slid her chair back to stand when he did. Neither of them spoke as he took her arm and they started out of the restaurant. Once they were in the main part of the hotel, Blue headed straight for the elevators.

The elevator ride to their suite was slow. Other guests came and went at nearly every floor. Though Blue kept a possessive hand at her back, she felt again the withdrawal that now seemed characteristic of him.

After what he'd told her about Charles, it didn't take a genius to figure out that Blue might want to damage him. Blue had come from a hard, poor background. In the weeks before the wedding, snippets of information had come to her, gossip mostly, but since she knew so little about Blue, she'd paid attention to each tidbit.

Prior to striking oil, Blue had been about to work himself to death. Unable to pay a full crew of cowhands, he'd taken up the slack himself. His financial credit had been spotless before the fall in cattle prices, but he'd allowed himself few comforts. She'd heard the house he'd lived in—which was located at the old ranch headquarters two miles from the new house and headquarters—had a dirt floor in at least one room.

A man who'd worked so hard and done without so

much to have his own ranch would naturally be outraged by anyone who would try to take it all away.
Particularly if that someone knew the real fortune in
the ranch wasn't in its grass or cattle, but in the earth
beneath it all.

When nothing worked to buy me out or run me off,
Blue had said. She'd heard he'd been plagued by
hardships that last year before he'd struck oil. Cattle
thefts, a couple of fires… Allison was suddenly sick
at heart.

Had Charles wanted Blue's land badly enough to
resort to criminal acts to get it? It wasn't unheard of
for a bank to refuse to grant an extension to a mortgage holder, though it was rare for one to refuse
someone with a good credit history who had had a
single bad year. It was unusual, though not illegal, to
begin foreclosure on a first time loan default. In which
case, a mortgagee with land collateral could qualify
for a second mortgage from another financial institu-
tion to pay off the first mortgage and hope for a better
year.

But what if Charles had talked other bankers in the
area into refusing to loan Blue money? Charles knew
most of the bankers in the counties surrounding theirs,
but would he have asked such a thing? Was the regard
other bankers had for him high enough for them to
do it?

Personally, even if Charles had no connection to
the other troubles on the Sumner Ranch, Allison saw
his rush to take everything Blue had worked so hard
for as greedy and criminal. Charles had married

money when he'd married Aunt Pet and he'd made a fortune many times over with his investments. He was a millionaire. Why on earth would he try to hurt someone as honest and hardworking as Blue Sumner? Even if he'd suspected there was oil on Blue's ranch, he couldn't have known it would be a huge strike. And even if he'd known, why prevent its rightful owner from getting it?

After what Charles had done to him, Blue might feel justified in seeing him ruined financially, just as Charles had tried to ruin him. Though she would never condone such an action, Allison might have understood the impulse, except that Aunt Pet would also be hurt.

In those next moments, she became so worried about Aunt Pet that she didn't register the precarious position she might be in herself.

Blue had his room key out for their door before it dawned on her that he might plan to use her to get back at Charles. His brisk, forceful move when he shoved the plastic key card into the slot, then pushed the door open increased her apprehension.

But when he slid an arm behind her back and leaned down to hook his other arm behind her knees to swing her off her feet, the jolt of terror she felt stopped her breath.

Blue's face was an inscrutable mask. His eyes were lit by a mixture of lust and lingering anger, his mouth a tight, harsh line. Allison braced her hands on his chest in wordless self-defense and stared up at him with wide eyes.

He hesitated. "Just carrying you over the threshold, Mrs. Sumner. It got neglected earlier." With that, he strode into the room as the heavy door swung closed after them.

Despite her faint move to signal she wanted to be set on her feet, Blue ignored it and stalked toward the bedroom door with her firmly in his arms.

Though Blue was still largely a stranger to her, he'd become at least familiar enough for her to feel a bit more ease around him. But his harsh profile made her feel truly estranged from him. By the time he set her on her feet next to the huge bed, she was trembling.

"This isn't a good idea," she blurted.

Her next breath stilled when Blue pulled her into his arms and his mouth landed demandingly on hers for a long, ravenous kiss.

Allison's hands were trapped between them. Alarmed at what he might have in mind now that she knew what Charles had done to him, she was far more immune to his kiss. She pressed mightily against his chest and labored to keep her lips stiff and together.

At just the moment she felt herself begin to weaken and give in, her resistance made him draw back. The lingering effects of his sensually forceful kiss made it difficult to get the words out.

Her soft, "Please, Blue," was breathless. Her continued pressure against his chest gained her another inch and her brain began to clear. "We need to talk."

"This isn't the time to talk," he said gruffly.

"I need to know your intentions." Her reply

stopped him just as he was leaning down for another kiss. His eyes went cool.

"About your uncle?"

Allison shook her head. "About everything. If you mean to use me to get back at Charles—if you mean to hurt Pet. Or me."

His dark brows drew together in displeasure. "You think I'd hurt you to get to him?"

His near growl increased her apprehension. She looked up at him, unable to conceal it.

"I don't know." Her soft candor made his expression harden. The fire in his eyes began to burn with anger rather than lust.

She hastily added, "Because I don't know you, I don't know what to think. You just told me about the appalling things Charles did to you, things that might make you want revenge. Because I don't know you, I'm worried about it. H-how do I know the big public wedding—your rush for sex—isn't part of some plan to embarrass Charles. Or me."

The swear word that burst from his lips shocked the color from her cheeks. He released her so suddenly that she almost lost her balance.

He stalked toward the huge windows that took up nearly the entire outside wall of the bedroom. She could tell by his swift, angry movements that he was ripping off his tie.

His low, "Get ready for bed," served only to elevate her fears. He was clearly not about to talk to her. The tie slid out of his collar with a snap and he wadded it into a ball.

Allison's sense about Blue, that he was a good man and a decent one, prompted her to try another tack.

"We haven't talked about what either of us wants in this marriage." Her quiet words seemed to have an effect. His angry movements stilled for several heartbeats before he tossed the tie toward a chair with normal force. Encouraged, she went on.

"If you mean for this to be a real marriage, then I would like it to be a real marriage also." She hesitated when he flipped back the facings of his suit jacket to shove his hands into his pants pockets. He kept his back to her.

Her voice went softer and trembled a bit. "I want children. I hope to be able to love my husband with all my heart, and I hope…I hope he can love me at least as much. That's why I don't want sex right away, under the circumstances. I want it to mean something…profound. I hope it will be an expression of mutual love and tenderness and trust that it might never be if—"

She couldn't get any other words out. She'd just confessed her deepest hopes for the future and she was suddenly terrified of Blue's reaction.

She saw the angry tension in him ease and felt her own tension ease. The sense that her words had had a positive effect allowed her to add, "Please. If those are the things you want also—"

His low, "Get ready for bed," was far less harsh this time and the rest of her tension slipped away.

She hesitated only a moment before she gathered

her night things from the closet and escaped to the bathroom.

When she stepped out of the bathroom a while later, the bedroom was dark. The drapes on the huge window had been closed. The only light came from the sitting room. Curious, she walked toward the open door, her bare feet making little sound on the carpet.

Blue sat slumped in one of the armchairs with a drink. His jacket was off, his shirttail was out and completely unbuttoned. He'd leaned his head against the chair back. He saw her the moment she stepped into the doorway and his eyes moved slowly down her white satin wrapper as if he were trying to see through it to her nightgown and what was beneath. His gaze came back up to catch the color in her fair cheeks.

"You're a virgin, aren't you?"

The question was a blatant indication that his thoughts were more on sex than on revenge. She took little comfort from the perception.

"As they say, I've never met the man who hung the moon," she answered quietly.

He took a sip of his drink but didn't take his eyes off her. "I never quite figured out how to hang the moon. Never thought I'd have to." He rested the half empty glass on the chair arm and took another long look at her.

She gave him a soft smile. "What did you think you'd have to do?"

When Blue smiled back, her breath stopped in her

throat. How handsome he looked when he smiled. She felt her attraction to him multiply.

"Used to be, I didn't think any woman would have me, so I didn't think about it. Always had too much work to do, no extra cash. I couldn't wine and dine 'em on a regular basis, though I did know how to get 'em into bed."

He smiled again, as if he were thinking about a pleasant memory. "Got so from time to time one of 'em would bring along a hot meal some Saturday night. When we got done eatin', one of us would make a move and I'd have a woman with me all night."

Allison didn't quite know how to take the information. She was embarrassed that he was disclosing details of his sexual history, but for once, he didn't seem so withdrawn from her. She'd told him earlier she wanted to talk. She knew of no other way for them to get to know and understand each other. It was only fair that he also got to pick the topic of their conversations. She just wasn't used to talking to a man about sex.

As if he'd just realized his choice of subject might not be the best, he added, "But just so you know, there hasn't been an endless parade of women through my bed. I haven't got any diseases and there aren't any Sumner kids growin' up somewhere." He let the silence stretch. "Yet."

"Why didn't you marry one of them?"

There was nothing more than a heartbeat between her question and his reply.

"I wanted you."

The silence wrapped around them. Allison couldn't help that his answer touched her. That strange new emotion she'd felt when he'd kissed her that Sunday afternoon began to stir, sending an odd warmth through her heart.

"You don't know me," she said softly.

"I know your reputation. You give your time to others with your charity work, you're kind to everyone and you're beautiful. I gambled that you're as perfect as you seem to be."

Allison laced her fingers together in front of her, and felt her face redden. "That's quite a fine compliment, but I'm afraid you've lost the gamble. I'm far from perfect. I lose my temper sometimes, there are days I don't want to do another minute's work for a charity and I actually told off Henrietta Cline, Marjorie Hampton and Elinor Johnson within the last year. I was so hard on Elinor Johnson that she still refuses to acknowledge my presence in church or on the street."

Blue actually chuckled and Allison was instantly taken with the sound of it. "God, I love to hear you talk. You still got some of that quick Yankee accent."

Allison's smile was interrupted by a yawn, and she jerked up a hand to stifle it. Blue rose immediately from his chair and came toward her.

"It's been a long day, Mrs. Sumner. I think we should go to bed." The low sound of his rough voice was sexy and Allison tensed. She still wasn't certain what his expectations were. And it was their wedding night.

Blue stopped in front of her, then reached out to touch her cheek with the back of his fingers. The next thing she knew both his hands were on her shoulders. He squeezed gently then eased his light grip. His hard fingers moved in small circles as if he were testing the feel of the smooth satin fabric.

His hands slowly moved off her shoulders and down her arms. When they reached her elbows, he moved his hands off her arms and gently gripped her waist. He pulled her slightly toward him and bent his head for a soft, gentle kiss that made her ache. When he withdrew, he leaned down slightly and swung her into his arms.

Taking only a moment to flip the wall switch that turned off the sitting room lamp, he strode confidently through the darkness to the side of the big bed. Allison held her breath as he lowered her feet to the floor and let her stand on her own. The bed had already been turned down, so he reached for the narrow sash of her wrapper and slowly, as if he were prolonging the action, untied the sash and let the ends fall softly to her sides.

This time when his hands came up to her shoulders, he'd slipped his fingers under the wrapper. He slid it off her shoulders with the same unhurried movement as he'd untied the sash.

He didn't kiss her on the mouth, though she was suddenly aching for him to, but he did lean down to kiss the delicate flesh of her neck, then brushed a second, lingering kiss on her shoulder. And then he pulled her wrapper all the way off and tossed it behind him to the foot of the bed.

"Go ahead and get in."

New tension twisted inside her. Did Blue expect to have a normal wedding night after all? As Allison climbed into the bed and drew the sheet and light blanket up, she shivered, as much from the fear and excitement of the question as from the air-conditioned air.

She lay back against the pillow and listened to the brisk sound of Blue undressing. She heard every move he made in the darkness. She heard his shirt come off, the belt hiss from the belt loops and the quiet zip and rustle that told her he'd removed his slacks.

She could make out his tall, wide-shouldered body as he walked around to the other side of the bed and drew back the covers. The big bed dipped when he got in. She stiffened when he reached for her and pulled her into his arms.

She was so tense she almost didn't realize he'd stopped moving. Now that he had one arm under her pillow, and the other across her waist, he relaxed. His rough, "Night, Miz Allis," prompted her to whisper, "Good night, Blue."

The strange sensation of lying in a man's embrace in a bed should have kept her awake for hours. Her accidental discovery that she was the only one who had worn clothes to bed should have been good for a totally sleepless night.

But the stressful day caught up with her almost immediately and she slept in her new husband's arms the whole night.

CHAPTER FIVE

IT WAS a new and pleasant sensation to wake up next to Blue. The drapes blocked a good share of the morning sun so she couldn't tell what time it was. The arm across her waist flexed and brought her solidly against his naked heat.

Allison tensed, but the feel of Blue's solid warmth was unexpectedly comfortable. If she had any hope at all of their marriage becoming more than a financial arrangement, she had to give moments like this a chance.

What she'd said to Blue the night before about the kind of marriage she wanted had been much more than a ploy to avoid sex. She truly wanted those things, though after she'd felt forced to marry Blue, she'd secretly despaired of ever having them.

The fact that Blue's rush for sex had been halted by her confession touched her. This small confirmation that he was a decent man made her soften toward him even more.

The arm across her waist moved and Blue's big hand curved around her ribs. His hand began to move, stroking lazily up and down her side, from just below her breast to her hip. The slow movement produced a tantalizing ache deep within her.

His hand stilled and Blue shifted up on his elbow

to lean over her. Heavy beard-stubble darkened his rugged jaw. His eyes, so blue and hungry in the soft light, searched hers. His fingers inched up and hesitated just beneath her breast. His thumb gently traced the swell and the light contact sent heat through her.

At just the moment he leaned down, she realized his intent. Self-consciousness made her jerk her hand up and press her fingers over her lips.

Her raspy, "Pardon—I have morning breath," and her abrupt shift away made his brows come together in surprise and amusement.

Allison slid from beneath his arm to scoot off the bed. Blue let her go and instead watched as she stood and faced him.

The amusement eased from his expression as he gazed at the clingy fit of the white satin gown that dipped low in front and in back from thin spaghetti straps. Realizing how exposed she was, Allison tried to reach for her satin wrap, only to find it had slid away somewhere and was tangled in the bedclothes.

Blue sat up in bed and leaned his back against the headboard. Allison walked around to the foot of the bed to search for the wrapper. The fact that Blue watched her every move with a faint smile on his face increased her self-consciousness.

"I'm glad you never met the man who hung the moon."

The words surprised her and made her glance up at him. He had no smile now and the piercing blue of his eyes smoldered.

Allison felt herself blush and looked down to continue her search. She found the satin wrap right away then, and hastily put it on. Once it was belted securely around her, she asked, "Would you like me to order breakfast?"

Blue shook his head. "Tell me what you want. I'll order it while you get dressed."

Her soft, "Thank you. I wouldn't mind steak and eggs with a bit of fruit," made him nod and reach for the bedside phone. She quickly selected her things and slipped into the bathroom to shower and dress for the day.

By the time breakfast was delivered to their room, they'd both showered and dressed. Allison had spread up the bed and moved more of her things from her suitcase to the dresser drawers. Blue had already taken care of his own clothes and personal items, and she liked that he hadn't automatically expected her to take over the chore.

Blue had ordered them a huge breakfast. They both had steak and eggs and a small fruit plate, but the coffee cake he'd also ordered was sinfully rich. They'd finished their meal and were sitting back with their coffee when Blue spoke.

"It's not too late to go on to someplace fancier for the honeymoon."

She lowered her coffee cup. "If it's something you'd like," she responded, then searched his face closely. They'd both agreed that Dallas was far enough to go for a honeymoon, but it wasn't quite fair to Blue to stay there if he wanted to go someplace else. Allison had traveled all her life, but she doubted

Blue had. Now that he had money and could do anything he wanted and go anywhere he pleased, she
didn't want to be the one to limit him.

"Never had a big hankerin' for exotic places," he
told her, "but then, I never had the time or the money.
Might want to someday. Could even go today if it's
something you want."

That he was thinking of what she wanted, and was
willing to change his plans to accommodate her, made
her feel close to him. She'd been glad they'd planned
to spend their honeymoon in Dallas. Blue had seemed
relieved when she'd suggested it, and she'd guessed
he might be more comfortable with her in familiar
surroundings. She certainly felt more at ease with him
in a place she knew well.

"I'm willing to go wherever you'd like, but I'm
just as content staying in Dallas."

"You're sure?"

Allison smiled. "I'm sure. It's very sweet of you
to ask."

To her surprise, his dark brows drew together and
lowered, as if what she'd said offended him.

Blue had never thought the word *sweet* would ever
describe him. But his bride had such a refined manner
of speech that he shouldn't have been surprised.
Sweet didn't seem very manly to him, but she'd
clearly meant no offense.

He was relieved that she seemed happy to stay in
Dallas. As she was so fond of pointing out in dozens
of different ways, they were strangers to each other.

On the other hand, maybe it would have been better if he had taken her to someplace like Paris.

Here, she knew her way around and didn't need to look to him for anything. Someplace like Paris might have put them on a little more equal footing.

But he was willing to cater to her. She was the focus and the prize for all his hard work and his spectacular run of good luck. He'd wanted her a long time, and now she was his.

Whatever he ended up doing about Charles Wallace, Allison Lancaster Sumner belonged to him. For now.

Their six days in Dallas went well. During the day, they shopped for a few more pieces of furniture for the house. They usually had breakfast in their room, but ate away from the hotel for lunch and supper.

They went to the opera and saw a play on two evenings. Blue politely tolerated the opera. He'd seemed to enjoy the play, but Allison had sensed his discomfort with both.

They made a trip to Neiman Marcus that had lasted most of an afternoon. Blue was fitted for another suit, but at his insistence, Allison tried on a handful of designer dresses and outfits he'd wanted to see her in. Though she had plenty of clothes, she indulged him. He'd seemed to enjoy the minifashion show as well as the sales associate's detailed explanations of what made each article of their couture collection so unique.

By the time she tried on the last outfit he'd wanted

to see her in, he'd already bought everything and had arranged to have it all delivered to their hotel.

The next day, they drove their rented car around Dallas. They ended up going to the finest Cadillac dealer in the city. Over her protests, Blue had her test-drive a Cadillac with every option possible. Once he pressured her and found out which color of car she favored, he promptly bought the car for her.

Blue's generosity worried her as much as it touched her. She'd protested the amount of money he was spending on her several times, until he'd finally gone grim.

"I've never had anyone to spoil and buy things for," he'd said gruffly. "The pleasure of having money and having a wife is to buy her things."

His remark had silenced her and she'd apologized. She'd gotten him to talk a bit more about himself that week. Though he'd been characteristically tight-lipped about the information, he did tell her that his mother had died when he was four and that his father had dropped completely out of the picture before he turned thirteen. He hadn't needed to add that they'd been poor and virtually homeless; she'd got the message.

At least she'd had Aunt Pet. And before Aunt Pet, she'd had a loving, secure home and affectionate, well-to-do parents. Blue had grown up poor and had had no one he could count on. The thought of his childhood poverty and loneliness, and the hard times and loneliness of his adult years, saddened her.

Though she wished he'd waited until their relationship was far more developed before he went on a spending spree, she didn't seriously protest again. Instead she showed natural gratitude and delight over the things he'd bought her and thanked him profusely.

That her thanks sometimes ended in a long, hot kiss made her uneasy. She didn't want either of them to equate gifts with kisses or more, but when Blue pulled her into his arms, she couldn't resist him.

At night, they lay together in the same bed, but nothing between them progressed beyond a few very carnal kisses. By the end of the week, Allison ached for Blue to do more than hold her. The fact that he hadn't tried was further proof that he'd taken her at her word on their wedding night and was willing to wait for deeper feelings between them.

The tenderness Allison began to feel toward him because of that and because of all the other little insights she now had into the man he was, made her feelings for him grow. Though she kept the knowledge to herself, she realized before they drove home to Chaney, that if Blue pressed her to consummate their marriage, he would be difficult to resist.

Because Blue used the cell phone to call Edward at the ranch when they were only a short distance from Chaney, Edward, the housekeeper, Mrs. Burns, and the cook, Miss Tilly, were all waiting on the veranda next to the front door for them to arrive.

Edward came forward the moment Blue slowed the car to a stop at the end of the walk. He opened

Allison's door and offered his hand to help her out of the car.

"Good afternoon, Mrs. Sumner. I trust you had a nice trip." His pleasant, though reserved expression was warm.

"Good afternoon, Edward. We had a very nice trip, thank you."

Blue was already out of the car and unloading their luggage from the trunk. Edward noticed and couldn't conceal his dismay. He politely excused himself to rush to the back of the car.

"Mr. Sumner, I shall take care of the luggage," Edward said, his voice firm.

When Blue shook his head and said, "I'll give you a hand," Edward came right back with, "You appear to have something much more pleasant than luggage to carry over the threshold, Mr. Sumner. Perhaps you shouldn't keep your bride waiting."

Blue's gaze sharpened on Edward's stiff expression, but then he seemed to change his mind. He glanced past Edward at Allison. "You're right about that, Edward. I'm obliged."

Blue came around the back of the car to Allison. "Come on, Mrs. Sumner," he said in a low voice. "Let's make this trip the official one." He then leaned down to sweep her into his arms.

Allison put her arms around his neck, much more comfortable with him than she'd been the night he'd carried her over the threshold to their hotel room.

As Blue strode past Mrs. Burns and Miss Tilly, he nodded politely, his quiet, "Ladies," as he passed a greeting. Allison had only a moment as she was carried past the two to greet them herself.

Once they were inside the huge home, Blue set her on her feet. Because the two women had followed them in, he whispered, "You suppose Edward'll be insulted if I give him a hand?"

Allison glanced back to see Edward step in with two suitcases and sit them down before he was back out the door.

Her light brow wrinkled. "I don't know. We never had a butler."

Mrs. Burns, who'd heard it all, stepped forward. After a hasty glance to make certain Edward was out of earshot, she leaned forward and said in a stage whisper, "Edward is very territorial, Mr. Sumner. He's quite a stickler for doing things his way."

That said, Mrs. Burns stepped back and folded her hands in front of her. By the time Edward returned with several shopping bags and boxes perfectly balanced, both Mrs. Burns and Miss Tilly stepped forward to assist him.

Allison and Blue watched the two women quickly divide Edward's load between them before they bustled off to the stairs to carry things up to the master suite.

Allison looked up at Blue. "It seems they've taken care of everything."

Blue was frowning. "Always thought I wanted someone to help me with the house chores. I got sick to death of eatin' my own cooking and trying to keep the place picked up and clean when I had so much outdoor work to do. Now I've got help, but it's hard to let them do everything that I pay 'em for. Seems impolite.''

Allison smiled. Charles thought nothing of being waited on hand and foot. In fact, Martha, their housekeeper/cook could never seem to do enough to please him. She approved of Blue's different attitude.

"I don't like to have the staff do things for me that I can do for myself, either," she told him. "I've always felt that they're employees, not servants or slaves."

Blue gave her one of his rare smiles. "We think along the same lines there." He started toward the stairs. "I'd like to get changed and get out to see how things've been going while we were gone."

Allison nodded. "Go ahead. I'll see if we have any messages before I unpack. It might be nice to have our first supper home in the dining room with our new china."

"I'll see you then," he said and turned to take the steps two at a time.

Allison watched him go. With every mile of the way back to Chaney, she'd sensed his increasing eagerness to be home. It confirmed that Blue was every bit the rancher/outdoorsman he'd always been. However hard his life had been while he'd struggled to hang on to his ranch and make something of it, in nearly every way that counted, it was obvious it had been a labor of pure love. Sudden wealth would probably not make much difference in that, which was something she also approved.

For a woman who'd always thought she'd marry a businessman and live in town or in the city, it was surprising to realize that she didn't mind that Blue was a rancher. Suddenly she looked forward to living in the country with a man who loved the land and meant to continue doing the hard work that went into keeping a ranch going.

Later, Allison was in the middle of unpacking when Aunt Pet called.

"Oh, my dear, you're home at last! Is everything all right with you?"

Allison smiled at the worry behind her aunt's question. She knew, although Pet had never said so directly, that Pet felt tremendous guilt and concern about Allison's marriage to Blue.

"Everything is fine with me, Aunt Pet. Blue is very nice. I hope that the two of you can become acquainted—I'm certain you'll like each other."

Allison didn't have to feign her enthusiasm. Sometime during that week, she'd got the sense that everything between her and Blue would eventually come right. Because she was seeing more and more how special he was, she was willing to wait for what she hoped to have with him. She didn't love him yet, but her affection for him was growing by the day.

Aunt Pet didn't seem comforted. All too soon, the topic switched to Charles and the bank.

"Charles is quite anxious to talk business with Mr. Sumner," Pet said. "He doesn't seem to realize that most people take a far longer honeymoon than the six days you have, so he's become quite a bear. Once he finds out the two of you have returned, he'll probably drive directly to the ranch.''

The information worried Allison. This was their first night together in their new home. She was planning a quiet supper and she was certain Blue's mind was on anything but Charles and the Chaney Bank. A feeling of foreboding welled up. Whatever Blue intended to do about Charles and the bank was better discussed at the bank during regular business hours. Something about bringing it to the house made her uneasy.

That was when she realized how much she already valued her marriage to Blue. Her desire to be a good wife included making his home life as pleasant as possible. It shocked her a little to discover that she'd suddenly become protective of him—just as a good wife would naturally be.

But then, as she was realizing, Blue'd had enough troubles in his life. If she could spare him a bit of Charles's aggravating penchant for badgering people, who were trying to relax, with business and the pursuit of the all-mighty next investment, she would.

''Please, Aunt Pet, don't mention that we're back just yet. I'll speak to Blue later. Perhaps he'll call the bank in the morning and make an appointment to see Charles there on Monday. This is our first night home, after all.''

There was only a small silence before Pet told her, ''Of course, dear. Charles can wait until business hours on Monday. I, for one, can wait until then now that I know everything will soon be all right. It's such a relief.''

It was no relief to Allison to think about the bank. Blue had been very noncommittal about what he intended to do, and she wasn't certain what she should do about it. Since Blue had revealed his business history with Charles, neither of them had spoken on the subject again.

Common sense told her it was foolish to think Blue would help the man who'd tried to take away his ranch, but fears for Aunt Pet made her pray he'd let bygones be bygones.

Her soft, ''Yes, it will be a relief, won't it?'' nearly choked her.

She heard a faint sound on the other end of the line and realized Pet was weeping. The sound distressed her and her feeling of foreboding multiplied. ''Aunt Pet? Are you all right?''

Pet's voice was shaky. ''Oh my, yes, dear heart. Please don't worry. I promise you that somehow, some way, I shall repay you for all you've had to endure to save the bank. If that—that *cowboy*—ever mistreats you or harms you in any way, you're to come home to me at once. We'll find some other solution—'' She was interrupted by a sniffle. ''I'm so sorry—none of this is your fault, yet you're being made to—''

Aunt Pet dissolved into tears and Allison gripped the phone. ''Aunt Pet? Please, Auntie, don't cry. I'm all right with Blue, *really*. Wait until I tell you about him—he really is quite a gentleman. He's very respectful and—'' Allison's hands tightened harder on the receiver. "I believe everything will work out with him, Aunt Pet. He's really not at all what you feared."

The only sound from the other end of the line was of Pet sniffling but trying to hide it by covering the mouthpiece of the phone. When she regained control, Allison's tense breath eased.

"Please forgive me. I've felt a lot of pressure of late. I don't mean to worry you by calling up, then squalling like a baby," Aunt Pet said in more normal tones, but Allison's heart was twisting. Pet was trying to put on a brave face, but she wasn't doing a very good job of it. "I'm relieved Mr. Sumner is behaving like a gentleman. It would be the best of all possible worlds if he turned out to be a wonderful husband and the two of you somehow fell in love."

She doubted her aunt heard her soft, "Yes, Auntie, me, too," because Pet went right on.

"Not like Charles and I."

Pet then changed the subject and Allison allowed it. Aunt Pet was a woman deeply unhappy with her marriage who, most times, bore it with grace and patience. It was lately, with all the trouble at the bank, that Pet's peaceful everything-is-excellent facade had started to crumble. She'd made more than one negative remark about her marriage recently.

It hurt to know that even if Blue worked out a business arrangement with Charles that would save the bank, no money arrangement could save Aunt Pet from remaining a deeply unhappy woman.

* * *

Blue walked to the big house. It was just before six p.m. Everything seemed as right as rain with the stock and the ranch. Money didn't worry him anymore. He now had most of the things he'd worked all his life for; he even had the woman he'd set his sights on.

The biggest problem wasn't that he finally had her, but that he wasn't certain what to do with her. If she'd been like any other female he'd ever slept with, they'd be lovers now. But she wasn't like those other women and, for the most part, he was glad she was different.

But the things that made her different were turning out to be things that threatened him. She'd knocked him between the eyes with her little wedding night speech about wanting to love her husband with all her heart and hoping he'd love her at least as much.

Because he didn't want to love her, what she'd said had put a burden on him. He didn't trust love, couldn't depend on it. As pretty as she was, as gentle and refined as she was, it shocked him to realize that her expectations had made him a little wary of her. And the more he thought about what she'd said, the closer that wariness came to fear.

Though he was a man who was used to hard times and had faced miles of life's bad roads, fear was an emotion he hadn't felt since he was a small child. And yet that old bugaboo had raised its ugly head. When she'd come out to the ranch that first time, her declaration about wanting to marry for love had started it. But by the time he knew she was his and she'd started the plans for the wedding, his old fears had slipped back into some forgotten crack in his feelings and stayed there.

Until he'd heard her say, *I hope to be able to love my husband with all my heart, and I hope he can love me at least as much...I want it to mean something profound...an expression of mutual love and tenderness and trust...*

The sick feeling had started again then. He could never admit to her that he also wanted those things, that he craved them—probably far more than she did. But the old wounds, which he'd thought had scabbed over and faded a long time ago, had opened up and started to ache.

He'd tasted the first bitter tang of fear then. That old fear of hoping and needing and loving, then having all that hope and need and love burned away by indifference and want and hate.

He didn't trust love. He trusted a solid handshake, a signature on a legal paper, a good horse and the terrible power of a man's heart to choose bad and do wrong.

He didn't trust Allison Lancaster Sumner. However sweet and perfect she was, he couldn't afford to love her, though she was free to love him as much as she wanted. Being the gentle person she was, she'd probably be happier if she thought she was in love with him. But he could never love her. He couldn't let himself.

She belonged to him now. She was his wife, but someday, she'd leave and find someone more worthy of her, someone more refined and well-bred like herself. Some man who wasn't afraid to love a woman and own up to it. A man who could truly love her back.

When she left him, he didn't want to hurt over it, he didn't want to eat his heart out and crawl into a bottle. He'd keep his kids—he'd give them the love he'd had so little of—but he'd let their mother go.

A fresh whiff of another old nemesis—despair—came in on his next breath. Clamping down hard on the feeling, he strode determinedly toward the house.

CHAPTER SIX

ALLISON was pleased by the fresh cut flowers in the crystal vase at one end of the dining-room table. The vase had been a wedding present. Two place settings of their new china, which had been a gift selected from her bridal registry, were set at the end of the long, polished table.

Blue would be sitting at the head of the table, with Allison to his right. Several heights of brass candle holders flanked the flower arrangement, their lit candles setting a romantic mood beneath the dimmed light of the grand chandelier above.

Allison had showered and changed into a flowing chiffon dress that was fitted at the bodice, then flared to a full, soft hem that ended just above her knees. The sleeveless dress with tiny rolled chiffon straps was several pale shades of yellow and was very feminine. It was one of the dresses Blue had bought for her in Dallas. She'd worn her hair up, with a few curly tendrils around her face and above her neck.

Blue had come into the house a half hour ago. Edward had informed her that her new husband had gone up the back stairs and would be down for supper shortly.

And so she waited, occasionally finding a reason to lean across the polished wood to adjust a bloom of the arrangement or slide a candle holder a fraction of an inch to a slightly better spot.

Nerves made her fuss. Now that they were home, would Blue still be content to only sleep with her beside him? Would *she* still be content?

The question heightened her edginess and sent a prickle of anticipation through her that made her glance toward the mantel clock over the fireplace at one end of the large room.

The gift she'd planned to give Blue on their first night home—if she felt optimistic about things between them—lay next to his place setting on a satin square artistically rumpled to display the small box.

Though she now doubted the wisdom of the gift, she left the gaily wrapped box where it was. The gift was as much a sentimental one as a valuable one. The gold cuff links with onyx settings had been her father's.

Her wedding gift to Blue, purchased with her own money, would be delivered the next day. Though she'd made arrangements for it prior to the wedding, she'd thought he would enjoy it more if they were home from their honeymoon before she gave it to him.

Because he'd spent so lavishly on her during their honeymoon, she now regretted the planned wait.

The mantel clock striking the half hour made her jump. At almost the same time, she heard Blue's booted step in the hall.

Blue walked into the formal dining room, caught off guard by the dim lighting. The light of the chandelier had been turned down in favor of the tall candles that sat on either side of the vase of flowers.

His bride stood near the head of the table, the pretty yellow dress he'd bought her glowing as if it were faded sunlight. Allison was so beautiful she stopped his breath. He saw the anxious, hopeful look on her face and felt a rush of heat.

The sense he had about her, that she'd begun to feel something for him, stirred his emotions. But a lifetime of craving love and never having it, sent a chill over him that froze everything tender in him except lust.

He resisted the urge to touch her. Instead he passed the head of the big table and walked behind her to pull her chair out in a silent invitation for her to sit.

The delicate, now familiar scent of her perfume wafted up to him. His fingers tightened on the chair back in silent resistance before they relaxed and fell away. He took his place at the head of the table and sat down.

Blue's rugged face was stern—as stern as she'd ever seen it. Once he seated her, Allison glanced in mute worry toward the small gift next to his plate, then forced herself to meet his gaze as he sat down. The fact that his expression didn't alter made her force a pleasant smile. Perhaps something had gone wrong. But things had been going well between them that day. What had happened to change that?

"Did everything with the ranch run smoothly while we were gone?" She couldn't seem to help that her eyes wavered a fraction from his in the direction of the gift.

His taciturn, "Smooth enough," sent an edge of disappointment through her that she made herself ignore.

"I had something I'd planned to give you on our first night home," she said, then waited for him to notice the box. "It's a sentimental sort of gift," she went on, her nerves twisting tighter as she made a small gesture toward the box, then watched nervously as he looked toward the spot she'd indicated.

Her soft, "They were my father's," nearly choked her.

The breath she'd just taken felt as if it had caught in her chest. Blue's stern features seemed to harden as he stared a moment at the gay ribbon and paper.

The seconds that passed made the air around them grow heavy and dull. Blue didn't react to the gift. He didn't reach for it, he didn't show a flicker of interest in it. Allison was suddenly filled with remorse.

His gruff, "My thanks," was the only appropriate reaction he made. The happy little box on the rumpled satin square now appeared forlorn. Allison's emotions started on a slow slide downward.

Edward appeared then with a large tray. Efficiently he served them both. His, "Will there be anything else madam...sir?" prompted Allison to shake her head.

Blue's low, "Thanks, no," made Edward disappear as quickly as he'd come in.

Allison looked down at her plate. She reached for

her linen napkin and spread it across her lap. Tense, battling hurt feelings because Blue seemed to have spurned her gift, her appetite vanished.

Nevertheless, she picked up her fork and determinedly began to eat. The heaviness between them grew thicker. Tension made her feel stiff and awkward.

Weeks of wedding preparations, days of being alone with Blue and finding potential for deep, loving feelings between them, suddenly seemed the foolishness of a romantic who had more fuzzy notions than common sense. Everything, from the wedding ceremony to their honeymoon and their return home to Blue's grand ranch mansion, now seemed to have been no more than an elegant stage production of a doomed play. One with all the right costumes, all the right stage directions, but no real heart and no real story that would ensure it would last much past opening night.

But Charles had bargained for a financial arrangement that he was almost certain to get, and Blue had gotten himself a sort of trophy wife that he'd chosen and virtually purchased so he wouldn't have to bother to court her. Or bother to learn to.

The sense that she'd been trapped into something far more difficult to solve than Charles's troubles at the bank made her spirits swing lower. The reminder that she'd married Blue to ease her Aunt Pet's worries made her feel only marginally better.

She'd had such hopes. Blue's reaction to her gift had crushed them and seemed a grim portent of things

to come. He'd heard her tell him the gift had sentimental value, that it had belonged to her father. She'd
confided to Blue days ago how close she'd been to
both her parents. Surely he'd realized the importance
of her giving him something that had once belonged
to her father.

It was inevitable that she'd start thinking about the
gift that was coming tomorrow. If she felt regret and
remorse for giving him the small gift, her regret and
remorse for the second, much larger gift was even
stronger.

The door chimes sent a melody of rich, perfect
tones into the silence of the large house. An unaccountable sense of dread seeped into her. Uneasy, she
quietly set her fork down and lowered her hand to her
lap as they heard Edward walk briskly down the hall
to the entry and the front door.

It seemed to take an eternity before he walked back
down the hall and stepped into the dining room.

"Mr. and Mrs. Charles Wallace to see you both,
sir. They are waiting in the front parlor. I've informed
them that you're still sitting dinner and that I shall
bring them a coffee tray while they wait."

Alarmed that Charles had burst in on them uninvited on their first night home, Allison's gaze streaked
to Blue's face.

His expression was stony. His low, "Thanks,
Edward," made the butler nod curtly before he started
off down the hall to the kitchen for the tray.

Allison couldn't help watching Blue's face as he
finished with his steak and calmly reached for the cof-

fee he'd preferred to wine. Though he didn't say a word to her and didn't lose his temper, it was clear he was angry.

Charles's pushiness had been honed over a lifetime of lording it over others. She knew suddenly that Blue might be one of the few people of her acquaintance who had the ability to push back. A life of hard living and scrambling to survive had no doubt made Blue quite formidable.

The precarious position that placed Aunt Petula in sent a fresh breath of alarm through her. She might also be in the middle, but at least she was now Blue's legal wife. Surely there was only so much he could do to her.

Every worry she'd had about Blue's possible desire for vengeance against Charles came storming up and she gripped the napkin on her lap with shaking fingers.

"My apologies," she said, her voice so soft it was barely above a whisper. "It's really quite rude for uninvited guests to drop in, particularly since it's our first night home. I hope—"

"Worried that I'll spoil the deal with Charles?"

Those intense blue eyes of his shifted and met hers. The impact of that burning gaze made her quail inwardly. There was no mistaking his anger now.

Her soft, "I don't know what you'll do," seemed to have some small impact. The fire in his eyes eased for a moment, but then blazed even higher than before.

"You got something you want to say to me before we go in there?"

Blue's question took her aback. "I don't understand—is there something you want me to say?" She gave her head a small shake. "I'm sorry for the intrusion."

With a calm that was chillingly opposite the anger she sensed in him, Blue pulled his napkin off his lap and tossed it beside his plate. He slid his chair back and stood, then stepped over to pull her chair out for her.

Allison wordlessly rose and laid her napkin aside. As she did, her gaze fell on the shiny little curls of ribbon that decorated the gift. The small bright cluster seemed to sparkle one last time, then fade. She made herself glance away, all too aware that the crisis ahead made everything too precarious to dwell on Blue's rejection of her gift.

Together they walked to the front parlor where Charles and Aunt Pet waited. The moment they stepped into the room, Charles ceased pacing the center of the floor and came straight toward Blue. Allison slowed, her attention going briefly to Aunt Pet, who was perched stiffly on the edge of a brocade chair.

Charles's smiling, boisterous, "Welcome home, Blue!" and his outstretched hand as he approached was met with cool silence. Instead of shaking Charles's hand, Blue caught Allison's elbow and prevented her from crossing the room to her aunt.

"Miz Allis? Might be you and your aunt would like

to have a private visit somewhere, catch up on things.''

Blue's suggestion sounded mild enough, but he was clearly ordering her to take her aunt elsewhere. Because Allison knew neither she nor Pet would be able to mediate anything between the two men, she said, ''Yes, Aunt Pet. We did some shopping in Dallas. Perhaps you'd like to see what we bought.''

Pet was so nervous that she immediately stood and came toward Allison. Her wary glance at Blue revealed her trepidation. As if she meant to stay out of arm's reach, she kept a careful distance from him before she stopped with Allison slightly between them. Her properly worded, ''Welcome home, Mr. Sumner, I hope you had a nice trip,'' was accompanied by an uncertain smile.

Blue merely nodded, his gaze shifting from Pet to her husband.

Allison took her aunt's hand and the two of them exited the parlor. Pet stepped closer to her as they walked toward the staircase, then glanced back as if to make certain they were safely out of earshot before she whispered, ''I'm so sorry, Allison. I didn't say a word to Charles about your return. I have no idea how he found out, but he refused to wait until tomorrow or Monday.''

Allison squeezed her hand. ''I'm sorry he didn't wait, but there's nothing either of us can do about it now.'' She made herself smile and thought of a way to distract them both. ''Let's walk out to the garage first.'' They bypassed the big staircase to walk down the hall to the back of the house. "Blue has been quite generous."

Even as she said the words and tried to give Pet the impression that she felt at ease about what was going on in the front parlor, Allison couldn't help that she felt sick.

She didn't know what to expect from her new husband. Marrying a man she didn't know gave her almost no confidence in what he'd choose to do about Charles and the bank. Charles had wronged Blue more than once. How could any of them expect him not to return the favor?

The question caused a twinge at the back of her neck. It wasn't long after she'd shown Aunt Pet her new car and they'd gone upstairs to see her new clothes, that the twinge began to intensify to an ache.

Once they were in the master bedroom, Aunt Pet closed the door, turned to Allison and took hold of her hands.

"Has he been decent to you, dear?"

Allison smiled. "Blue's been quite decent to me, Aunt Pet. He's really a polite man."

Petula gave her a searching look. "Forgive me for bringing this all up again, but…he's not been brutish…in *that* way?" Her cheeks glowed a crimson color at her reference to sex.

"Not at all, Auntie. He's been very patient. He understands that we don't know each other well enough yet."

"You're certain?" Pet persisted anxiously.

"I'm certain. Blue has been more a gentleman in

some ways than a lot of men who are considered well-bred.'' She smiled again to reassure her aunt.

Pet stared deeply into her eyes a moment, then appeared to be satisfied with her answers. ''All right, dear, but please, if there's ever a moment that he mistreats you or you feel frightened of him, please don't hesitate to come right home.'' She gave Allison's hands a firm squeeze. ''And I mean that.''

''Thank you,'' Allison said softly, touched at her aunt's concern for her, ''but it won't be necessary.''

By the time Edward came upstairs to inform Aunt Pet that Charles was waiting in the front hall to leave, Allison's headache was worse. It was all she could do to conceal her discomfort long enough for Pet to be gone so she could take something for it.

The moment Pet left the bedroom, Allison went directly to the medicine cabinet in the master bath. She didn't often get stress headaches, but when she did, they were excruciating. The well-stocked cabinet yielded several analgesics to choose from, and Allison quickly downed a full dose.

She'd managed to weather the stress of the past few weeks, but Charles's behavior that night—and her secret worry over what Blue would do about it—seemed to have been the last straw.

She debated about going down to find out right away what had happened between Charles and Blue, but decided it was late enough now that Blue would be coming upstairs. She knew he meant to return to his early work routine now that they were home, so she assumed that also meant an early bedtime for him.

Because of her headache, she decided to have an early night, too, and went through the routine of preparing for bed. After she put her hair up to keep it reasonably dry, she undressed and stepped into the large Plexiglas shower cubicle next to the Jacuzzi tub in the roomy master bath. In moments, jets of hot water pelted down on her. She stood quietly, letting the pressurized water pound the back of her neck and shoulders with the heat she hoped would ease the tension there. When at last she felt relief, she finished her shower and got out to dry off and dress.

Weary from the day, that night's disruption and her headache, all she wanted to do was go to bed and get some sleep. She snapped off the bathroom light and stepped into the dimly lit bedroom.

Blue stood in front of the doors to the balcony that faced the rear of the house, his back to her. She read instantly the tension in his tall, strong frame. She noted he'd already removed his boots—they sat beside the padded chest at the foot of the bed. She also noticed that only one of the two balcony doors was open and that he could see her reflection in the door he'd left closed.

"Looks like I'm not the only one going to bed early."

His low voice gave her no clue to what had gone on between him and Charles, so she told him, "I have quite a headache."

"Did you guess I sent your uncle off without makin' a firm deal?"

His words were quiet, but carried an edge of sarcasm she almost missed. But she heard it faintly, and something in her came to full alert.

"As I said, I wasn't certain what you'd do. It was rude to drop by so unexpectedly. Aunt Pet was quite embarrassed." Allison's headache was better, which meant the aspirin was working, but the last thing she wanted was more upset.

"So now you have a headache."

There was no mistaking the skepticism in his tone.

"I sometimes get tension headaches," she said as she walked toward the bed and pulled down the comforter and sheet. She straightened and looked over at him. "A little aspirin and some sleep usually cures them."

Blue turned toward her, then reached for the edge of the balcony door to close it. His gaze was sharp as he searched her face, then dropped to scan her slim form all the way to her bare feet.

"It's a little early in the marriage to claim a headache, isn't it? A simple no would have done the trick."

Allison saw the grim set of his ruggedly handsome face as he started toward her. Something about the way he was looking at her sent a shiver through her middle. She sensed his anger, but there was also something dark and turbulent behind the look he was giving her.

She watched his advance, but couldn't move. It was as if he had some strange sort of power over her. She felt threatened, she felt fear, but her legs were suddenly too leaden to move.

Her soft, "Is something wrong?" made his grim expression darken.

Blue stopped before her and lifted a hand to her cheek. His eyes were blazing down at her as if they were lasers while he brushed the knuckle of one finger down her smooth cheek, then eased it to her throat. With the tip of that finger, he drew a line down her chest to her breast, but stopped just short of the goal.

"I can't sleep next to you one more night without having you." The blunt words sent a spasm of feminine excitement through her.

She tried to swallow the sudden dryness in her throat. "W-we still don't—"

"Doesn't matter. There's only so much you and I are ever going to know about each other, only so much we're ever gonna feel. Right now, I want kids, and I want one by spring."

It didn't take a mathematician to figure out that she'd have to get pregnant almost right away. Allison shook her head. "I want children also, but not that soon. We need a year, maybe more for—"

"As I said, there's only so much we're ever gonna know about each other. Sex doesn't have to mean anything profound, it just needs to be good and happen regular."

Allison couldn't conceal her dismay. "I can't have sex with you, not under those circumstances."

Blue's hand slipped around her and pulled her against him. He bent down. She felt the harsh gust of his breath and turned her face away. His lips landed on the tender flesh of her neck. At the same time, his other arm came around her and lashed her tightly against him. There was no mistaking his arousal. Or his determination.

Allison's hands were trapped between them, and she pushed with all her might. If anything, her efforts gained her only a fraction of an inch. Blue's mouth became more voracious. The openmouthed kisses he pressed to her neck were interspersed with gentle bites.

She felt the anger in him recede, felt the difference in the way he held her, but she didn't understand how she knew it, except that he'd gentled somehow. His passion, however, was overwhelming and she trembled as she felt her body begin to respond.

His passion was more a threat to her than his anger had ever been. She felt her resistance melt and had to struggle to shore up her will. She couldn't make love—couldn't have sex—with a man she didn't truly know, even if he was her husband. And she couldn't possibly love a man who'd as much as said he would never love her. She couldn't give herself to such a man.

But suddenly she found herself on her back in the big bed, her nightgown and wrapper shoved to her waist and Blue's big body beside her. His jean-clad leg slid over her thigh and abraded her smooth skin, effectively pinning her to the mattress.

She kept her hands braced against his chest, but he loomed over her.

Her desperate, ''Please, Blue, don't,'' had no effect and she watched helplessly as he leaned down to kiss her. The last second turn of her head only delayed what he had in mind. He gently pursued her mouth until his lips covered hers in a soul-shaking kiss.

His lips opened hers and his tongue plunged deep while he slid his hand between them and untied her wrapper. He pulled the wrapper open and slid the strap of her nightgown down to pull half the bodice to her waist.

He ignored her futile attempt to cover herself, but made his kiss softer, gentler, and so persuasive that she felt herself begin to melt.

As if he knew precisely how to touch a woman in a way that ensured her compliance, he fitted his hard palm around her breast, then focused on her sensitive nipple.

Allison suddenly couldn't fight the wild storm of sensation he provoked and felt herself tumble toward that deep dark place where reason fled and desire ruled. She knew then that her body's violent response to him gave him complete control. Her last coherent thought—that there had to be some way to stop him, to stop *herself*—evaporated beneath the heat of his lips and his hands.

And slowly, Allison found herself reacting to him, responding to the aggressive seduction that made mincemeat of her reserve and her will. Her effort to push him away ended when she slid her hands up his chest to wrap around his neck. The painfully intense arousal he brought her to made her as eager to wantonly touch him as he touched her.

Somehow, piece by piece, their clothing came off.

Somehow, amid all the soft sounds of rough tanned flesh on smooth white skin, and soft sighs and pounding hearts, two bodies came together. Two hearts bonded in a way neither was quite prepared for, then everything evaporated in a conflagration of need and hunger and sensation.

CHAPTER SEVEN

BLUE left his sleeping bride long before daybreak. The sweet knowledge that she really had been a virgin played on his male pride like an aphrodisiac. He remembered then what she'd said about never having met the man who'd hung the moon, and the heady, masculine thrill of seducing her began to drag on his conscience.

He'd rushed her into sex. He'd taken brutal advantage of her inexperience, and few of his intentions had been honorable. He'd truly not been able to think about lying next to her one more night without taking her, but he'd also wanted to change her mind about love. To show her that love wasn't necessary or needed.

He hadn't been able to tell if she'd been telling the truth about not knowing her aunt and uncle were coming over. He'd thought at first that she'd invited them, but wouldn't own up to it. Part of the reason he'd seduced her had been to create a new bond of loyalty to him, and break some of her strong family ties.

He cared for Allison, he damned sure felt tender and hungry for her, but he didn't love her. He didn't want to. He did, however, want her loyalty to be exclusively his.

And because he'd become a little afraid of the idea

that she might someday fancy that she was in love with him, he'd figured rushing her into sex—putting their marriage on the level of sex—might be the one chance he had to spoil her notions about love.

Now that he'd taken her, he'd discovered that sex was better between a husband and wife. Sex had been intoxicating with her, but in the end, sex was all it had been. And because in his mind, sex had never meant love, it made sense to him that after last night, it wouldn't mean love to Allison, either.

Why those thoughts caused a heaviness in his chest wasn't something he wanted to examine too closely.

By the time Allison awoke, it was almost nine o'clock. She was aware of the emptiness beside her before she was fully awake. The depth of the sweet, tender feelings she had now for Blue were astonishing. She'd never felt so exposed, so close, to anyone in her life as she'd felt to Blue last night. She'd never imagined passion could be as sharp, as fiercely gentle as it had been. She'd never guessed her body could feel what Blue had made her feel.

But as she lay there thinking, awash in the memory of his kisses and the feel of his hard, strong body and the way they'd made love, she began to regret that it had happened so soon.

Now she remembered that there had been no tender words between them, no whispers of love, no declarations. She understood then what place she would truly occupy in her husband's life.

* * *

The six-year-old black quarter horse mare was magnificent. Expertly trained as a cutting horse, the mare had competed in enough cutting horse competitions to show promise of being a champion. The purchase of the mare had seriously dented Allison's trust fund.

And though the mare was beautiful and a true credit to her breed, the extravagant gesture she represented now made Allison cringe.

But she had no wish for her loveless marriage to Blue to stay that way. And she had no wish for divorce.

While she watched the groom walk the ebony mare around to exercise her after the long hours in the horse trailer, she realized she was probably guilty of trying to buy Blue's affection.

Because Blue was a horseman and a working rancher, she'd thought a good cutting horse would be the most appreciated and unique gift she could give him. And because he was now a very wealthy man, she couldn't quite picture herself giving him something small that he could easily buy for himself on his next trip to Dallas.

She was preoccupied with his reaction to her gift the night before. She had no idea what had become of it, and she was afraid to ask. She couldn't imagine anything worse than for Blue to react the same way to the mare.

Tortured by regret and dread, she reluctantly followed the groom as he led the beautiful black mare down the long lane to the stables.

* * *

Blue was hot, bathed in sweat and grit, and hungry. The bull they'd brought in that morning had a wire cut that had torn open his chest and shoulder. It had taken Blue and three others to maneuver the pain-crazed animal into the custom-made squeeze chute the vet had trucked out to the ranch. The doc had sedated the huge animal, and as the bull had started to succumb to the anesthetic, the small engine and pulley system on the special chute had laid the bull over on his side.

After examining and irrigating the wounds, the vet had sewn the bull up rapidly, administered a large syringe of antibiotic and gave instructions for the animal's recovery from the anesthetic and for his care the next several days.

After the vet had left on another call and they'd got the woozy bull on his feet, Blue caught sight of Allison walking toward him down the dirt alley that bisected the network of corrals.

Dressed in a white sleeveless blouse, designer jeans and Western boots that still carried the shine of new, her light hair fell to her shoulders as perfectly as if she'd just brushed it.

The sight of her delicate, blond beauty, against a backdrop of raw wood plank rails, dusty confined cattle and the assortment of ranch buildings, was arresting. Her utter femininity stirred everything masculine in him and his mouth went dry. And when she got close enough, he could tell the flush on her cheeks had nothing to do with the effects of the sun.

The shy look in her eyes, even though she made

herself meet his gaze, sent a sting of guilt through him. He stepped away from the fence, mumbled a gruff, ''I'll check with you later, Jim,'' then walked to meet her.

Once they were almost at arm's length from each other, they stopped. Allison broke eye contact and glanced past him to the bull, who stood weakly in the upright squeeze chute.

''You have an injured animal. Am I interrupting?''

That soft voice moved along something in his chest and sent a thrill straight through him.

''All done. But you ought not be out in the noon sun with no hat and bare arms.''

Allison glanced from the bull to Blue's face, touched by his concern. It gave her a glimmer of hope. ''I wasn't planning to be out long this time, though I would like to see everything. I don't know a lot about ranching or how things get done here, but I'd like to learn.'' She offered a pleasant smile. It had occurred to her that Blue might not want her to have any contact with the actual operation of his ranch. He might have definite ideas about what he considered her place and his.

''Didn't know you were interested.'' He glanced away briefly, then back to her. ''If you are, you'll have to wear something on your arms and dig up a hat.''

Encouraged that he was responding positively—and protectively—to her interest in the ranch, she felt a bit more at ease about giving him the mare.

But nervousness made her forget her planned

speech to lead up to giving him her gift, and she got out a slightly rushed, "I bought you a wedding present a couple of weeks ago. I wanted to wait until we were home before I gave it to you, but it's arrived and I'd like to give it to you now."

Blue's expression closed and seemed to harden. Allison's heart fell but she tried not to show it. "I know you weren't too impressed by my gift at supper last night, but I'm h-hoping this is one you'll like." The small stutter made her catch her breath in mortification, and she found herself scrambling to save face.

Her forced smile trembled tellingly. "If you don't like it, I'm not certain what to do, unless the previous owner would consider taking her back."

Allison remained silent, but his blue gaze veered from hers. Allison felt sick. She'd obviously made a huge mistake. Blue's ungraciousness on the subject of gifts seemed out of character, but it hurt terribly.

"You were also very unhappy with my gift last night," she said quietly. "You seem angry that I'm giving you another one." His harsh gaze swung back to her and she paused to take a steadying breath. "But if you can't accept my gifts, I can't keep the ones you bought me in Dallas, not the clothes or the car."

With that, she turned and walked with stiff dignity to the stable, then up the lane to the house.

Blue didn't come to the house for lunch, though it was clear that Edward had expected him. When he brought Allison's lunch into the dining room for her, he wordlessly whisked away Blue's place setting when he went out.

Later, Allison went upstairs to make some phone calls from the master bedroom, but she glanced frequently out the balcony doors, hoping for any sign of Blue.

Much of the activity at the barns and corrals was obscured by the buildings themselves, but even when she caught a glimpse of someone, it wasn't Blue. No black mare was ever led out of the stable, and the pretty animal hadn't been let out into a corral.

The calls Allison made were to the handful of charities she worked with. Vacation Bible School would be starting at her church on Monday morning, so she called the program coordinator to confirm her plans to teach the prekindergarten class. They discussed Allison's ideas to match her lesson plans with this year's theme, Show Jesus to the World.

She eventually went into one of the spare bedrooms where Edward had installed a telephone and stored her charity things, and got out the huge box she'd packed her Bible School materials in. Determined to distract herself, she laid everything out on the large bed in that room, then reviewed it all and made additional notes. She got out her scissors and the knee-high stack of magazines beside the desk, which she'd selected particularly for their picture assortments, and began to leaf through their pages. She planned to use the pictures to illustrate several examples of how the children could "Show Jesus to the World" by their good deeds and good attitudes.

As the day wore on, Allison's spirits sagged low. Eventually she finished Bible School preparations and packed everything into the box the way she wanted and set the box near the door along with a second stack of magazines she'd previewed for appropriateness for her preschoolers to cut things out of.

By the time she went in for supper, Blue still hadn't returned. This time, her place was the only one set at the table. When she asked Edward about it, he reported that Blue was on the range somewhere and might not be back to the house until very late.

After picking at her supper, Allison went for a walk and ended up at the stable. The black mare was munching grain in her stall and welcomed Allison with a nicker as she stopped at the stall door. The big horse put her black head over the stall door for a pat. Allison stroked the mare's long nose, complimented her on her very white and distinctive lightning bolt blaze, then bid the mare a soft good-night and eventually wandered back to the house.

It was late when Blue went up to the bedroom for a shower. He didn't turn on a light when he stepped into the room, and he closed the hall door quietly before he carried his boots across the carpet to the bathroom.

Once he showered and came out, he went straight to his side of the big bed to ease between the sheets. Allison was already in bed, and maybe had been asleep for hours. She didn't make a sound or a move when he settled beside her.

It had taken him all this time to come to grips with her gifts. The tiny box from the night before had been safely squirreled away in the top drawer of his armoire. He'd opened it last night while Allison had been in the shower.

He'd not had many gifts in his life, so when she'd given him that one—a special one with sentiment attached—it felt as if she'd handed him a live rattler.

The whole subject had hit him like a mule kick to the chest. He hadn't been prepared for his feelings about such a thing. It had made him think of all the other times—birthdays, Christmases, special occasions—when he'd felt as if he was the only kid in the world who had no one who cared enough to remember him with a gift.

It hadn't seemed to matter that he was now a grown man and had long ago forgotten about such things. Seeing that festive-looking little present with its curly gold ribbon wrapped up just for him had brought it all back. He was a man, but he'd suddenly relived the hurt of a lonely kid, the shame of being the only one Santa forgot.

The cuff links were handsome, but the mare was one of the finest horses he'd ever laid eyes on. He was unworthy of either gift. And never more than when he recalled the stark pain in Allison's lovely blue eyes both times when his own emotions had struck him dumb.

And now, he couldn't remember a time in his life when he'd felt more ashamed of himself. Leaving Allison with the impression that he didn't like or want either of her gifts was one shame he'd brought on himself.

How could he tell her how her thoughtfulness had made him feel? He never spoke of his feelings, never put them into words. The whole idea of telling her about the story behind his bad reaction struck terror in his heart.

Because he was truly sorry, and because he craved her tenderness and secretly prayed for her forgiveness, he rolled toward her. He touched the silken skin of her arm, then dropped his hand to her waist and slid it around her to ease her back against him.

She made a small sound and murmured something he didn't catch. Because he was certain she was asleep, he pressed a tender kiss to her ear then turned his face to rest his rough cheek against the sweet smoothness of hers.

He didn't want to love her. He couldn't, no matter how much he thought of her, no matter how privileged he felt to lie beside her and touch her.

A few moments later, the craving he'd had all day made him ease away and gently roll her onto her back. She stirred then, just as he leaned down to kiss her. When her hand came up sleepily to his cheek, he deepened the kiss. She didn't resist him at all, and somehow, sex that night became something much more than he had in mind.

"Oh, Allison, we've missed you!"

Lizabeth Morgan hurried to Allison and threw her

arms around her for a quick hug. "How's the new bride?"

Allison blushed and Liz laughed. "I don't blame you, girl! If I was lucky enough to catch a man like Blue Sumner, I'd not only blush, I'd keep him in bed for a month!"

Liz's naughty comment made Allison giggle and shush her. "Hardly the topic for the front steps of a church before Sunday service," she admonished, but her eyes were twinkling with the first lightheartedness she'd felt in what seemed like weeks.

"So," Liz chattered on as they walked up the last steps to the church door, "where's that handsome sinner you married a week ago yesterday?"

Liz had been her maid of honor, but Allison had managed to confide little of her true relationship with Blue. As if she'd seen right through Allison's reticence, Liz had loyally not asked many probing questions, though she'd pestered her with a frequent litany along the lines of, "Are you sure about marrying him? Are you sure he's the one? What's the rush?"

Allison treasured her friend for her honesty, common sense and her entertaining bluntness. Liz was not Charles's favorite person and Liz felt exactly the same about him. To Aunt Pet, Liz was the happy, boisterous best friend of the niece she loved, so she'd accepted Liz long ago and seemed to enjoy her company. Allison didn't know what Blue would make of her friend once he was around her a while, but despite the problems in their marriage, she hoped he would be tolerant.

Liz leaned close to confide, "Aunt Pet came in a bit ago. I don't want to worry you, but her eyes were a little puffy and she looked tired. Charles stayed home, as usual."

Liz followed as Allison made her way to the pew her aunt sat in. Both sat down next to Pet, who greeted them quietly, but with obvious relief.

The service started then with a nice blend of traditional hymns and contemporary worship music. The pastor preached on patience which, he said, usually went hand in hand with trying to understand others, especially people who could sometimes be difficult to get along with. The message seemed quite appropriate for her situation with Blue and gave Allison food for thought.

After church, Liz insisted the three of them go to one of the nicer restaurants in town. Though Pet was initially reserved, Liz managed to make her laugh a time or two, and soon the three of them were relaxed and had a good time. Liz was the first one to leave once they finished eating and talking. Allison and Pet lingered over a last cup of coffee.

"I understand Blue will be coming in to the bank tomorrow morning," Pet began. "Charles seems to have calmed somewhat after their talk the other night."

Allison shook her head. "Blue didn't say a lot about how things had gone. I got the impression that he'd not made a firm agreement."

"That's understandable," Pet commented, but the hint of worry about her indicated she didn't understand at all. "He has a right to make decisions about his own money. As you pointed out to Charles more than once, there is no written agreement between the two of them."

Pet couldn't look her in the eye those next few moments. Not even Allison's soft, "You seem very worried," encouraged her to do so.

Aunt Pet stirred her creamed coffee and appeared to be laboring to control her emotions. Allison waited in suspense for her to speak.

"Charles hasn't been himself for some time, Allison. I was thinking his upset was due solely to the problems the bank's having, but I'm afraid he might also be having another affair."

Ironically Allison felt a bit better. Charles had never been faithful to Pet, so the information was nothing new or worse than usual. Though they lived in the same house, Petula and Charles had separate bedrooms and virtually separate lives, and had for as long as Allison could remember. Charles lived for the bank, and Pet lived for her charities. Charles kept his dalliances discreet, and Pet rarely let on that she knew, though Allison suspected her aunt truly did know about each one.

"Is there something different about this woman?" It was a bold question for Allison to ask, but she sensed Pet wanted to talk. It had only been in the past two years or so that Pet had begun to confide in her about such things.

Pet kept her eyes firmly fixed on the tabletop,

though she held her head as regally as always. "This one has borne him a child."

Allison stared at her aunt, stunned at the news. "What makes you think so?"

"I was at the bank not long after a sheriff's deputy walked out of Charles's office. I happened to be there waiting for Marjorie to finish with some paperwork so we could go for lunch, and apparently Charles wasn't aware I was close by. A few minutes after the deputy left, Charles threw open his office door and marched through the bank. He appeared to be furious.

"That's when I decided to see what was going on. Because Meg, his secretary, appeared to be more surprised that he'd rushed out of the bank than the fact that I'd stopped by to say hello, she told me I could wait for him in his private office."

Petula paused, then glanced up at her at last. "I'm not one for snooping around in the things of others, but I was in Charles's office and Meg closed the door so I could have privacy. That's when I noticed a wad of papers on the floor next to Charles's trash can and walked over to pick them up."

"What were they?"

Pet took a steadying breath. "A court summons advising him of a paternity suit, filed by a woman with a name I didn't recognize. Her home address is outside the county, so she doesn't live nearby."

Allison felt sympathy for her aunt and reached across the table to grip Pet's hand. "I'm sorry, Aunt Pet. That can't have been easy for you to discover."

"It wasn't easy, but I'm glad I know. If it ever

comes out…'' she said, then shivered. "It will be quite a scandal, but at least now I have some warning.''

"What will you do?"

"I have no idea. Other than hold my head up and continue doing good things for people who need someone, I have no idea what I *can* do. Unless I try to contact this woman myself to see if she can be persuaded to drop her suit and keep silent. Of course, the child will need suitable financial support, but that can be easily arranged without a formal hearing.''

Allison added, "Unless he's not the child's father.''

Aunt Pet nodded. "I'd thought of that, too, but surely the woman wouldn't dare begin a lawsuit, where there'd be a demand for blood tests to determine paternity, if she wasn't completely certain who the child's father is.''

They both went silent for a while. Pet sipped her coffee, but her hand trembled.

"Is there anything I can do?'' Allison hated that it seemed such an empty offer, in view of the fact that there probably was nothing to be done, but she felt as if she had to do something.

Pet shook her head. "No, dear, there's nothing. Sometimes life doesn't run smoothly. This isn't the first time in the history of bad marriages that such a thing has happened. It won't be the last, though I hope to manage my part in this little drama with some grace.''

"I'm so sorry, Auntie,'' Allison said sincerely.

"I'm sorry also, but perhaps it's time I made a few

decisions. Past time, in fact. I'll be doing a lot of thinking in the next few weeks.''

Allison sensed the direction Pet's thoughts might take. "Are you thinking of…divorcing?"

The question made Petula give her a searching look. "I don't know why, when I've tolerated things as they've been for so long, but—'' she paused ''—I'd be a complete fool if I didn't consider it now.'' She gave a delicate shrug. "It's entirely possible that Charles might believe he's in love with this woman and want this baby. I'd always found it odd that Charles never seemed to want a child of his own, but perhaps he just didn't want that deep a tie to me. If I stepped out of the picture, perhaps it would be to the child's benefit.''

Allison reached across the table with both hands. Pet reached for her at the same instant and they gripped each other's fingers.

"Whatever you decide to do, I'll support you in any way I possibly can, you know that,'' she said.

Pet's eyes were teary, but the smile she gave was strong and reassuring. "I know that, my dear. You've always been a good child, perfect in every way, and the most profound joy of my life.''

Now Allison was teary and bit her lip to keep from crying. When she was in control again, she asked, "Why don't you come to the ranch for the afternoon? We could be daring and change into something sturdy and perhaps Blue would give us a tour of everything. Either him or one of his men. It would be completely different from what you're used to, and might be a wonderful distraction. I know you've always loved horses. Blue owns quite a few. If you'd like to go riding, I'm certain he'll let us. You haven't ridden in so long.''

Petula nodded and smiled a little, apparently grateful for the invitation. ''And I do so miss riding. I lost interest in it after my sweet little Maria passed away. Afterward, I simply became too busy to find her replacement. By the way, I didn't ask but, how did Blue like the mare?''

Allison should have realized her aunt would ask, and she scrambled to think of something to say that wouldn't make Blue look like an ogre.

''I think I managed to surprise him.''

It was the truth, though far from the complete truth. But after the pastor's sermon that morning, she'd decided to set aside her hurt feelings and find out why Blue had reacted to her gifts as he had. Blue had so many fine qualities and had treated her well enough that she was coming to the conclusion that his rejection hadn't been motivated by cruelty.

Thinking of him triggered the memory of their lovemaking the night before. He'd been so tender with her. She'd finally managed to go to sleep, but he'd awakened her when he'd come to bed. She should have resisted him, but all he'd had to do was touch her and any thought of withdrawing from him scattered. He'd been gentle, taking his time, making certain she was fully awake and willing before he aroused her to a fever pitch. This time, he'd used endearments.

Precious and *sweet darlin'*. The memory of the fervor and strain in his deep, husky voice when he'd said the words still had the power to send a flash of heat and weakness through her. This morning, she'd been disappointed to again wake up alone.

"Oh, my, I don't know whether I should go riding," Aunt Pet fretted aloud, breaking into her thoughts. "It's been at least three years since I was on a horse."

Though Pet was shaking her head, Allison could tell from the spark of excitement in her aunt's eyes that the idea strongly appealed to her.

"Then let's do it," she urged. "Please, Auntie, it would be so good for you."

Petula suddenly smiled as if she were an excited child. "But you should call Blue first and make certain it's all right with him. It wouldn't be good form for me to just show up." Her enthusiastic smile dimmed a bit. "I'm still very sorry about bursting in on the two of you the other night."

"We both know it was Charles's idea, Aunt. Please forget about it." Allison released Pet's fingers and hurriedly gathered up her purse. "I'll go use a pay phone and let Blue know we're on our way." She got out her wallet and tossed two large bills on the table to pay the check, making certain enough was included to give the waitress a respectable tip, before she rose to go off in search of the pay phone.

Blue wasn't at the house. She learned from her call to the foreman's office, located at the end of one of the barns, that Blue was on the range checking the stock. Because he had a cell phone with him, the foreman gave her the number and she finally reached him.

"Do you mind if I bring Aunt Pet out for the afternoon? We were hoping for a small tour of the ranch buildings and to see a bit of the ranch, but Aunt Pet would especially enjoy being able to ride one of your horses. She's a competent equestrian."

The silence on the line crackled with a bit of static, and went on for several moments. Either Blue hadn't heard everything she'd said or his silence was a prelude to refusing her.

Worried he might say no and that Pet's feelings would be hurt, she added a soft, "Please, Blue. It would mean a lot to me to be able to bring my aunt out for a visit. And for her to be able to go riding."

"Have the two of you got clothes that'll keep you from being fried alive?"

His gruff question relieved her. "We can both wear the jeans and long-sleeved shirts I bought to wear around the ranch. I have two pairs of boots, so all we'll need are a couple of hats. We could buy those at the Wal-Mart on our way out."

"Edward bought a few to have on hand for guests. Jim can show you around and get you a couple of horses." And then the line went dead.

Jim can show you around and get you a couple of horses. The words crushed her enthusiasm. She'd hoped Blue would show them around. But now, after two days of waking up alone and being alone all day the day before, she couldn't help getting the clear impression that he was deliberately keeping her at a distance.

Until that moment, she hadn't realized the depth of her growing feelings for Blue. The pain of being brushed off helped her find it.

CHAPTER EIGHT

ALLISON and Petula arrived back at the ranch and went quickly upstairs to change into riding clothes. Because they were virtually the same size, Allison's jeans and blouses fit Pet as well as her own clothing did. Pet's feet were a half size smaller, but Allison's boots were a reasonable fit.

Once downstairs, Edward brought them a selection of hats from the coatroom off the kitchen. Either the hats were too tight or too large. Opting for the larger hats, they put them on, then glanced over at each other and promptly burst into laughter.

"I'm sorry, Aunt Pet," Allison said when she was able to stop. "Our hats are a bit oversized."

Pet rolled her eyes and the adolescent gesture made her seem younger. "No doubt we look cartoonish. These hats must have been made for giants."

Impulsively Pet turned to Edward, who looked on dutifully. "What do you think, Edward? Do we look like a pair of clean-shaven Yosemite Sams?"

"Hardly, madam," he said tactfully, his British accent betraying a cheerful lilt that Allison hadn't heard before, "More like two very lovely ladies wearing garden hats—Texas style garden hats, of course."

Petula's light brows rose so high they disappeared beneath her hat. "My, what a sweet remark, Edward.

Suddenly I feel like hatching a plot to steal you away from my niece.''

A hint of pleasure flashed through his dark eyes and a faint flush seeped into his stern cheeks. ''Thank you very much, madam. I'm flattered.''

As if he were suddenly embarrassed, Edward abruptly glanced from Pet to Allison. ''Mr. Sumner phoned just as the two of you were coming downstairs. He's requested that I take you on a tour of the headquarters. I was recently granted that same tour, and I have quite a good memory for details. If this is agreeable to you, madam, I shall require a few minutes to change into outdoor gear.''

Allison smiled. ''Of course, Edward. It would be very nice of you to show us around. Take all the time you need. We'll wait.''

Edward nodded to each of them, then turned to walk to the backstairs and go up to his suite of rooms. Allison turned to Aunt Pet and caught a wistful look in her eyes. The wistful look turned sad. Aunt Pet looked over at her, then blushed self-consciously when she realized Allison had been watching her. ''It's quite pleasant for a man to make gracious comments to the ladies. Of course, I realize I stand in your shadow, but it was a small boost to the ego, even so.''

Allison caught her aunt in an affectionate embrace that knocked both their hats askew. ''Aunt Pet, you're a beautiful woman, not only on the outside, but on the inside as well. Charles is a fool.''

Petula hugged her fiercely a moment, then drew back to straighten her hat. ''Thank you, but let's not spoil our little adventure with talk of Charles.'' Her smile trembled a bit, but then it steadied. ''Particularly when there are more gracious gentlemen about.''

Later, well into the tour Edward gave them of the headquarters, Allison realized that there were frequent moments of eye contact between Edward and her aunt. Though neither of them made an overtly flirtatious remark—Edward was quite properly behaved and Aunt Pet was exactly the same—there was no way to mistake the handful of lingering glances between the two.

Edward had changed into a blue plaid Western shirt with blue piping around the yoke and pearl snaps. The jeans he had on were the deep, dark blue of unwashed denim. His boots were black. He'd brought down his own Stetson, a black wide-brimmed cattleman's hat that completed the handsome picture he made in his Western clothes. Allison soon got the impression that Edward had a secret love for the west and for Texas in particular. And, unless she was hallucinating, he was at least mildly attracted to Aunt Pet.

Later, Petula chose a flashy sorrel mare to ride and recommended another sorrel mare for Allison. Edward surprised them both by selecting a horse for himself. While the stable hand saddled Allison's mount and Petula's, Edward efficiently saddled his own.

And when they mounted up and rode down an alley between the corrals for the range, Edward kept a sharp eye on them both until he seemed certain of their competence, then led the way on a small tour of the

ranch that he promised would be pleasant and pictur-
esque.

Allison eventually lagged behind Edward and Pet.
Concern for Pet and the years of loneliness she'd lived
made Allison keep close watch. However pitiful her
marriage was, Petula was a married woman. She was
also a very vulnerable one. As the time passed,
Allison began to see just how vulnerable her Aunt Pet
was when she began to lose her reserve and flirted
gently with Edward.

Allison did the best she could to distract her aunt
without being obvious. Petula had suffered a long
time in her marriage. This thing with Charles's paternity suit might have been the last straw.

How could she find some way to restrain her aunt
and keep her from doing something Pet would be
mortified about later on? As Allison rode along with
Edward and Pet, and watched her aunt's fascination
with Blue's butler deepen, Allison had no idea how
to accomplish it.

"How did your aunt like her visit?"

Allison started at the sound of Blue's deep voice
and glanced up from the book she was reading. She
was sore from the horseback ride and the outdoor air
had made her sleepier than usual. Truth to tell, she'd
been about to nod off. Blue's arrival in their bedroom
brought her fully awake.

"I didn't hear you come up the stairs—Aunt Pet
was thrilled to visit." Allison sat up straighter against
the pillows she'd placed between her back and the

headboard. She'd gone to bed to sit up and read for a bit. "Thank you for allowing her to come out and ride one of your horses. She used to go riding every day before her horse died a few years ago. She hasn't ridden since."

Blue walked to the foot of the bed and his gaze searched her face so intently that she felt herself blush. He was dressed in another chambray shirt and worn denims. She could tell from the dust that clung to his clothes that he'd just come in from the range.

"Does she aim to come out here every day to ride?" The question sounded mild, but Allison couldn't tell if he approved of the notion or not.

"I doubt it. When she still had Maria, she kept her at a stable closer to town." Allison hesitated. "If she did, would that bother you?"

Blue's eyes never wavered from hers. "I don't know. She seems nice enough. Probably too polite to be a bother."

Allison smiled at his perception. "Yes, she is. She was the one who wanted me to call you to ask permission to visit."

Blue looked faintly uncomfortable. "She doesn't need to ask my permission to come out. It's just her husband I want to have some warning about."

Allison watched his face. The faint stirring of desire that had begun the moment she'd heard his voice began to intensify. She sensed his concession about her aunt was a big one for him to make. She doubted he was a man who was used to lots of people going in and out of his house. He was accustomed to his men and the household staff, but perhaps his wife's family members and friends might be another story.

"I'm glad, Blue. Thank you. My aunt means a lot to me."

His expression seemed to harden a bit. "You know I'm goin' in to talk to Charles tomorrow."

"Yes. And do you remember Vacation Bible School starts at church in the morning?" She'd decided it best not to let either of them focus solely on Blue's trip to the bank. He might think she was trying to pressure him about it.

As if he was relieved that she wasn't pressing him about what he'd do, he nodded once. "Nine o'clock to eleven. I'll drop you off, talk to Charles, then pick you up when I get done."

As if that was the end of the discussion as far as he was concerned, Blue turned and strode toward the bathroom, then closed the door behind him.

In moments, Allison heard the shower go on. Her eyelids suddenly too heavy to read, she set her book on the night table and switched off the lamp. She slid down in the bed. Now that all the lights were off except for the soft light from the lamp on Blue's side of the big bed, she wasn't feeling quite as sleepy.

Nevertheless, she must have dozed, because she didn't realize he'd finished his shower until she felt the mattress dip when he got into bed. She opened her eyes and saw he'd snapped off his lamp. She glanced his way in the darkness, feeling her heart rate accelerate as he settled against her side, his shadowed face looming over hers.

She expected him to kiss her and felt a hot rush of excitement. She lifted her hand to touch the hard muscle of his upper arm, then was disappointed when he didn't move.

"My thanks for the mare."

The low words and the edge of emotion behind them caught her off guard.

She immediately realized that this might be her one opportunity to get Blue to explain his earlier reactions to both her gifts. But, lying there in the dark, hearing the hint of strong emotion and restraint in his voice, she suddenly sensed the answer.

Perhaps because of Blue's childhood poverty, and the loneliness and isolation of his adult life, he hadn't received many gifts. A hard man of few words who kept his feelings rigidly in check, might not be prepared to react any other way to her gifts than he had. She'd just decided not to seek a confirmation of that when he surprised her by admitting it.

"Haven't been given too many presents in my life. That's not said to make you feel sorry for me." The gruff edge in his voice warned her from doing that, but it also betrayed his extreme discomfort with making an explanation. "It's just to let you know the reason for how I acted." He paused. "I'm proud you gave me something that belonged to your daddy, and that mare is one of the finest pieces of horseflesh I ever laid eyes on. I thank you."

By the time he finished with his almost terse speech, tears were leaking from the corners of her eyes. She reached up with both hands and placed her palms on his lean cheeks.

Her soft, "You're welcome, Blue. I'm glad you liked them," was soft, and she was grateful she'd managed to keep a teary sound from her voice. "Thank you for telling me. I understand now."

With that, she raised up to close the few inches between her mouth and his. Her tender feelings for him blossomed as she touched her lips to his.

Blue's lips suddenly bore down on hers, gently pressing her head back down on the pillow. He made love to her then. The poignant feelings between them burst into a passion so hot and fierce that it left them both trembling with exhaustion in its aftermath.

"Miss Allie! Miss Allie!"

Allison had seen Johnny Bond fall, and had already started in his direction at a run when he cried for her.

After Bible School, she and some of the children had been playing touch-tag on the church lawn. Because some of the parents were late picking up their children, Allison had organized the game to keep the little ones occupied. Luckily, some of the older children stayed behind to help her. Sure enough five-year-old Johnny had been "it" and had chased another boy too close to the concrete parking lot before he tripped and fell on his hands and knees at the edge of the rough surface.

Allison was beside him in an instant, gathering him into her arms.

"Oh, honey, I'm so sorry!"

Blue had just parked his car on the street when he saw the boy fall. Allison had literally run to the boy, and now sat on the grass with the kid on her lap.

She brushed the little boy's dark hair out of his eyes, said something to him, then gingerly inspected his bare knees and the palms he'd turned up to show her. Blue got to them and felt a shaft of pure pleasure when she glanced up and recognized him. He saw the smile of welcome in her eyes, along with a look of relief that made him feel ten feet tall.

"Better get this one fixed up," he said briskly. "I'll carry him in."

The boy shrank away from the tall stranger until Allison assured him that it was all right and quickly introduced Blue as her new husband. The boy looked up at him with new respect and allowed Blue to pluck him off Allison's lap. Allison asked the older children to mind the others carefully for a few moments.

Once inside the church, Allison directed Blue down the stairs to the small bathroom off her basement classroom. Blue set the boy on the counter next to the sink and stepped back to watch as Allison gently washed the boy's abrasions with warm water and soapy paper towels.

The boy began to cry, but Allison's frequent pauses and soothing words helped get the boy through it.

Blue suddenly felt every gentle touch of her hands as if she'd touched him. The peculiar sensation made his heart pound and sent a sweet feeling over his skin that connected with every atom in his body. Both adults cringed in sympathy for the teary boy when

Allison had to apply an antiseptic cream to his raw skin.

Need sent a stroke of lightning through Blue as he watched Allison's tender ministrations. God help him, but he couldn't remember clearly that anyone but a nurse or doctor had ever taken care of his scrapes and hurts. It was damned sure he'd never been comforted.

Suddenly memories of childhood injuries—skinned knees, smashed fingers, cut hands and broken bones, even the time he'd fallen off a fence and ripped his side open on the head of a protruding nail—seemed to crowd into that tiny room. There had been no one to doctor and comfort and croon sympathetically to him, no mother alive to do it, no father sober enough to notice and no adult, other than the occasional doctor or nurse, who had taken on the chore.

And yet Allison lavished affection and attention on this boy—someone else's child—as if he was the only kid in the history of the world who had ever skinned himself up.

The fact that Blue had never known an Allison Lancaster Sumner in all his growing up years made the sudden realization that he knew one now—at last—especially poignant.

Emotions that were anathema to him rose and pounded against the wide, hard wall he'd erected around his heart. With every beat of blood through his body, emotion thundered painfully against his only defense.

The room closed in on him like a stout rope on a calf, and he took it as long as he could stand before he abruptly stepped out. Escaping the small bathroom didn't make things much better, but at least he could get a full breath. And though he couldn't see what more Allison did for the boy, what he had seen had been burned forever on his mind and heart.

Blue was so quiet on the ride home that Allison's worry over what he'd done about Charles escalated close to panic.

She hadn't told him anything about Pet's discovery about the paternity suit. She'd been afraid to. Though she felt guilty about it, she'd feared what Blue might do about the bank if he knew.

Aunt Pet hadn't come to any decision about her marriage, but Allison suspected Pet would eventually choose to stay with Charles. If Charles had seemed as furious as Pet had said, perhaps he had no intention of being rid of her so he could marry the mother of his child. Charles was such an arrogant, cold man that Allison had trouble picturing him being truly in love with anyone. It was certain the child only figured to be a nuisance in his life.

Besides, Petula Wallace was well loved by everyone. She was known in their small town and throughout the county as an angel of mercy, a beautiful, rich woman who genuinely cared about others and gave unstintingly of her money, time and attention to the sick and those in need. Divorcing Petula for a woman he'd had an affair with would forever ruin Charles's reputation and cause many more problems for the bank that Charles truly did love.

Allison was certain she'd have to think of a tactful way to ask Blue what he'd decided to do about the bank, when he suddenly told her.

"I transferred a certain amount of money into a new account with Chaney Bank," he said grimly. "I gave Charles a second amount of money to use for a couple of mortgage investments."

Though Allison was certain the dollar amounts in both cases were far lower than what Charles had hoped for, perhaps it was enough.

"Told him you weren't responsible for his hiring decisions about that college friend of yours."

Allison was startled that Blue had found out about John Blake's embezzlement. But then, she wouldn't put it past Charles to try to use a revelation like that to get more money out of Blue. After all, it had been one of the pressures he'd used so successfully on her.

"I also told him he needed to call in the law and let them handle things with this John Blake. I won't give him access to another dollar until he does."

Allison's soft, "Was he angry?" made Blue's mouth quirk humorlessly.

"He tried to talk me into more, but I could tell he was straining to keep from cussing me out. One of the good things about bein' rich is some people'd rather bite their tongues off before they chance offending you."

Allison smiled, relieved he'd come through with his part of the bargain with Charles, but proud of him for maintaining the upper hand. She told him so, but Blue ignored the bit of praise.

"If what I gave him isn't enough to save his bank, then there's no savin' it."

"Thank you, Blue. I'm glad you didn't put everything in Chaney Bank. Charles hasn't shown his usual professionalism of late." Her brow crinkled with worry. "There's no way the money you put in the bank and invested could be lost, is there?"

"Not unless Charles steals it himself." He turned to briefly glance at her. "I had a man at the meeting who handles my money and investments. Nothing that we agreed to puts the money in jeopardy. The investment part isn't especially risky this time." He glanced ahead to watch the highway. "Charles wasn't happy to find out my man already handles things for me, but he had to accept it."

Allison released a tense breath. "Then it's all over. The crisis has passed."

"Maybe."

Blue let his remark signal the end of the conversation. Allison could tell by the stern set of his profile that he'd said everything he wanted to. His low, "Maybe," could have meant anything, but it was probably an acknowledgment that he'd given Charles no more than a minimum of what he'd truly wanted from him. She doubted Blue knew about the paternity suit. He reached over to snap on the radio for a weather report just before they got to the ranch and Allison was distracted from thinking about Charles's private problem.

They had lunch together when they arrived home. Blue rushed through his meal, then left the house to get back to work long before Allison finished eating. She got the distinct impression that he was eager to get away from the house—away from her specifically—then chided herself for taking it that way. The world didn't revolve around her.

But there was no getting away from the fact that Blue's world didn't revolve around her. His ranch was his first love. Because he was a man who didn't believe in love, he'd probably invested everything he might normally feel for other people—for a wife in particular—into his ranch.

She pushed away the dismal thought. Blue had changed toward her. There was no way she could discount his tenderness, or the way he seemed to be trying to overcome his lifelong habit of being a loner. Blue had weathered a lot of huge changes in his life the past two years. Perhaps once they'd lived together for a while, his attitude about loving her would change.

Because she had such hope, she began to relax. Though she was certain now that she was in love with Blue, she could wait for him to love her. However long it took for him to overcome his resistance to the whole notion of love, she believed with all her heart that Blue was a man worth being patient for.

Allison finished her meal, then told Edward where she could be reached, before she changed her clothes, picked up her handbag, then went out to the garage to her car. She was due at the small town hospital to read for some of the patients, children and adults, who

had no visitors in the afternoons, or to simply visit
with them or play cards, and give their spirits a lift.

It was amazing how lighthearted she felt as she
drove to town. She thought immediately about Aunt
Pet and wondered if Charles had given her the official
good news that the bank was on its way to solvency.
She'd give Pet a call from the hospital when she got
a chance. She might even stop by Pet's house if she
finished at the hospital early enough to avoid Charles.

Supper that night was the same as the night before:
lonely. Blue stayed on the range until very late, so
Allison ate in the big dining room by herself. Later,
she wandered through the house, making mental notes
of the things that were still needed to complete fur-
nishing it. Blue had said no more about the purchase
of anything additional. Perhaps it would be best, now
that many of the basic furnishings had been bought,
to collect the rest more slowly, though there were still
three upstairs bedrooms that contained no furniture at
all.

The empty bedrooms reminded her of what Blue
had said about wanting a child by spring. She had not
told him then—he'd caught her so by surprise with
both his declaration to have a child right away and
his sudden push to consummate their marriage—that
she'd gone on the pill within two days of agreeing to
marry him. Unless she was one of the rare women the
pill didn't work for, there would be no child by
spring.

Because they'd been lovers these past few days, she

should have found some way to tell him that she was using a contraceptive. But it was a difficult subject to bring up when they spent so little time together. She couldn't quite picture herself saying, during one of the few meals they'd shared, "Oh, by the way, I'm on the pill." During their ride to town that morning then later, when they'd driven home, they'd both been preoccupied with the bank. It had never entered her mind to bring up the subject of contraception, though even that might not have been the proper time, either.

Now she remembered Charles's paternity suit, and her worries began to multiply. Perhaps she should have told Blue about Charles's latest problem before he'd gone to the bank that morning. Instinct warned her he wouldn't approve, of either Charles's predicament or the fact that she'd not told him about it immediately.

On the other hand, she fully expected Pet would stay married to Charles. Petula was too important a woman for Charles to discard, and Pet loathed anything that hinted of scandal. For Pet, divorce at this late date, after years of tolerating Charles's infidelities, would be out of the question.

But because Allison was worried about not telling Blue about the pill, she suddenly began to rethink things about Charles. This time, there was a child involved, plus a paternity suit that might become very public. Now she recalled the shy looks Pet had given Edward and the little flirtations she'd indulged in.

Pet had always had very firm notions about morals and proper behavior. But the fact that she appeared to

have eased a bit over the line with Edward might be
an indication that she'd finally had enough of Charles.

By the time Allison went to bed, her worries had
escalated. She should have told Blue about Charles,
she should have told him that she was on the pill. She
had not meant to keep secrets from him, but when she
thought of things from his point of view, what she'd
done seemed quite serious.

She laid in the bed alone a long time fretting. If
she knew Blue better, if things were more normal in
their marriage, she might not have got herself into this
fix. It was almost a relief when Blue came upstairs.
She would talk to him now, straighten everything out.
But by the time he finished his shower and came to
bed later, he touched her in a way that let her know
he wasn't interested in talk.

By the time she realized that he might have planned
it that way, they were both too far gone to stop.
Afterward, Blue pulled her against his side and went
instantly to sleep. Worry kept sleep away from her for
hours.

CHAPTER NINE

ALLISON tried to wake up early enough to have time to talk to Blue. Because she'd not slept well, by the time she did sleep, she was dead to the world. Her alarm clock went off at seven, but Blue was long gone.

She drove to town for her Bible School class, then stayed in town for a quick lunch at a fast-food drive-in, before she went to the hospital. She worked in the newborn nursery for a while, helping feed babies and change diapers. Later, she went to the pediatric ward to read and play quiet games with several of the children there. It was almost six before she finished for the day.

When she'd realized she would be at the hospital later than she'd planned, she'd called Edward to let him know. Edward reported then that he hadn't heard from Blue, but that supper would be ready for them whenever they got home.

Allison was walking down the long back hall of the hospital, meaning to go out through the emergency department exit to the lot where her car was parked, when she saw from a distance that Petula and her housekeeper, Martha, were coming through the automatic doors.

Martha commandeered the nearest wheelchair and

139

quickly settled Pet into it. The moment Allison saw that—and the harsh bruise and bleeding cut on her aunt's pale cheek—she broke into a run down the busy hall. She reached them just as Martha pulled the wheelchair to a halt in front of the admissions desk.

"Aunt Pet!" Allison touched her aunt's hand and automatically inspected her injured cheek. "What's happened?"

Pet's eyes flinched from hers and she pressed the small damp cloth that held a few chunks of ice over the wound, more as if to hide it from view than to ease the swelling. "I'll be all right—nothing to worry about." Pet's voice was choked.

Martha made a disapproving sound, but didn't remark. Anything the three of them might have said next was lost in the flurry of questions the clerk asked. When the clerk asked how the injury had happened, Pet was vague. "A small collision. Is Dr. Evans on duty?"

"He is," the clerk answered as she handed over two papers for Pet to sign. The clerk smiled sympathetically at Pet when she signed and handed back the papers. "And you're in luck, Mrs. Wallace. Not too much traffic through here yet this evening, so Dr. Evans can probably see you right away."

Just as the clerk said, a nurse came to the desk immediately to wheel Pet to an examination room. Martha and Allison followed along. Once the nurse had checked Pet's vitals, she asked how the injury had happened. Pet's repeat of "A small collision" rang even more hollow than the first time, but the nurse wrote it down, and asked Pet how her car had come out of it.

Pet appeared at a loss for words. "My car?" It took her a second. "Oh—my car. It's fine. Not a scratch."

Allison stared at her aunt. Pet was lying, and not very well. She couldn't remember a time in her life when she'd heard her aunt lie. A feeling of dread seeped into her.

Martha issued another, more disapproving sound that the nurse was oblivious to as she closed her file and issued a cheerful, "Dr. Evans should be in soon, Mrs. Wallace. Sorry to see you need to use the ER, but I'm relieved the injury appears relatively minor. We should be able to fix you right up."

Pet's gentle, "Thank you, dear," and her trembling effort at a firm smile made Allison's heart ache. Something was very wrong.

The moment the nurse had gone out and closed the door, Martha advanced on Pet from the corner she'd been standing in. "You need to tell them how this happened, Miz Pet."

Pet closed her eyes wearily and a small tear dampened a lash. "Please, Martha, don't."

Allison stepped closer to Pet. "How did it happen?"

Pet bowed her head slightly as if bearing a heavy weight. Martha reached over and put her arm around her friend's shoulder and said much less sternly, "You've been through enough, Miz Pet. No sense you goin' through somethin' like this on account of him."

Allison felt sick. A spark of rage flared and began to burn wildly in her heart. Because she suddenly knew what had happened, her soft, "On account of *whom?*" was low and angry.

Pet bowed her head further and tears fairly spurted from her eyes. Martha sent Allison a worried look and Allison released Pet's hand to step closer and put her arm around her aunt's thin waist.

When Pet couldn't answer, Martha glared over at Allison. "It's that damned Charles. He came home and Pet finally told him she knows about that paternity suit. He yelled and threw things around—broke that little china doll Miz Pet's so fond of. I was listening at the door, so the minute he started throwing things, I opened the door and went in. Before I could get to Pet, he up and slapped her so hard he knocked her against the fireplace. While she was on the floor, he was about to kick her leg when I shoved him away."

Shocked, Allison felt the color drain from her face. Her soft, "Oh, God," was the only prayer she could manage. The idea that Charles had slapped her aunt and would have kicked her had Martha not intervened made her so sick she thought she'd faint.

Charles had never struck Pet. He was often surly and ungracious, but he'd never laid a hand on her. And it was just like Martha to be close by to step into the room when Charles started on a tirade.

Allison felt tears on her own face as she leaned over and pressed a gentle kiss on Pet's uninjured cheek. When she straightened, she reached over and took Martha's free hand to grip it.

"Thank you, Martha. You're always so good to us, but this was above and beyond the call of duty or friendship."

Martha actually blushed, her harsh features softening as she looked at Pet. "I got enough of ol' Charles today. I'm hopin' Miz Pet finally did, too, 'cause there ain't no way she'll ever be safe 'round him again." Her harsh features hardened again. "If she thinks she can go on livin' with him, then she's gonna have to do it without me."

The ultimatum made Pet lift her head. Her teary eyes looked bewildered and panicked when they met Martha's. "You'd leave?"

"I'd leave right this minute if I thought you'd let that animal anywhere near you again. While you were in the bathroom at home, I called the sheriff. He should be comin' along anytime, so you need to tell him what happened. And none of that 'small collision' stuff, neither."

Pet shook her head. "I couldn't possibly…"

Martha was relentless. "You *can* possibly. Don't matter who Charles is, he smacked you and woulda done more. You do all that work for the battered women's shelter, but now you're suddenly too good and your life is too fancy to own up to this?"

"N-no, no, I'm not too good. But Charles…the bank—"

"Charles needs to know right now, the first time, that he can't do this to you and get away with it." Martha was immovable. "Besides, he ain't worth the dust on your shoes."

Allison's head was swirling with pain and emotion and outrage. "Martha's right, Aunt Pet. You must speak to the sheriff and file a police report."

Pet was shaking her head, overwhelmed. Allison leaned close and hugged her aunt. Martha hugged them both.

Later that night, the three of them drove to the Sumner Ranch. Allison went with Pet and Martha to help pack some things for them both. Deputies were looking for Charles, but the sheriff himself had come to the house with them for protection.

Sheriff Lem Reynolds remembered the time his wife was so badly injured in a car wreck that it had taken her months to recover. He remembered more that Petula Wallace had come to his house daily, patiently helping his wife relearn to read and write and do general math, while she badgered and bribed her to do every bit of her physical therapy. And when his wife had become so discouraged by all those agonizing months of pain and relearning that she'd gone in search of one of his revolvers, it was Pet who had sensed during her visit that day that something was wrong. Petula Wallace had cared enough about his wife to come back after he'd gone off to work that night. She'd gotten there in time to discover his wife on the back porch with a gun. She'd talked Sandy out of killing herself. Because of Pet Wallace, Sheriff Reynolds still had his beautiful wife and she'd recovered so well that she'd been able to present him with two beautiful children.

A man didn't forget that kind of thing, and he didn't stop feeling grateful. When the three women finished packing, the sheriff followed Pet's car, which Martha drove for her, and Allison's all the way to the Sumner Ranch.

Once Allison and Martha got Pet settled comfortably in one of the bedrooms upstairs, Allison helped Edward set up a rollaway bed for Martha in the same bedroom. Allison had tried to talk Martha into taking the other furnished bedroom next to the one Pet was in, but Martha refused.

"Pet might rest more at ease if I stay with her," Martha had said pointedly.

Edward was grim, but he'd raced around in an almost unbutlerlike manner to bring the three women a tray of food heaped high with everything he and the cook could think of to tempt them to eat.

Allison left her aunt in Martha's care while she got ready to go find Blue. Edward got a chair for the hall near Pet's door so he could be on hand should either woman want anything.

She changed into jeans and a shirt and boots. Blue wasn't at the house, so she decided to seek him out to tell him about Pet and Martha and why she felt so strongly that they needed to stay at the ranch the next few days. She hoped he wouldn't mind.

She found Blue at the stable, pulling a loose shoe off one of the horses. He seemed surprised to see her, and it warmed her when she saw his surprise switch instantly to pleasure as he untied the bay gelding and led him into a stall.

"You're a long way from the house at this time of night." The faint smile that softened the hard line of his mouth let her know the remark wasn't meant as a criticism. He unhooked the gelding's lead and stepped out of the stall.

She stopped when she reached him. Though he seemed glad to see her, she dreaded his reaction to her news. She tried to think of an easy way to tell him. As if he sensed something was wrong, his faint smile faded.

"What is it?"

"Something happened to Aunt Pet early this evening. She'll be all right, but I brought her and her housekeeper, Martha, to the ranch. I'd like them to stay on a few days until Aunt Pet decides what she's going to do."

Allison's hands were clasped together in front of her. Her heart trembled when his eyes took on a flat look. "I know it's quite an imposition…"

"What happened to her?"

"Charles—" Her throat closed with emotion. Shock and anger and worry overcame her those next moments, and she couldn't speak.

Blue closed the stall gate and stepped close to place his big hands on her shoulders.

"What about Charles?" The question was harsh, as if he'd already sensed what had happened. Somehow that made it easier for her to speak. She gave him a brief account of what had happened.

"Did she call the sheriff?" Though Blue's question was calm, she felt as if she was staring up into twin fires of pure fury.

"Pet is mortified, but she filed a police report and asked for a restraining order against Charles. Sheriff Reynolds thought it best that she stay someplace safe for the next few days, until he gets things sorted out."

"So you brought them here." His grim tone gave her no clue about whether he approved of the idea or not.

Her soft, "I hope you don't mind," and the way her voice suddenly wavered made him gently tighten his grip on her narrow shoulders.

"She'll be safe here. Edward is around as much for security as anything."

Allison sagged with relief. Blue pulled her into his arms. Her arms went around his lean middle and she pressed herself tightly against him, her damp cheek resting against his shirtfront. Suddenly she felt safe. The shock of Charles's attack on Pet receded.

"Thank you, Blue. I can't tell you how much it means to be able to have her here and know she's safe."

"Where's Charles now?"

"No one knows. The sheriff and two of his deputies are looking for him."

"I'll walk you to the house, then I'll go down to the bunkhouse and have a talk with the men. Charles probably won't show his face here, but it might pay to have everyone on the lookout."

Grateful that Blue took it all as seriously as she

did, and that he was so willing to do what he could to help protect Pet, Allison hugged him tightly and reveled in the way they walked, each with an arm around the other all the way to the house. When they got into the ranch kitchen, the gentle kiss he pressed to her forehead was wonderfully consoling. He left her right away to go talk to his men.

Those next two days were somber. At Blue's and Pet's insistence, Allison maintained her Bible School and hospital schedule. Sheriff Reynolds came by the house the next evening to report that he'd discreetly arrested Charles at the bank that morning, but that the judge had set bail at such a low amount that Charles was only gone from the bank for the length of a long lunch.

He warned Pet that the news would surely come out, but he assured her that the scandal she was so worried about would never reflect negatively on her or Allison because of the way folks felt about them. After the sheriff left, Pet retreated to her room.

Though Martha hovered and Edward was always nearby, Pet withdrew from everyone and spent the days in bed.

The day after Charles's arrest, the phone at the ranch rang constantly with calls from longtime friends and well-wishers who had heard the news. Flowers were delivered almost hourly, and several people stopped by the house. Edward managed to field the flurry with calmness and aplomb, but Pet refused to take calls or to leave her room.

By that night, Allison began to worry about her aunt's increasingly depressed state of mind.

Blue hated the takeover of his home. Though he felt sorry for Petula and was outraged at what Charles had done, he hadn't realized until Pet and Martha had moved in how much he resented Pet's close relationship with his bride.

It was a hell of a way for him to feel, particularly since he shouldn't have cared that much. He didn't mean to fall in love with Allison, so why should he care that others loved her and that she loved them?

But everything Allison said and did and thought seemed to revolve around her aunt, and he felt such a sting of jealousy he could hardly keep quiet.

As he'd known from the beginning, if Allison's loyalty was ever put to the test, he'd always be her second choice. His brief effort to begin to separate her and her aunt on their wedding day had fallen flat that night when she'd let him know how much she thought of her aunt. He'd had to back off.

While he knew Pet couldn't help the predicament she was in, he began to resent the fact that she'd spent the last two days in bed. He couldn't understand why she would behave that way, why she would put everyone out and make them worry, but those thoughts made him feel mean and hard-hearted.

He'd had Allison to himself for such a short time. Though he didn't love her, he was forced to admit he missed her terribly. Which angered him because she'd gone nowhere and still slept with him every night.

Friday morning, when he knew Allison had gone to Bible School and Martha had gone with Edward to pick up a few more things at Aunt Pet's house, he walked back to the house. Except for his cook and housekeeper, Pet was alone.

The time had come for someone to do something. He didn't let himself waver as he entered the house and strode across the kitchen. Remembering to remove his hat, he hung it on a wall peg near the back stairs, then pounded up the steps to the second floor.

Blue stopped at the bedroom across from his and tapped on the door. His low, "Miz Pet? I need to have a word with you," sounded as if he meant business.

He heard a quiet, "Just a moment, dear," then felt a peculiar sensation in his chest at the endearment. But Petula regularly called everyone "dear." It meant nothing special in his case, so he made himself ignore it.

He heard footsteps, then the sound of the knob turning. Pet opened her door a few inches and peered out at him.

Her cheek was an ugly yellow, the cut still prominent on her fine skin, but it was healing nicely. Her light hair was uncombed, she wore no makeup and she was still in her robe.

Feeling a bit impatient that at ten a.m. she wasn't up and dressed and ready for the day, and knowing he couldn't carry on a conversation with her from the hall, he gave her as stern a look as he figured he needed to.

"I can't talk to you till you get dressed. I'll meet you downstairs in the den in twenty minutes."

His no-nonsense tone caused Pet's blue eyes to widen. He'd spooked her and now he felt as abusive as Charles. Nevertheless, they had to talk. Pet had been coddled for two days and nothing had changed. However much money she had, if she divorced Charles she'd have to buck up and make her own way in the world. Someone had to toughen her up, or she'd never be any good, for herself or anyone else.

Blue turned and walked back the way he'd come. He went quickly downstairs to the kitchen, pausing only long enough to ask Mrs. Burns to bring him a coffee tray with two cups, before he went to the den at the front of the big house to wait.

Almost exactly twenty minutes later, Pet appeared in the open door of the den. Her hair was styled the way she usually wore it, she was dressed in a nice blouse and slacks and she'd made up her face so well the bruise hardly showed. She was wearing jewelry and looked right as rain to him.

He stood briefly because it was proper, then motioned her toward the wing chair opposite the one he sat down in. When she saw the coffee tray on the low table between them, she automatically poured coffee for them both, handed his over and took the other cup and saucer for her own.

"I imagine you've grown quite tired of me, haven't you, Mr. Sumner?"

Her statement caught him off guard. It was as if

she'd read his mind. He took a sip of coffee while he studied her face.

"I don't understand how a woman who's done so much for people, who's helped so many others through their hard times, can suddenly take to her bed when something happens to her."

His blunt words fell hard between them, though he'd tried to say them kindly. Because Pet seemed to be able to take it, he went on. "Your niece has been worried sick over you, and Martha would probably like to visit the daughter and new grandbaby she's got in San Antone."

Pet looked surprised, then distressed. "New grandbaby? Martha didn't mention—"

"Martha's been worried over you," he went on without mercy, "how you're keepin' to yourself. She didn't want any of us to mention the baby to you, 'cause she knew you'd make her go. She said there was no way she could leave until you felt better."

Petula stared over at him in horror then set her cup down. "I didn't realize..."

"Well, now you do."

The silence in the room pounded Blue's conscience. He was trying to jar Pet out of her self-pity, but what did he know about fragile aristocrats? If she was as fragile as she looked right now, his stern talk would probably put her in the hospital.

He remembered how much she liked to ride horses and gave her a searching look. "Can you ride in those clothes?"

Pet clearly hadn't recovered from his first little assault. It took her a moment to follow the change of subject. She glanced down at herself a moment as if she'd not been able to recall what she was wearing. She looked up at him.

"No, but…Martha packed something for me to ride in, and my boots."

His tough, "Go get 'em," made her flinch. He made himself ignore her reaction. "A ride'll do you good. I need to check the stock. You might as well come along."

Blue held his breath. Petula looked shocked. Just when he wondered if she was going to faint or holler or run upstairs and lock herself in her room, she seemed to recover.

"Yes, I believe a ride would be good," she said then. "I'll just go upstairs and change."

Though she got up with the same regal grace that was also second nature to Allison, Pet made it to the door before she suddenly broke into an unladylike rush toward the front stairs. Blue sat listening to her run up the steps.

After a few minutes, he got up and walked out into the entry hall to move unhurriedly through the house to the back door. He got his hat on the way, put it on, then tugged it down snugly.

God knew if he'd ever see Allison's aunt again.

CHAPTER TEN

ALLISON rushed home to eat lunch and see how Pet was before she went back to town for an afternoon at the hospital. When she stepped in the back door, she discovered an uproar in the kitchen.

Edward and Martha had squared off and Mrs. Burns and Miss Tilly were looking on worriedly.

"Mr. Blue don't know nothin' about Miz Pet," Martha was saying.

Edward stood stiffly, one brow raised as he looked down at the much shorter Martha, who glared up at him.

"Mr. Sumner is not known for mistreating others, madam. If he took Miss Pet on a horseback ride, you may be certain that she's being properly looked after."

Martha shook her head adamantly. "Miz Pet was in no state to be chased outta her bed and run over half of Texas!"

Edward appeared unruffled. "Nevertheless, madam, Mr. Sumner is in charge, and I suspect he's acted on nothing less than the very best intentions toward Miss Pet. I assure you she could be in no better hands."

Martha's face flushed as she continued to argue. "Miz Pet's afraid of Mr. Blue."

Both of Edward's brows arched high. "Then perhaps once she's spent a bit of time with him, she'll understand that she has nothing to fear."

Martha took a deep breath that seemed to puff her up. Allison chose that moment to make her presence known. The level of conflict in the kitchen had been too intense for anyone to notice her arrival.

"I'm certain Edward is right, Martha."

All eyes turned in her direction. Martha immediately rushed over to plead her side of the argument.

"Mr. Blue waited till you were gone and Edward and I went to the house in town before he made Miz Pet leave her room and go out riding. You saw her this mornin' yourself. She wasn't ready for anything that would strain her, much less to be dragged over this ranch on a horse."

Allison took Martha's hand. Though she suddenly had her own doubts about what Blue had done, she couldn't bring herself to think he meant ill against her aunt.

"I'm certain Blue is taking good care of her. Some time outdoors in the fresh air might be just what she needs to lift her spirits."

The quiet confidence Allison hoped to exude seemed to affect Martha, though she wasn't entirely convinced.

"I mean no offense to you, Miz Allison, but I can't help but wonder what he's thinking of, to bother her like that."

"Me, too, Martha, but let's wait before we get too upset." Allison gave her a soft smile.

Martha finally began to calm. Because she was normally a very sensible woman, and fair-minded, she turned back to Edward.

"I been lookin' out for Miz Pet a lotta years," she said gruffly. "Might be I jumped to some conclusions—but Mr. Blue oughtta of talked it over with somebody else before he took this notion."

Edward gave a reserved nod. "Perhaps, madam, but I believe we can rely on him to treat Miss Pet with care."

Martha made a sound to let everyone know that she was reserving judgment, but she subsided. She glanced toward Allison. "We brung back some more of Miz Pet's things, including some boxes of keepsakes and family things that were up in the attic. No sense lettin' ol' Charles get at those. I'll go take care of them till Miz Pet gets back." She glanced at them all. "Ain't got an appetite for lunch anyway."

"Thank you, Martha." Allison kept her smile in place until she was certain Martha was too far down the hall to the front entry to hear. She turned to Edward.

"I do wish Blue had discussed it with me first."

Edward gave her a kind look. "Mr. Sumner is quite unused to discussing things with others, though I'm certain that will change as he adjusts to married life. Perhaps he discovered that your aunt seemed improved and was prompted to offer a horseback ride. She did seem to quite enjoy being out-of-doors Sunday last."

Allison relaxed. "Yes, she loves to ride. I'm sorry

Martha reacted so strongly. She's been with my aunt for years now."

"Yes," Edward agreed pleasantly. "Loyalty is quite a fine character trait. I do understand Miss Martha's protectiveness, in light of the recent incident, though I don't agree that it was necessary in this case. I'm certain when Miss Petula returns, everyone will see how beneficial her outing has been."

"I'm sure you're right," she murmured, but she suddenly had no appetite herself. She did try to eat something. And though it was hard, she had to force herself to get back to town and the hospital. Because Petula hadn't returned to the house by the time she left, Allison almost didn't go. But there were people at the hospital who were counting on her. She'd just have to trust that Blue was taking care of her aunt, however long they were absent from the main house.

When Allison got back home at five o'clock, Aunt Petula still hadn't returned. Though he'd already informed Martha, who stood nearby with Mrs. Burns and Miss Tilly, Edward calmly reported to Allison that he'd managed to have contact with Blue via a cell phone that one of the ranch hands had taken out to him.

Aunt Pet had worked with a haying crew that morning, eaten lunch at the cookhouse with the ranch hands, but had gone to another part of the ranch to help Blue check water tanks and the handful of windmills that pumped water into the tanks.

Allison was stunned by the report. Even Edward

had grown solemn. Aunt Pet was unused to hard labor of any sort, and it sounded as if everything she'd been exposed to that day was far beyond the kind of activity she was used to.

Moments after Edward gave her his report, the back door opened and Aunt Pet stepped into the kitchen.

Petula walked as if she'd aged forty years. Her overlarge hat was askew, her blond hair hung in tired strands from beneath the hat and she was covered with a layer of Texas dust. She had a tear on one sleeve, a stray straw of hay stuck to her shoulder and a smear of cow manure on the knee of her jeans. She'd sweated off most of her makeup and her blue eyes were dazed with exhaustion.

Allison was horrified. When Pet reached up to remove her hat, Allison saw the dark grease stains on her hands and that her normally well-tended fingernails were filthy and pared short.

When Pet realized that everyone at the house was standing in the kitchen, staring at her in shock, she gave them all a lovely smile.

"There're quite a lot of interesting things to do on a ranch," she declared. Her smile brightened. "I even got to fix one of the windmills!" As if she found the sight of the grim faces around her amusing, she laughed. "Do I look that bad?

"I am quite done in," she said as she made a wry face, "but I assure you all that I feel better after a day of ranch work—if you could call my small contribution work—than I've felt in years."

Petula started stiffly toward the back stairs, then

grimaced and immediately halted. "Though I doubt I'll make it up the steps with any sort of grace..."

Allison was at her side in a moment, as was Martha. They each took one of Pet's arms to assist her, but Pet gave a soft gasp.

Edward heard and promptly rushed over to offer his assistance. "If I may, Miss Petula," he began stiffly, "might I suggest that someone carry you up the stairs?"

When the three of them glanced up at him in surprise, he blushed. "Of course, with Miss Allison and Miss Martha to supervise."

Petula beamed him a smile. "Why, Edward, what a thoughtful suggestion. I would very much appreciate it if you would carry me up the stairs." Petula's gaze wavered to meet Allison's rounded eyes and give her a quick wink.

The wink startled a giggle out of Allison, but Martha, who had followed it all, made a grumpy sound. Allison instantly made her face go sober, but her heart was soaring.

It was reassuring to see Aunt Pet in a lighthearted mood. Whatever had happened that day with Blue, however "done in" her aunt was now, Pet seemed happy and playful—more than restored.

Edward leaned down and carefully eased Petula into his arms. Petula's arms found their way around his neck. Edward tried not to look into the twinkling glimmer in Petula's eyes, but his eyes were twinkling just as happily. He strode toward the back stairs and started up them at a steady pace.

Martha and Allison followed along, though Martha was the only one who truly "supervised." When they reached the upstairs hall, Martha caught her arm and held her back just long enough to whisper harshly, "Now I wonder what that one's up to."

Allison shrugged. At the moment, she didn't care. Though she was exhausted, Petula Wallace now seemed genuinely happy. The crisis had passed, and for the first time, Allison sensed that things would go well for her. Pet had some difficult decisions ahead, but she now seemed equal to them.

By the time Allison left Martha to help Pet with her shower, Edward had gone downstairs. Blue hadn't come in from the range yet and Allison was eager to see him.

After she'd brought Pet and Martha to the ranch, they'd barely had time to be alone, much less to talk to each other. Blue, perhaps out of consideration, had made no demands in bed at night.

Now that Pet had recovered, Allison realized how focused she'd been on Pet's troubles. Apparently Blue wasn't the only one who needed to adjust to married life.

Remembering her earlier upset, because Blue hadn't discussed taking Petula out of the house for the day, Allison was reminded of the things she hadn't discussed with him.

Charles's paternity case and her use of the pill had completely slipped her mind these past days. And the longer she delayed telling Blue about them, the more seriously he might take her silence.

Allison changed clothes for dinner, then was frustrated when she was the only one at the table. Edward had taken a tray upstairs for Petula and Martha, but Blue hadn't come to the house yet.

She ate because she was suddenly starving. Afterward, she changed into outdoor clothing and was about to go off in search of Blue when Edward caught her and passed along a message.

"Mr. Sumner sent word that he won't be home until late."

Allison thanked Edward for the message, but she was disappointed. Was Blue worried that she'd be angry about today? Or was this another case of Blue preferring his first love—his ranch—to his wife?

She doubted very much if Blue worried about riling her. If she'd been a more volatile kind of woman, perhaps he would have. But Blue probably did prefer the ranch he loved to the wife whom he didn't. The fact depressed her, but she wasn't ready to give up on him.

Since it was Friday night, Allison treated herself to a long bubble bath, then did some reading before she finally became too tired to keep her eyes open. Though she'd tried to wait up for Blue, she didn't make it past eleven p.m.

According to Edward, who always made it a point to stay up until he was in for the night, forcing Pet out of the house into the fresh air for a day of exhausting activity had been considered a "rousing success by all."

When he'd asked Edward how everyone had taken
it, prior to seeing the result, Edward tactfully glossed
over Martha's reaction. But Blue had figured on
Martha taking it bad. It pleased him when Edward
reported that his bride had not only given his actions
the benefit of the doubt, but that she'd defended him.

Blue hadn't expected that, and the news sent such
a shaft of sunlight across his heart that he felt the
sweet warmth of it spread clear through him.

And Pet seemed to have lost her fear of him. She'd
stuck with him the whole day, until he'd had to make
her go to the house for the night. She been a willing
little helper, and game for anything, even when he'd
had her climb up a windmill with him to replace a
couple of parts. He hadn't expected that, either, but it
made him feel good.

Allison was asleep when he got upstairs. He showered and shaved, then grabbed his discarded towel off
the counter to drop it down the laundry chute. Too
late, he realized he'd managed to drag Allison's handbag off the counter with the towel. The contents of
the bag dumped and spilled all over the floor. He'd
leaned down to pick everything up, when he spied a
round, flat disk.

He'd never known a lot about women's things, especially the personal things they carried around with
them, but he could read the word Contraceptive just
fine.

Allison was on the pill, and maybe had been for
some time. He remembered clearly telling her he

wanted a child by spring. He remembered just as clearly that she hadn't said a word about this.

As Blue put her things back into the handbag, he thought about it. Though he wouldn't have believed Allison would be dishonest with him on purpose, he was worried now that she had been.

Maybe she was the kind of woman who liked other people's kids, and maybe even sometimes thought she'd like to have kids of her own, but when push came to shove, she didn't really want any. The darker thought, that maybe she just didn't want a child with him, was one he dismissed. At first.

He had passable looks, lots of money and he'd saved her uncle's bank. But, when you put a man like him up against a woman of breeding and background, he was a mongrel. Besides, she might also bear him a hellish resentment for forcing her to marry him.

What other plans had she had for her life before he'd taken it over? It hadn't mattered much to him before, but now that he cared about her, what she wanted mattered very much.

He'd known all along that she'd never stay married to him. He'd accepted that, he expected her to be like everyone else who had had a place in his life. He'd wanted her to leave him with children, at least one child, but as long as she was on the pill, she'd never conceive.

Blue felt the warmth drain out of him. Old feelings of rejection and loss swelled up to add new torments. He did his best to ignore them, but he was only partially successful.

When he snapped off the light and went into the dark bedroom, he went straight to his side of the bed and climbed in beside his wife. Emotion nearly choked him. Want and need churned so fiercely inside him that he couldn't help but touch her.

And when she turned toward him in the darkness, just because his touch had made her wake, he couldn't keep himself from taking her. He refused to think of it as lovemaking, but the way he touched her, the way they came together, made it impossible for his brain to keep its grip on the word sex.

Saturday went much the same for Blue as every day at the ranch had so far. He was up early and gone before Allison awoke.

Pet got up shortly after seven a.m. when Allison did. The two of them and Martha ate breakfast together. Pet disclosed her plan to consult an attorney on Monday to represent her in her divorce.

After a quick breakfast, Pet and Martha went to town to find a supply of thank-you cards to post to everyone who had sent flowers. When they returned, Pet went into the den and spent the rest of the morning returning the calls of some of the many well-wishers who had called the ranch to inquire about her. That afternoon, she then called the charities she was involved with and set up a schedule for the next week.

By that evening, Petula announced that she'd bought a plane ticket for Martha to go visit her new grandbaby. Martha would be leaving the next afternoon and Pet planned to drive her to the airport.

When Blue again came in late, Allison was determined to have a talk with him. She'd attended her last church service without him, and tomorrow was Sunday. Because Blue seemed unusually withdrawn from her, she made the mistake of bringing up the milder subject of church attendance and Sunday work first.

Once Blue agreed to go with her, he touched her and managed to obliterate all thought of expanding their discussion to the subject of the pill and Charles's paternity suit. After a very carnal kiss, neither was in any mood for talk.

The next morning, Blue was up and gone by the time Allison awoke. Just when she thought he'd changed his mind about going to church, he came in, took a quick shower, then solemnly dressed for the service.

He wore a dark suit and used her father's onyx cuff links. Allison wore one of the pretty summer dresses he'd bought her in Dallas. Blue was no more talkative on the ride to Chaney than he'd been at breakfast. Though he wasn't the talkative type, Allison sensed that something was bothering him.

Later, in church, he held up his half of the hymnal they shared, but he didn't sing. He seemed attentive to the pastor's message, bowed his head respectfully for the prayers, but the pleasant service did little to lift what Allison began to think was a touch of gloom.

Did the church service bring back some unpleasant memory for him? Her second thought was that he probably had never been instructed as a child on the importance of church attendance. Perhaps that was why he didn't seem to know any of the songs. That thought led to another. Perhaps he was going to the service only because she'd insisted, and he now resented it. But none of that really accounted for the shadowy silence between them.

Later, they drove home. Their large Sunday lunch together was pleasant. Blue asked Martha to join them before they left for the airport. Allison suspected Blue might have liked for Edward, Mrs. Burns and Miss Tilly to join them at the big table also, but Edward had probably nixed the idea.

Edward did seem to have some very firm notions of how things in the household should be run, though he waffled a bit on the subject of Aunt Pet. More than once, Edward had behaved in a less than rigid manner toward her aunt. Allison needed no clearer confirmation of the growing attraction between the two.

She even mentioned it to Blue when they went out riding that afternoon, but he didn't remark on the subject beyond a quiet, "I noticed." Blue had been restless hanging around the house. Because he'd seemed to take her insistence that he attend church with her and not work on Sunday as an unspoken expectation of him to stay inside at the house the entire day, she'd decided that not working didn't mean not riding.

It was amazing how much of Blue's tension eased once they were on horseback, riding in the direction Allison had heard his former house stood. Just when Blue started angling away from the old headquarters in the distance, Allison stopped him.

"I'd like to see the old headquarters," she told him. Blue glanced her way, but didn't make eye contact. His expression was grim.

"Nothin' much to see. It's old and run-down. I expect to have it torn down by winter."

Allison looked over at him. "I understand it's quite an old house. Do you think it might have some historical significance?"

"You've been working with the historical society too long," he chided gently, but she sensed the new tension in him. "The only historical significance it has is that I lived there for more than six years. No matter how many times I patched the roof, a drip always found me when it rained, the cold air still comes through strong enough to move the curtains, and there's still a hand pump over the kitchen sink. I had to pipe running water into the bathroom for a shower, sink and commode. Had to cut up a closet to put the bathroom in, since there was only an outhouse when I bought it."

"You've worked very hard in your life, haven't you?"

Her soft question silenced him for several moments. The gloom she'd sensed about him was suddenly strong. When he didn't answer her question, she reined her horse in the direction of the old headquarters. "I'd like to have a look."

Blue actually reached over to seize her horse's reins. Now his eyes met hers directly, and the burning look in them stunned her.

"No." The hard set of his face, and the faint bleakness his burning gaze couldn't quite conceal, emphasized his refusal.

Allison placed her hand gently over his and saw the immediate effect when his gaze shifted down to look at it.

"I'm no snob, Blue," she began softly. "I've never looked down on anyone who had less. If you'd rather I not go to the old house, I won't." She paused when his gaze lifted from her hand to focus into the distance.

"I think—" Emotion overwhelmed her. It was more than the sympathy she felt for this proud man who was still insecure enough about his background to be ashamed that he'd lived for years in an old house that had a room with a dirt floor. A man still so ashamed of his poverty that he couldn't bear for his own wife to see evidence of it.

"I think you're one of the finest people I know," she said, struggling to keep her voice from trembling with her feelings. "What you came from doesn't bother or disgust me, and never will. It's who you are without that old house and without your fortune that matters to me."

She paused again, hoping he'd look at her, hoping he was really listening to her. Because she'd just realized how very deeply she loved this proud, hard, complex man.

She made her quiet words a confession. "I'm in love with who you are, Blue, not with what you have now or with what you didn't have in the past. If you lost everything tomorrow, I'd still love you, I'd still want to be with you. Even if it meant living in your old house, or living in a trailer on a ranch somewhere while you work for someone else.''

Those words finally earned her his complete attention. But instead of accepting the love she'd just declared for him, his eyes were burning with an anger and cynicism that shocked her.

Blue heard every soft word. Each syllable shot a hot dart that impacted painfully on something raw inside him.

She didn't mean it. Love was something different for her than it was for him. When love failed her, it would hurt, but she was too secure for a loss of love to destroy her.

He suddenly had to shield himself from the beautiful mirage her declaration of love called up for him. If he let love become part of things between them, losing her later would be agony. He had to stop her talk of love. In the long run, it would be kinder for them both if he stopped it now.

''Don't make meaningless love pledges to me, Miz Allis. I don't want your love,'' he growled, the anger in his voice making his words harsh and brutal.

Allison stared, shocked, as his fiery gaze held hers and his words pounded her heart.

''We got married because I needed a wife and your family needed my money, not because either of us needed love. I want a child by spring. If spring comes and you aren't carryin', I'll divorce you so fast it'll make your head spin.''

The vicious words made her feel faint. She couldn't

breathe, her shock was so profound. Somehow, she got in a bit of air past the strangling pain in her throat.

Her whispered, "You don't mean those hateful things," made his lips tighten and the muscles of his jaw flex. Suddenly he yanked the reins out of her limp fingers. He spurred his horse. Both horses stepped forward with a jolt. Allison grabbed dazedly for the saddle horn and rode numbly along. Blue glanced back to make certain she was hanging on, before he spurred his horse again and they galloped toward the old headquarters.

By the time he stopped the horses, they'd reached the old barn. Blue dismounted, dropped both sets of reins over a wood rail of the corral, then came around his horse to reach up and pull her from her saddle.

The fury in him was terrifying. He took her arm, then led her to the old house on the other side of the ranch yard. When he reached the porch, he wrenched the door open, then pulled her through before he shoved the inside door and sent it banging against the kitchen wall. The inside of the house was dim, but there was enough light coming through the old curtains and thin drapes to reveal the shabby condition of the house itself and its sparse, ugly furnishings. The smell of earth and leather and old wood permeated the place.

It was not the worst house she'd ever been in. Actually it appeared quite sturdy and quaint. With new wallpaper, paint and a new finish on the wood floors, all it would take was a careful collection of basic furniture to make it comfortable and attractive.

But Blue seemed to believe it was a terrible place. He dragged her from room to room, forcing her to look at everything as he pointed out what he considered evidence of poverty and worthlessness. He showed her the second bedroom at the back of the house and the hard-packed dirt floor beneath the tarp that covered it.

By the time they ended up in the other bedroom, Allison's heart was traumatized. Not by the conditions in the house, but by Blue's towering anger. She couldn't help shrinking back when he turned to her.

He didn't yell, but his low voice was starkly challenging. "Think you could live in a dump like this, Miz Allison Lancaster Sumner? Think you could shower in that metal shower stall and wash your dishes in the kitchen after you pumped a sink full of water and a couple baby frogs came out of the spout? And how about this bed?"

He dragged her forward, and pushed her close to the iron bed with its old, sagging mattress. Her knee bumped the mattress and startled a field mouse out of a tattered hole to send it scurrying across the faded fabric.

Blue leaned so close that his breath gusted hotly against her cheek. "Could you lay beneath me on that bed at night and be happy? Or would you cry for the fine things you've always had, like the clean, expensive sheets and the top-of-the-line mattress you had under your beautiful back last night?"

As if he meant to go the whole way to shocking her, his arms came around her from behind and his hands covered her breasts. "Just how turned on could a woman like you get, if she had to spend the rest of her life sleeping in that bed, in this house, with a man who'd never make enough money to buy her a fine dress or her kids more than a little extra candy at Christmas?"

Allison felt the complete gentleness in the hands that cupped her breasts. Blue hadn't harmed her body. She knew with absolute certainty that he never would, no matter what the provocation. She was shaking from the angry words he'd thrown in her face, but she'd also heard the terrible pain behind the things he'd said. Something in him had broken, and this flood of anger was evidence of it.

She knew she would never see a more terrifying display of the effects of the emotional deprivation Blue had endured in his life, and she forgave him instantly.

Her hands trembled as she lifted them and placed them over his. She leaned against him, pressing her back gently into his heat.

She didn't realize that her face was wet with tears until she heard them in her voice. "I don't care what you say to me, Blue, I don't care what you show me. You'll never do anything that will make me love you less than I love you right now."

After a few thundering moments, his hands went slack. He released her and his arms fell away. He stepped back. Allison turned and looked up onto an expression as hard and unfathomable as weathered granite. The look in his eyes was flat and almost dead-looking.

However much his anger had frightened her before, this terrible cold and lack of emotion cut at her heart in a way that caught her off guard. His voice was low.

"I haven't changed my mind about what I want from you," he said. "When you really get down to it, I want your body for sex, and sex for the children it could give me if you weren't on the pill."

Allison's breath caught. Somehow, he'd guessed she was on the pill. But the rest of what he said was even more shocking. *I want your body for sex, and sex for the children it could give me.* The words stung, and were a clear effort to degrade the tender feelings between them.

But she hadn't misunderstood his care for her. It showed itself in every touch, in everything he did, and made itself heard in every gruff word. She knew he loved her, even if only a little. The war inside him had to be fierce, otherwise he could never have said the things to her that he had.

The emotional aftermath of this shocking confrontation was starting to crash down on her, but she made herself withstand it. Blue was worth her patience, he was worth enduring this temporary pain, he was worthy of her love. But if she wasn't strong enough to be as tough as he was, she'd lose him.

"I never expected that you would turn out to be a liar, Blue," she said calmly. "You're only saying these awful things to me because you know I've guessed the real truth. That you love me, but you're terrified by it.''

Blue's eyes were suddenly blazing again, the dead-look in them banished by the outrage that took its place. The word ''liar'' had the right effect. Allison went on softly, aiming for the thing she felt certain might get through to him.

''But if you can't let yourself risk loving me, maybe you won't be able to risk loving the child I might give you. And, if you're not able to risk loving your own child, what will you really have to offer instead? Money? A fine house?'' Allison didn't let her gaze waver from the fiery wildness in his eyes as she tried to pierce the shield around his heart.

''What did you want most when you were a child, Blue Sumner? Being poor wasn't what hurt you, you weren't starved for 'things.' What you wanted most, what you needed and were so hungry for, was a loving mother and a steady, sober father who would make a loving, secure home for you. If you'd had enough love, poverty wouldn't have mattered—you might not even have noticed you were poor.'' Her voice went softer for one last stroke. ''If you'd had enough love, my love wouldn't scare you. And the fact that you love me wouldn't terrify you so.''

Blue was so stiff with anger now that she thought he would explode. For all her calm bravado, her knees were rubbery and she was shaking. She'd crossed too many lines with Blue, blasted through too many boundaries with what she'd said. If her instincts were wrong, he would never forgive her. If she lost him because she'd taken this risk, she might never forgive herself.

Blue suddenly swung away from her. He was gone from the house almost as quickly, stalking through it and out into the late-afternoon sunlight as she started to follow. Allison stopped at the open kitchen door and watched him grab his horse's reins and leap into the saddle. The horse shot out of the ranch yard at a gallop. Allison watched until Blue and his horse were a speck on the horizon.

After a last walk through the house, she went out, closing the door to the kitchen securely, then the porch door.

Still dazed by the trauma of the showdown between them and numb with reaction, Allison got her horse, mounted and rode slowly back to the new headquarters.

CHAPTER ELEVEN

THOSE next days were some of the worst of Allison's life. Because Aunt Pet was still around, she put up a calm, cheery front. Aunt Pet remarked once on the fact that she was pale and seemed tired, but Allison discovered she possessed a bit of modest acting ability. She managed to convince her aunt that the excitement of the last weeks and her heavier volunteer schedule was the cause.

She almost never saw Blue. He was up well before dawn, and he came to the house for bed only after he thought she was asleep. Every night they would lay next to each other, the silence between them thundering in the still room. Blue was so stiff beside her most of the night that she wondered if either of them ever truly slept.

Aunt Pet consulted an attorney, filed for divorce and had the papers served on Charles at the bank. When she insisted that Charles move out of the house, he refused. Until Sheriff Reynolds went to speak to him one evening on an unofficial visit and managed to convince him.

She and Aunt Pet speculated about what the sheriff had said to Charles to accomplish that, but Allison secretly suspected Sheriff Reynolds might have resorted to force. Neither man said a word about it.

By the end of the week, Martha had returned from

San Antonio, and she and Petula had moved back into Pet's home. Without them, Blue's huge house seemed cavernous and lonely.

At first, Allison put in more hours at the hospital and more time with the church daycare, where she also donated her time. She worked through the long evenings at the new animal shelter where every dog or cat brought in was cared for until a home was found for them. Because the animals were never euthanized, the shelter was always desperate for people to donate their time and money.

Despite Blue's nearly complete avoidance of her and her dismal feelings about that, she tried to have faith that things would get better between them. She spoke to no one about her troubles with Blue, but often in those days, she slipped away to the church to think things over.

It was during one of those first quiet visits to the church that she remembered Blue's initial reaction to her gifts and how hurt she'd been. The memory of his confession later when he'd apologized to her and thanked her, still seemed so wonderful that it brought tears to her eyes. Blue was a good man. She had to believe he'd come around. It was not in his nature to be cruel, whatever he'd said to her that afternoon. He was too fair-minded and considerate of others not to eventually see that he was being unreasonable on the subject of love. If he could just overcome his pain and mistrust, she'd never let him down.

It was late that second week when Allison decided she'd had enough. She canceled her work for the day and changed into riding clothes. One of the stable hands saddled a horse for her. She found out where Blue was working, then set out in the direction of one of the hay barns that was a distance from the new headquarters.

An inner radar that was always peculiarly attuned to Allison's presence hummed in his chest. Before he even caught sight of her riding out to the hay barn where he was doing repairs, he sensed her.

While she was still a long way out, he sent the two men working with him to another task on another part of the ranch. The sun was getting too high to work on the barn roof much longer anyway. He pretended not to notice the knowing look the two men gave each other when they caught sight of his wife.

His wife. Of all the things he owned, of all the things he treasured, Allison, *his wife,* was so far and away the most precious to him, he wasn't certain how he stood it. Especially after he'd said the hateful things he'd said, after the way he'd spurned her love.

Because he did love her. She'd been right to call him a liar, because that's exactly what he was. Not that he'd set out to be a liar, but because the truth had seemed such a terrible thing to face that he'd pretended it didn't exist.

The truth was, he'd loved Allison long before he'd decided to marry her, long before he struck oil and got rich. He'd loved her longer than she'd even known he was alive.

One of the joys of his life had been that time she'd got a flat tire on a gravel road. Because he followed any tidbit of information he ever read or heard about her, he'd known she'd been over to the Caseys' little ranch, helping out with the kids while their mother had gone into the hospital for surgery.

Because it had been one of those endlessly lonely days, he'd found an excuse to drive down the old road that went past Casey's on the pretense of checking the part of his fence that ran parallel to it. It had been an adolescent impulse, but he'd been hoping for a glimpse of Allison if they passed on the road.

But instead of some fleeting glimpse, he'd found her stranded by a flat tire. She'd managed to get out the jack and the spare tire, but he'd arrived before she would have had to change it herself. One of the pleasures and torments of his adult life had been changing that tire for her, catching her watching him, listening to her soft sweet voice as she'd thanked him for coming along and doing such a nice thing for her.

His feet hadn't touched the ground for days afterward. It had been one of the few times in his life that he'd allowed himself to indulge in such foolish joy. Foolish joy, but safe, because at the time, Allison Lancaster had been so far out of his universe she might as well have been from another planet.

The moment he'd struck oil and become a millionaire, he'd been launched into her orbit. But he'd also been in unfamiliar territory. He'd managed to get her, to take advantage of her uncle's greed so she'd marry him, but once he had her, he'd realized how dangerous his feelings for her were.

He'd gone so far wrong the other day when he'd spoke rough to her, he was certain neither of them would ever get over it. It was certain she'd never forgive him. He reckoned he'd have to live for the rest of his days with the bitter knowledge that he'd spoiled her love for him, maybe even killed it.

Remorse gave his heart another heavy jolt. He wished he could take back every hateful word he'd said to her. If she wanted him to cut out his heart to make it right, he would. But he didn't know what she wanted. It might be kinder to give her an out, to offer her a divorce.

The notion made him sick, but it might be the only thing he could do to make up for things. As he used the ladder and got down from the roof, he tried to toughen his heart. But the high, wide wall that used to do most of that for him was broken down. That day in the bedroom of the old house, it had shattered like a dried-up clay pot.

When he got to the foot of the ladder and stepped on solid ground, he grabbed his shirt off a sawhorse and stepped into the shade just inside the wide doors of the hay barn. The sweet smell of hay was familiar to him, and the scent was about the only comfort he was able to feel right now.

Allison slowed her horse when she was several feet from the hay barn, then walked the horse in.

Blue was drinking ice water from a steel thermos. He capped the lid and set the thermos aside as she drew her horse to a halt.

"What're you doin' out in this hot sun, Miz Allis? It's gonna be a scorcher."

Allison's heart lifted. Considering Blue had barely spoken to her the past two weeks, it was a lot for him to say. The fact that he seemed to care that she was out in the Texas heat made her think he might still care about her.

"Might as well climb down and come into the shade."

Allison dismounted and led the horse past him through the huge doors. She tossed the reins over an old rail. The smell of hay was strong and sweet. She took a fortifying breath of it and turned to see Blue was facing her while he finished buttoning his shirt.

He was so tall and strong and rugged. His black Stetson was tipped back slightly on his head and the straight dark hair she could see beneath his hat brim was curled with perspiration. His big hands managed the buttons on his shirt with a masculine grace that reminded her of their wedding day, when he'd unbuttoned her dress.

The memory of what that had felt like—what it felt like any time he touched her, sent a quake of heat through her. His eyes were fixed on hers, but he'd carefully shielded whatever he might be thinking. Her courage began to fail her, and she had to force herself go through with what she'd planned to say.

"I've come to tell you that I know what you're doing."

It surprised her to see that he continued to watch her calmly, as if what she'd said had made him only mildly curious. There was no trace of anger in his look. She sensed he wasn't on guard, though he seemed tense, almost as if he was bracing himself for something.

His voice was somber. "What am I doing?"

Allison took a nervous breath. "I think you're putting me to the test, making things difficult so you can see what I'll do. I think I understand why, but I came to tell you that you might as well give me a passing grade. Because I'm not going to leave you unless you physically throw me out of your house. Even then, I'll never stop loving you."

It was a bold declaration, but this was no time to mince words. Blue's expression made her feel sad, though she couldn't have said why. His jaw had firmed, but he gave no outward indication of melancholy.

"You might feel that way now," he said, his voice low and faintly rough, "but what about next year? Five years?"

She caught the glimmer of bleakness that flashed past his calm facade. "Love is more than a rush of hormones and sentiment, Blue. It's also a commitment." She stopped briefly. Blue suddenly seemed easy to speak to, easy to reach. She smiled softly. "By the way, there will be no child by next spring. I've decided I'm not ready to share you just yet."

Blue glanced down, his hat brim shielding his eyes. She felt her heart squeeze at the gesture. The feeling of melancholy grew stronger.

"What about the other day? The things I said..."

She battled the strong sting of tears, but kept silent to give him time to finish speaking.

"I should never have said hard words to you. You've never been anything but kind to me. Patient. More than I deserve."

His hat brim came up and he looked over at her

with an intensity that was almost painful. "I had no cause to talk to you that way. I wish I could take the words back and make them like they never got said. But I can't and I'm sorry. I hope you can forgive me."

Allison was overwhelmed. "I forgave you right away."

She moved toward him. Hesitantly at first then, unable to stop herself, she ran to him. He caught her in a fierce hug that lifted her feet off the ground. She hugged him just as fiercely. She pressed her mouth against his shoulder to muffle a sob, but the next ones were torn from her.

Blue placed desperate kisses to her hair. "Don't cry, baby," he whispered gruffly. "I can't bear the sound of it." The pain in his voice touched her.

She drew back only far enough to see his stricken expression. She placed a hand gently to his cheek. "These are happy tears, Blue. I love you so much."

He didn't answer, but kissed her cheek then crushed her against him. His voice was ragged. "I love you. You're more precious to me than I can ever tell you— oh, God…"

The words were a fervent prayer. Suddenly, the kisses he'd placed in her hair weren't enough. He found her mouth and their lips fused hotly.

Before she realized he'd moved, he laid her down on a raft of fragrant hay bales. He didn't break off the kiss. It was several more moments before he slid his mouth off hers and he drew back to look down at her.

"I think I fell in love with you the afternoon I saw

you in front of the movie house downtown. Some Disney movie was playin' and you were there with about a half dozen little kids. They were holdin' hands, goin' two by two right along behind you like a double row of baby ducks.'' His face was so solemn that she reached up to touch his cheek. It was as if something new had blossomed inside him, something good that sent a torrent of words and happiness flooding out.

''You had on a pink dress with little straps that tied on the shoulders. Your skirt was short enough for me to see what fine legs you had, but it was your face that kept me looking. And your kind eyes. I watched you with those kids. There was one who had an ornery look about him, but he was a little angel with you.''

Allison stared up at him, surprised and thrilled by the story. ''Where were you? I would have noticed you.''

''I was sittin' in my truck, waiting for the stoplight to change. Other than the fact that I sat through the next three lights while I ogled you, there was no reason you would have seen me. You were so far above me and my life. You were a sweet dream that made me watch for you every time I went to town.''

''I wish I'd known you then.''

Blue shook his head. ''I wasn't fit for you. I may not be now, but there's no way I'm gonna give you back. If you really do love me and want to stay, I'll do my best to make sure you're never sorry.''

''Oh, Blue, I love you so much.'' She lifted up to close those few inches between them. Blue met her halfway, and his heart at last soared free.

EPILOGUE

BLUE and Allison Sumner stood at the altar of the
Chaney Community Church at another wedding more
than a year later.

This time, Blue was the best man for his former
butler, Edward Stansbury, who was now the proud
owner of the small Texas ranch that he'd saved all
his life to buy. Edward was dressed in a black
Western suit with a string tie and black dress cowboy
boots that had been polished to a mirror shine. He'd
quit being a butler and gone Texan, and intended to
live out his life as a gentleman rancher with the
woman of his dreams at his side.

Allison was matron of honor for the bride. Aunt
Petula was dressed in an ivory linen suit with a matching hat that had a short stiff veil. Her skin was tanned
these days, and her face was radiant with joy. She
was going to be a rancher's wife. She meant to work
alongside her man and have the kind of loving marriage and happy life she'd never had with her former
husband.

Behind them, the church was packed with wedding
guests. Sheriff Lem Reynolds had just given the bride
away, and was walking back down the church aisle to
where his beautiful wife sat, her green eyes tearing
up.

He sat down quietly, grinned at her, then passed

her a huge white hanky. As he sat back in the pew, his enjoyment of the wedding service was made sweeter by the memory of his happy task two weeks ago.

He'd gone to Chaney Bank with federal bank authorities, presented Charles Wallace with the warrant for his arrest for embezzling, then had the added pleasure of having Charles spend a significant number of hours as a guest in his jail before he and his new lawyer could get in front of a judge.

Allison's friend John Blake had been found working in a bank in Austin. An intense investigation turned up no evidence that the young man had stolen a thing. In fact, Blake's record and reputation were spotless.

Charles's record turned out to be less than spotless. Thanks to a tip from one of Charles's own employees, federal officials had dug deep into the bank's workings and come up with enough evidence to arrest Charles for embezzling the bank's money on a scale that made Lem Reynolds's scalp tingle.

No one was too sorry that Charles might face a few years in jail. Not even the woman who claimed she'd given birth out-of-wedlock to his child. The woman had dropped her paternity suit months ago after Petula had approached her. Because everyone knew that Charles was going to fight the suit to the end, even though paternity tests had proved he was the father, Petula had stepped in on the child's behalf. She'd set up a very generous plan to see that the woman had more than enough financial support to raise her son, including the full payment of college expenses for the little boy when the time came.

But, that was just like Petula. It did Lem's heart good to see a fine woman like her find a decent man good enough to make her happy.

In fact, along with Allison and her husband, Blue, the four of them were just one happy group of folks. Like him and his Sandy.

Lem Reynolds raised his arm to rest it on the pew behind his wife's shoulders, then sat back to enjoy the wedding.

Next month don't miss –

A CHILD FOR CHRISTMAS

Christmas: a kiss under the mistletoe, a caress by the fire. In these three festive romances Christmas is also a time for receiving the best gifts of all – a child, the man of your dreams, and a new family to call your own...

On sale 5th December 2003

Available at most branches of WHSmith, Tesco, Martins, Borders, Eason, Sainsbury's and all good paperback bookshops.

1103/05

Modern Romance™
...seduction and passion guaranteed

Tender Romance™
...love affairs that last a lifetime

Medical Romance™
...medical drama on the pulse

Historical Romance™
...rich, vivid and passionate

Sensual Romance™
...sassy, sexy and seductive

Blaze Romance™
...the temperature's rising

27 new titles every month.

Live the emotion

MILLS & BOON

BETTY NEELS

THE
CHRISTMAS COLLECTION

On sale 5th December 2003

*Available at most branches of WH Smith, Tesco, Martins, Borders,
Eason, Sainsbury's and all good paperback bookshops.*

MILLS & BOON

It Happened One

CHRISTMAS

Three *brand-new* Christmas
romances with an urban *twist!*

SUSAN WIGGS   NANCY WARREN   JULIE MCBRIDE

On sale 5th December 2003

*Available at most branches of WHSmith, Tesco, Martins, Borders,
Eason, Sainsbury's and all good paperback bookshops.*

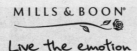